Exercises in Econometrics

Exercises
in Econometrics

P. C. B. PHILLIPS
Professor of Econometrics, University of Birmingham

M. R. WICKENS
Reader in Econometrics, University of Essex

Volume II

Philip Allan/Ballinger Publishing Company

Published jointly 1978 by

PHILIP ALLAN PUBLISHERS LIMITED
MARKET PLACE
DEDDINGTON
OXFORD OX5 4SE

BALLINGER PUBLISHING COMPANY
17 DUNSTER STREET
HARVARD SQUARE
CAMBRIDGE
MASSACHUSETTS 02138

0 86003 006 7 Volume I
0 86003 009 1 Volume II

Typeset by The Alden Press Ltd, London
Printed in the United States of America

Contents

3. THE MULTIVARIATE LINEAR MODEL *116*

0   Introduction *116*

1   Questions *118*

2   Supplementary Questions *125*

3   Solutions *129*

4. FURTHER ASPECTS OF THE LINEAR MODEL *161*

0   Introduction *161*

1   Questions *161*

4.1 R^2, the variance of an OLS estimate and multicollinearity; 4.2 Multicollinearity
and principal components; 4.3 Specification bias due to omitted variables;
4.4 Conditional and mixed regression; 4.5 The effects of including unnecessary
variables; 4.6 Seasonal variation; 4.7 Deseasonalised models; 4.8 Models with linear
segments; 4.9 Heteroscedasticity and OLS; 4.10 Properties of OLS with autoregressive
errors; 4.11 Cochrane−Orcutt and ML estimation; 4.12 Asymptotic properties
of the Durbin−Watson statistic; 4.13 Missing observations; 4.14 Covariance model;
4.15 Error components model; 4.16 Comparison of covariance and error components
models; 4.17 Aggregation bias and tests for perfect aggregation; 4.18 Application
of specification bias.

2   Supplementary Questions *168*

4.19 Using extraneous information; 4.20 Testing linear restrictions; 4.21 Dummy
variables and the covariance model; 4.22 GLS and tests of linear restrictions;
4.23 Multiple comparisons test; 4.24 Poisson distributed errors; 4.25 Quarterly
dummy variables; 4.26 Models with linear segments; 4.27 Testing for structural change
using recursions; 4.28 An application of testing for autocorrelation and seasonal
variation; 4.29 The finite sample distribution of the MLE of the linear model with
AR(1) errors using Monte Carlo simulations; 4.30 Testing for serial correlation;
4.31 Numerical optimisation methods and AR(1) errors; 4.32 Covariance
analysis; 4.33 Modelling equation and error dynamics.

3   Solutions *177*

5. FURTHER STOCHASTIC MODELS *217*

0   Introduction *217*

1   Questions *217*

5.1 Consistency of MDE in non-linear models; 5.2 MLE and MDE in non-linear
models; 5.3 Asymptotic efficiency of MDE in non-linear models; 5.4 Consistency
of MDE in a non-linear model; 5.5 Asymptotic distribution of MDE in models
non-linear in coefficients; 5.6 Iterative estimation of a linear model with a non-linear

restriction on the coefficients; 5.7 Estimation of the multivariate linear model with
non-linear cross equation restrictions; 5.8 Orthogonal regression; 5.9 Unobservable
variables; 5.10 Estimation of the vintage Cobb—Douglas production function.

2   Supplementary Questions *223*

5.11 Estimation with a non-linear restriction; 5.12 OLS with errors of measurement;
5.13 Estimation with proxy variables; 5.14 Estimating macro and micro equations
with errors of measurement; 5.15 Estimation of equations with errors in variables
by OLS and instrumental variables; 5.16 Estimation using the method of moments.

3   Solutions *228*

APPENDIX *xix*

BIBLIOGRAPHY *xxvi*
INDEX *xxxiii*

VOLUME II

PREFACE *xi*

LIST OF SYMBOLS AND ABBREVIATIONS *xiv*

6. SIMULTANEOUS EQUATIONS MODELS *267*

0   Introduction *267*

1   Questions *268*

6.1 Identifiability and the simultaneous equation bias of OLS; 6.2 Identification
of equations and models using homogeneous restrictions; 6.3 Identification using
non-homogeneous restrictions; 6.4 Identification using cross equation restrictions;
6.5 Identifiability of a given structure; 6.6 Calculation of 2SLS estimates; 6.7 Choice
of instruments in the IV estimator; 6.8 Calculation of a confidence interval for a
2SLS estimate; 6.9 Choice of dependent variable and 2SLS; 6.10 Asymptotic
distribution of OLS; 6.11 Asymptotic distribution of ILS; 6.12 Calculation of LIML
and a test for over identifying restrictions; 6.13 Derivation of FIML, FIML as an
iterated IV estimator, 3SLS as an asymptotically efficient non-iterated estimator;
6.14 3SLS for models with a diagonal error covariance matrix and just-identified

2   Supplementary Questions *281*

3   Solutions *291*

7. DYNAMIC MODELS *374*

0   Introduction *374*

1   Questions *374*

2   Supplementary Questions *388*

3   Solutions *401*

Preface

This book provides a set of worked and unworked exercises to supplement the main textbook material in econometrics. It is written partly for students who are commencing undergraduate work in econometrics and who have some prior knowledge of statistics, and partly for students who are undertaking more advanced undergraduate and graduate instruction. We also hope that the book will prove useful to teachers by providing material for classroom discussion and to research workers by going a small way towards bridging the gap between the textbook and the rapidly expanding literature in this field.

The book attempts to supplement the existing econometric literature in two ways. First, in our experience, students very often find that the textbook they are assigned does not prepare them adequately to solve the sort of problems they face in examinations. They are not shown in a direct way how the theory can be used to solve such problems and they are not provided with similar questions which they can attempt on their own. Second, with the increasing output of econometric research, the coverage of the established econometrics textbooks is seen to be less complete. This problem is of particular concern to advanced students searching for a recent overview of the subject and to beginning research workers who often feel the need for a simpler introduction to the recent literature, more particularly in the technical areas.

In this book we provide exercises both on econometric theory and applied econometrics that cover most of the material in introductory and advanced econometric textbooks. In addition, we have constructed problems based on more recent research in order to introduce the reader to some new results. As far as possible, we have included more than one question on each topic. We have provided a fairly detailed solution to (at least) one of these questions; the other questions are intended to be supplementary and are left either for the reader to answer on his own or for classroom discussion.

The material within each chapter is organised in the same way. At the start of each chapter we have a brief introduction to the subject matter of the chapter and, where this is appropriate, an outline of the notation that is to be used. The next two sections contain all of the questions in the chapter: first, those questions for which worked solutions are provided; and, second, the supplementary questions. The final section in each chapter contains the solutions. The questions and solutions are separated to encourage the reader to attempt the exercises alone before looking at the solutions that are provided. The questions are arranged and the solutions are written to enable the reader to proceed naturally from one question to the next. Knowledge of topics which are treated later in the book is not usually required. Where appropriate, the solution includes some discussion of the relevant econometric theory; and we have made such discussions more detailed in those solutions which relate to more recent research. Naturally, when the theory has already been explained in an earlier solution, it is not repeated, but reference is made to that previous solution. Moreover, to assist those readers who will wish to use the book in conjunction with a textbook, we have given references, as far as possible, to the major textbooks.

Although the questions are arranged in order of their topic, they are not always arranged in order of difficulty. But, when a topic is first introduced, it is usually done through simpler questions; and we have sometimes used numerical exercises to clarify the manipulations that are involved in a particular procedure. Subsequent questions on the same topic then tend to be of increasing difficulty. Therefore, both beginning and advanced students should find questions of interest throughout the book. Some questions deal with various aspects of applied work in econometrics and these questions are included towards the end of each chapter.

The book is divided into two volumes and this has enabled us to cover a fairly wide range of topics in the exercises. Volume I covers most of the usual textbook material dealing with regression techniques and their application in econometrics. Chapter 1 of this volume is concerned with a number of methodological issues that arise in the use of econometric techniques including the underlying concept of an econometric model and fundamental problems such as aggregation, causality and the distinction between recursive and interdependent systems. We also consider the problem of extracting and comparing the sampling distribution of least squares and other estimators in simple bivariate models allowing for serial correlation and errors of measurement. A large part of the remainder of the volume concentrates on methods of estimation and inference that apply to models that are linear in both variables and parameters (Chapters 2 and 4). There are many exercises illustrating standard results on the linear regression model. Most of these are contained in Chapter 2 and a number of extensions dealing with autocorrelated errors, multicollinearity, missing observations and seasonal adjustment are given in Chapter 4. We also consider multiple equation models with across equation parameter restrictions (Chapter 3) and covariance and error component models (Chapter 4). In

Chapter 5 we deal with non-linear regression models and models with errors in variables.

Volume II contains two chapters and deals with models of simultaneous equations (Chapter 6) and dynamic models (Chapter 7). Chapter 6 contains a number of introductory questions on identifiability and the use of single equation estimators such as two stage least squares and limited information maximum likelihood. A number of numerical questions have been included, as in Volume I, to lay out the sequence of manipulations needed to compute estimates and confidence intervals. The remaining questions in Chapter 6 deal with more advanced topics such as identifiability in the presence of cross equation parameter restrictions, systems methods of estimation, some simpler finite sample theory (Nagar's moment approximations and Edgeworth approximations) and an introduction to non-linear simultaneous equations models. Chapter 7 covers problems such as the identification of parameters in dynamic models with serially correlated errors, the consistent estimation of dynamic models with serially correlated errors, distributed lag models, continuous time models and models of markets in disequilibrium, as well as a number of applied questions. Much of the material in Chapter 7 has not yet appeared in textbooks and will, we hope, be of particular interest to advanced students and research workers.

Two major omissions from the book should also be noted: time series regression by spectral methods and the use of Bayesian methods in econometrics. These omissions were made with reluctance through pressure of space and time.

We are greatly indebted to the University of Auckland, the Australian National University and the Universities of Birmingham, Bristol, Essex, London and York for their permission to use questions which have appeared in their examinations. Where we have used questions from these examinations, or adapted them for our purpose here, this has been clearly indicated. Although it is impossible to give due credit to particular people in such cases, we acknowledge with special thanks that the following are among the authors of some of these questions: A.R. Bergstrom, R. Bowden, A. Chesher, J. Durbin, L.G. Godfrey, D.F. Hendry, G. Mizon, A.R. Pagan, J. Richmond, J.D. Sargan and K.F. Wallis. We are also grateful to J. Richmond, W. Barnett, V.B. Hall, E. Maasoumi and M. Prior for their comments on earlier versions of some of the questions and solutions. They are, of course, absolved from blame for any of the errors that remain.

Finally, it is with great pleasure that we thank Mrs Lucy Lowther, Mrs Sheila Ogden and Mrs Phyllis Pattenden for their skill, patience and good spirits in preparing the typescript.

P.C.B. PHILLIPS
M.R. WICKENS
July 1978

List of Symbols and Abbreviations

The following table comprises a list of principal symbols and abbreviations used in the book.

Symbol or Abbreviation	Meaning	Reference
A'	Transpose of the matrix A	
A^*	Complex conjugate transpose of the matrix A	
AESS_i	Additional explained sum of squares due to including variable i	p. 76
BAN	Best asymptotically normal	p. 146–147
b_{OLS}	Ordinary least squares estimator	p. 56
b_{GLS}	Generalised least squares estimator	p. 194
BLUE	Best linear unbiased estimator	
CES	Constant elasticity of substitution	
Const.	Constant	
CUAN	Consistent and uniformly asymptotically normal	p. 146
χ_n^2	Chi-squared distribution (or variable) with n degrees of freedom	p. 62

$\chi_n^2(\alpha)$	$P(\chi_n^2 > \chi_n^2(\alpha)) = \alpha$; $100\alpha\%$ significance point of the χ_n^2 distribution	
DW	Durbin–Watson statistic	p. 200
$E(\ )$	Mathematical expectation	
ESS	Explained sum of squares	p. 37
F_{n_1, n_2}	F distribution (or variable) with n_1 and n_2 degrees of freedom	p. 62
$F_{n_1, n_2}(\alpha)$	$P(F_{n_1, n_2} > F_{n_1, n_2}(\alpha)) = \alpha$; $100\alpha\%$ significance point of the F_{n_1, n_2} distribution	p. 63
FIML	Full information maximum likelihood	p. 274
GLS	Generalised least squares	p. 42
H_A	Hypothesis A	
i	$\sqrt{-1}$; complex constant	
$i(x)$	$= (2\pi)^{-1/2} \exp\left(-\frac{1}{2}x^2\right)$; standard normal density	
$I(x)$	$= \int_{-\infty}^{x} i(t)\,dt$; standard normal distribution function	
i_A	$A \times 1$ sum vector each of whose components is unity	p. 167
I_n	Identity matrix of order $n \times n$	p. 167
$\mathrm{Im}(\ )$	Imaginary part of a complex quantity	
J_A	$A \times A$ matrix each of whose components is unity	p. 167
LIML	Limited information maximum likelihood	p. 290
$\ln(\ )$	natural logarithm	
M_{xx}	$= T^{-1} \sum_{t=1}^{T} x_t x_t'$, sample moment matrix	p. 57

MLE	Maximum likelihood estimator	
$n!$	$= 1, 2, \ldots n; n$ factorial	
$N(\mu, \Sigma)$	Normal distribution with mean vector μ and co-variance matrix Σ	
$O(\ ), o(\ )$	Order of magnitude symbols	Cramér (1946, Ch. 20)
$O_p(\ ), o_p(\ )$	Probability order symbols	p. 107 and Mann and Wald (1943)
OLS	Ordinary least squares	p. 37
$\mathrm{plim}_{T \to \infty}, \mathrm{plim}$	Probability limit as $T \to \infty$	
R^2	Coefficient of determination	p. 61
$\bar{R}^2$	Corrected coefficient of determination	p. 61
$\mathrm{Re}(\ )$	Real part of a complex quantity	
RSS	Residual sum of squares	p. 37
RSS_A	Residual sum of squares from a regression under Hypothesis A	p. 64
$\mathrm{RSS}_{y \cdot 123\ldots}$	Residual sum of squares from regression of y on $x_1, x_2, x_3, \ldots$	p. 68
$r_{y1 \cdot 2}$	Partial correlation coefficient between y and χ_1, given χ_2	p. 68
t, n	Integers unless otherwise specified	
T	Integer representing sample size unless otherwise specified	
$\mathrm{SE}(\hat{\gamma})$	Standard error of the estimator $\hat{\gamma}$	p. 67

$\text{tr}(A)$	$= \sum\limits_{i=1}^{\min(m,\,n)} a_{ii}$ Trace of the matrix $A =$ $(a_{ij})_{m \times n}$	
TSS	Total sum of squares	p. 62
$\text{vec}\,(A)$	$nm \times 1$ vector of the components of the $n \times m$ matrix A, by rows	p. xix
$\overline{\text{vec}}\,(A)$	$nm \times 1$ vector of the components of the $n \times m$ matrix A, by columns	p. xxii
V_{OLS}	Covariance matrix of the least squares estimator	p. 193
V_{GLS}	Covariance matrix of the generalised least squares estimator	p. 193
ΔX_t	$= X_t - X_{t-1}$; differencing operator	
LX_t	$= X_{t-1}$; log operator	
$\otimes$	Kronecker matrix product (right hand)	pp. xix—xx
2SLS	Two stage least squares	p. 272
3SLS	Three stage least squares	p. 274

To Emily and Ruth

CHAPTER 6

Simultaneous Equations Models

0. INTRODUCTION

In the formulation of econometric models, economic theory often leads us to consider systems of equations which relate a large number of inter-dependent variables. These variables can usually be regarded as being jointly determined by the system and it often happens that one or more of these variables may appear as explanatory variables in the specification of an equation designed to explain movements in another variable. Systems of equations which fit this description differ from the models we have considered in Chapter 3 and elsewhere in this book. They come within the framework of simultaneous equation models in econometrics and a large body of theory has been developed which deals with the statistical treatment of such systems. The questions in this chapter will concentrate on various aspects of this theory and illustrate the application of theory by numerical examples and instances of applied studies.

In our notation we will continue our use of y and x to represent (vectors of) endogenous and exogenous variables, respectively; and y_t and x_t represent the sample observations of y and x in period t. We write the structural form of a system of n simultaneous equations as

$$By_t + Cx_t = u_t \tag{6.0.1}$$

or

$$Aw_t = u_t \tag{6.0.2}$$

where $B(n \times n)$, $C(n \times m)$ and $A = (B \vdots C)$ $[n \times (n + m)]$ are matrices of coefficients and u_t is a vector of random disturbances with zero mean and covariance matrix Σ for all t. The reduced form of (6.0.1) is written as

$$y_t = Px_t + v_t$$

where $P = -B^{-1}C$ and $v_t = B^{-1}u_t$. We write the covariance matrix of v_t as $E(v_tv_t') = \Omega$. When we consider a single equation of (6.0.1) we often use the notation

$$y_i = Z_i \delta_i + u_i \qquad\qquad (6.0.3)$$

where $y_i' = (y_{i1}, \ldots, y_{iT})$ is a vector of T sample observations of the ith endogenous variable, $Z_i = [Y_i \vdots X_i]$ is a matrix of observations of included endogenous variables (Y_i) and included exogenous variables (X_i) and $u_i' = (u_{i1}, \ldots, u_{iT})$ is the vector of disturbances on this equation.

1. QUESTIONS

Question 6.1

The market for a certain good is expressed by the following equations

$$D_t = \alpha_0 - \alpha_1 p_t + \alpha_2 y_2 + u_{1t} \qquad (\alpha_1, \alpha_2 > 0)$$
$$S_t = \beta_0 + \beta_1 p_t + u_{2t} \qquad (\beta_1 > 0)$$
$$D_t = S_t$$

where D_t is the quantity demanded, S_t the quantity supplied, y_t is income which is taken to be non-random and exogenous, u_{1t} and u_{2t} are serially uncorrelated disturbances with zero means, variance σ_1^2 and σ_2^2 and covariance σ_{12} for all t.
(a) Examine the identifiability of the model.
(b) Assuming that $\lim_{T \to \infty} T^{-1} \Sigma_{t=1}^{T} y_t^2$ is finite and non-zero, derive the simultaneous equation bias in the OLS estimator of β_1.
(c) If $\sigma_{12} = 0$ would you expect this bias to be positive or negative? Explain.

(University of Essex BA Examinations, 1975.)

Question 6.2

Consider the following model:

$$y_{1t} \qquad\qquad + c_{11}x_{1t} \qquad\qquad = u_{1t}$$
$$b_{21}y_{1t} + \qquad y_{2t} \qquad + c_{21}x_{1t} \qquad\qquad = u_{2t}$$
$$b_{32}y_{2t} + y_{3t} + c_{31}x_{1t} + c_{32}x_{2t} = u_{3t}$$

where the y_{it} are endogenous variables, the x_{it} are exogenous variables and the u_{it} are disturbances with $E(u_{it}) = 0, E(u_{it}u_{jt}) = \sigma_{ij}$ for all i, j and t and $E(u_{it}u_{js}) = 0$ for $t \neq s$.
(a) Consider the identification of each equation of this model in the following cases:
  (i) no further information is known,
  (ii) $c_{31} = 0$, and

(iii) $b_{21} + c_{21} = 0$.

(b) Obtain the reduced form of the model and hence examine the identifiability of the whole model.

(c) Comment on these statements:

(i) '... we shall be content with the fact that the rank condition is satisfied in nearly every case when the order condition is.' (Christ, 1966, p. 331);

(ii) 'Intuitively, identifiability requires restrictions.' (Goldberger, 1964, p. 316).

Question 6.3

Examine the identification of each equation of the following model

$$y_{1t} + b_{12}y_{2t} + c_{11}x_{1t} = u_{1t}$$
$$b_{21}y_{1t} + y_{2t} + c_{21}x_{1t} + c_{22}x_{2t} = u_{2t}$$

where the y_{it} are endogenous variables, the x_{it} are exogenous variables and the u_{it} are disturbances with $E(u_{it}) = 0$, $E(u_{it}u_{jt}) = \sigma_{ij}$ for all i, j and t and $E(u_{it}u_{js}) = 0$ for $t \neq s$:

(a) when no further information is available;

(b) when $b_{21} + c_{21} = 1$;

(c) when the covariance matrix of the structural disturbances is

$$\Sigma = \begin{pmatrix} \sigma_{11} & 0 \\ 0 & \sigma_{22} \end{pmatrix}.$$

Question 6.4

In the model

$$y_{1t} = b_{12}y_{2t} + c_{11}x_{1t} + u_{1t} \tag{6.4.1}$$
$$y_{2t} = b_{21}y_{1t} + c_{21}x_{1t} + u_{2t} \tag{6.4.2}$$

the y_{it} are endogenous variables, the x_{jt} are exogenous variables and the u_{it} are serially independent random disturbances that are identically distributed with zero means and non-singular covariance matrix for all t. It is known that the parameters in this model satisfy the cross equation restrictions

$$b_{12} + b_{21} = 1 \tag{6.4.3}$$

and

$$c_{11} - c_{21} = 0 \tag{6.4.4}$$

(a) Discuss the identifiability of the parameters in the above model.

(b) Consider, in particular, the identifiability of the structure in which $b_{12} = -1, b_{21} = 2, c_{11} = 1$ and $c_{21} = 1$.

Question 6.5

In the model

$$y_{1t} = b_{12} y_{2t} + c_{11} x_{1t} + u_{1t}$$

$$y_{2t} = b_{23} y_{3t} + c_{22} x_{2t} + u_{2t}$$

$$y_{3t} = b_{31} y_{1t} + c_{32} x_{2t} + u_{3t}$$

the y_{it}, x_{it} and u_{it} are endogenous variables, exogenous variables and stochastic disturbances, respectively. It is known that the u_{it} are serially independent, have zero mean and non-singular covariance matrix but are otherwise unrestricted.

(a) Discuss the identifiability of the parameters in the above model.
(b) Consider, in particular, the identifiability of the structure in which $b_{12} = 1, b_{23} = 2, b_{31} = 4, c_{11} = 5, c_{22} = 6$ and $c_{32} = -3$.
(Adapted from University of Essex MA examinations, 1974.)

Question 6.6

Consider the following model

$$y_{1t} = b_{12} y_{2t} + c_{11} x_{1t} + u_{1t} \tag{6.6.1}$$

$$y_{2t} = b_{21} y_{1t} + c_{22} x_{2t} + c_{23} x_{3t} + u_{2t} \tag{6.6.2}$$

$$y_{3t} = b_{31} y_{1t} + b_{32} y_{2t} + c_{33} x_{3t} + u_{3t} \tag{6.6.3}$$

where the y_{it} are endogenous variables and the x_{it} are exogenous variables which we assume to be non-random and whose moment matrix we assume to have a finite positive definite limit as the sample size tends to infinity. The random disturbances u_{it} are distributed with zero means and finite second moments; it is also assumed that $E(u_{is}u_{jt}) = 0$ for all i, j and $s \neq t$.

(a) Using the method of two-stage least-squares, find consistent estimates of the parameters b_{12} and c_{11} given the following sample moment matrix:

	y_1	y_2	y_3	x_1	x_2	x_3
y_1	25	10	15	30	35	40
y_2	10	60	20	-20	50	80
y_3	15	20	400	50	-75	360
x_1	30	-20	50	200	0	0
x_2	35	50	-75	0	250	0
x_3	40	80	360	0	0	400

(b) Suggest an alternative method of obtaining consistent estimates of the same parameters which involves fewer calculations. Compare the final estimates you obtain by both methods.

(Adapted from University of Essex BA examinations, 1973.)

Question 6.7

The structural equation

$$y = Z\delta + u \tag{6.7.1}$$

is estimated by the method of instrumental variables and the resulting estimator of δ is denoted by d. Z is a matrix of observations of k explanatory variables and X is a matrix of observations of p instrumental variables $k \leqslant p < T$. The limiting distribution of $X'u/\sqrt{T}$ is assumed to be $N(0, \sigma^2 M_{xx})$, where $\lim_{T \to \infty} X'X/T = M_{xx}$.
(a) For the special case where $k = p = 1$, show that the variance of the limiting distribution of $\sqrt{T}(d - \delta)$ decreases as the large sample correlation between Z and X increases.
(b) Examine the effect on the covariance matrix of the limiting distribution of $\sqrt{T}(d - \delta)$ of using additional instrumental variables.

Question 6.8

In the model

$$y_{1t} + \alpha y_{2t} = u_{1t}$$
$$y_{2t} + \beta y_{1t} + \gamma x_{1t} + \delta x_{2t} = u_{2t}$$

the y_{it} are endogenous variables, the x_{it} are exogenous variables and the u_{it} are random disturbances.

Given the following sample second moment matrix based on 100 observations

	y_1	y_2	x_1	x_2
y_1	10	6	2	10
y_2	6	40	10	10
x_1	2	10	5	5
x_2	10	10	5	25

(a) calculate the two-stage least-squares estimate of α;
(b) find an approximate 95% confidence interval for α when $T = 50$.

(Adapted from University of Essex BA examinations, 1976 and University of Auckland BA examinations, 1972.)

Question 6.9

(a) Show that the 2SLS estimators of b and c in the overidentified equation

$$y_1 = by_2 + cx_1 + u \tag{6.9.1}$$

are unaltered if y_1 is replaced by its reduced form estimator $\hat{y}_1$.
(b) Let the 2SLS estimator of b be $\hat{b}_1$ when y_1 is treated as the dependent variable and $\hat{b}_2$ when y_2 is made the dependent variable. Show that $\hat{b}_1/\hat{b}_2 \leqslant 1$.

(Adapted from University of London BSc examinations, 1970).

Question 6.10

Consider the following model

$$y_{1t} = b_{12}y_{2t} + c_{12}x_{2t} + u_{1t} \tag{6.10.1}$$

$$y_{2t} = b_{21}y_{1t} + c_{21}x_{1t} + c_{23}x_{3t} + u_{2t} \tag{6.10.2}$$

where the y_{it} are endogenous variables and the x_{it} are non-random exogenous variables. The random disturbances u_{it} are serially independent and are distributed with zero means and finite second moments given by

$$E(u_{1t}^2) = 5, \quad E(u_{1t}u_{2t}) = 1, \quad E(u_{2t}^2) = 1$$

identically for all t. The limit of the matrix $T^{-1}\sum_{t=1}^{T} x_t x_t'$ where $x_t' = (x_{1t}, x_{2t}, x_{3t})$, is known to be

	x_1	x_2	x_3
x_1	1	1	0
x_2	1	2	0
x_3	0	0	1

The true values of the parameters in the above model are:
$b_{12} = 1, b_{21} = 2, c_{12} = 2, c_{21} = 3, c_{23} = 1.$

(a) Find the probability limit of the ordinary least squares estimator of the vector $\delta' = (b_{12}, c_{12})$.

(b) Derive the covariance matrix of the limiting distribution of $\sqrt{T}(\delta^* - \delta)$ where δ^* is the two-stage least-squares estimator of δ.

(c) Consider the model (6.7.1) in which the true values of the coefficients are given by $b_{12} = 1, b_{21} = 0, c_{12} = 0, c_{21} = 3, c_{23} = 0$ and the first and second moments of the u_{it} are as before. Briefly describe how you would attempt to derive the limiting distribution of $\sqrt{T}(\hat{b}_{12} - \bar{b}_{12})$, where $\hat{b}_{12}$ is the ordinary least squares estimator of b_{12} and $\bar{b}_{12} = \text{plim}_{T \to \infty} \hat{b}_{12}$. Indicate any difficulties you expect to arise in this derivation.

Question 6.11

Consider the stochastic model

$$C_t = \alpha + \beta Y_t + u_t$$

$$Y_t = C_t + I_t$$

where Y_t is real net national income in period t, C_t real consumption in period t and I_t real investment in period t; u_t is a serially independent random disturbance with $E(u_t) = 0$ and $E(u_t^2) = \sigma^2$ for all t. I_t is assumed to be non-random and the limit of $T^{-1} \Sigma_{t=1}^{T} (I_t - \bar{I})^2$ as $T \to \infty$ is a finite positive number.

Find the limiting distribution of $(\hat{\alpha}, \hat{\beta})$, the indirect least squares estimator of (α, β).

Question 6.12

In the model

$$y_{1t} + b_{12} y_{2t} + c_{11} x_{1t} = u_{1t}$$

$$y_{2t} + b_{21} y_{1t} + c_{22} x_{2t} + c_{23} x_{3t} = u_{2t}$$

the y_{it} are endogenous variables, the x_{it} are exogenous variables and $u_t' = (u_{1t}, u_{2t})$ is a vector of serially independent random disturbances with $E(u_t) = 0$ and the same non-singular covariance matrix for each t.

Given the following sample second moment matrix

	y_1	y_2	x_1	x_2	x_3
y_1	14	6	2	3	0
y_2	6	10	2	1	0
x_1	2	2	1	0	0
x_2	3	1	0	1	0
x_3	0	0	0	0	1

(a) Calculate the limited information maximum likelihood estimates of b_{12} and c_{11}.
(b) Calculate a statistic for testing the null hypothesis that the over-identifying restrictions imposed on the first equation are correct.

(Adapted from University of Essex MA examinations, 1976.)

Question 6.13

(a) Show how the FIML estimator of the coefficient matrices in the simultaneous equations model (6.0.1) may be derived.
(b) Explain why the FIML estimator can be interpreted as an iterated instrumental variable estimator.
(c) Explain why the 3SLS estimator is a non-iterated instrumental variable estimator.
(d) Hence show that 3SLS is asymptotically as efficient as FIML.

Question 6.14

(a) Examine the properties of the 3SLS estimator of the coefficients of a system of linear equations
    (i) when the contemporaneous covariance matrix of the disturbances is diagonal, and
    (ii) when each equation is just identified.
(b) If a subset of the equations of the system are just identified, obtain an expression for the 3SLS estimator of the coefficients of the remaining equations.

Question 6.15

In the model

$$y_{1t} + b_{12}y_{2t} + c_{11}x_{1t} = u_{1t} \tag{6.15.1}$$

$$b_{21}y_{1t} + y_{2t} + c_{22}x_{2t} = u_{2t} \tag{6.15.2}$$

the y_{it} are endogenous variables, the x_{it} are exogenous variables and the

u_{it} are serially independent random disturbances which have the same bivariate normal distribution with zero mean and non-singular covariance matrix for each value of t.

(a) How would you obtain full information maximum likelihood (FIML) estimates of the coefficients of the above model?

(b) Prove that your procedure yields the FIML estimates.

(Adapted from University of Auckland MA, MCom examinations, 1967.)

Question 6.16

In the model

$$y_{1t} = b_{12}y_{2t} + u_{1t} \tag{6.16.1}$$

$$y_{2t} = b_{21}y_{1t} + c_{21}x_{1t} + c_{22}x_{2t} + u_{2t} \tag{6.16.2}$$

the y_{it} are endogenous variables, the x_{it} are exogenous variables and the u_{it} are serially independent random disturbances which have the same bivariate normal distribution with zero mean and non-singular covariance matrix for each value of t.

Find the full information maximum likelihood estimate of the parameter b_{12} in the above model, using the following sample second moment matrix.

	y_1	y_2	x_1	x_2
y_1	10	8	2	10
y_2	8	40	10	10
x_1	2	10	5	5
x_2	10	10	5	25

(Adapted from University of Auckland MA, MCom examinations, 1965.)

Question 6.17

In the model

$$y_{1t} = \alpha y_{2t} + u_{1t} \tag{6.17.1}$$

$$y_{2t} = \beta x_{1t} + \gamma x_{2t} + u_{2t} \tag{6.17.2}$$

the y_{it} are endogenous variables, the x_{it} are exogenous variables and the u_{it} are serially independent random disturbances which have the same bivariate normal distribution for each value of t with $E(u_{1t}) = E(u_{2t}) = 0$, $E(u_{1t}^2) = \sigma^2$, $E(u_{1t}u_{2t}) = \sigma^2$, and $E(u_{2t}^2) = 2\sigma^2$, where σ^2 is an unknown scalar. You are given the following matrix of sample second moments:

	y_1	y_2	x_1	x_2
y_1	10	2	3	1
y_2	2	5	1	1
x_1	3	1	1	1
x_2	1	1	1	1

(a) Find the full information maximum likelihood (FIML) estimates of α, β and γ.

(b) Is it possible to find asymptotically efficient estimates of α, β and γ by using three-stage least squares?

(Adapted, in part, from University of Essex BA, MA examinations, 1976.)

Question 6.18

The following model

$$B_1 y_{1t} + B_2 y_{2t} + C_1 x_{1t} = u_{1t} \qquad (t = 1, \ldots, T) \qquad (6.18.1)$$

is an n_1 equation sub-system of an n-equation structural model. Whilst the coefficients of (6.18.1) incorporate *a priori* restrictions, the coefficients of the remaining $n_2 = n - n_1$ equations of the system remain unrestricted. It is known, however, that in the complete model the vector of endogenous variables is $y_t' = (y_{1t}', y_{2t}')$, the vector of predetermined variables is $x_t' = (x_{1t}', x_{2t}')$, and the vector of disturbances is $u_t' = (u_{1t}', u_{2t}')$, which is serially independent and is distributed as a $N(0, \Sigma)$ variable with $\Sigma = \{\Sigma_{ij}\}$ for $(i, j = 1, 2)$. Σ is non-singular.

(a) Show how the maximum likelihood estimator of the coefficients of the sub-system (6.18.1) can be obtained by using FIML on a complete model consisting of (6.18.1) and the unrestricted reduced form equations associated with y_{2t}.

(b) Suggest an asymptotically equivalent non-iterative instrumental variable estimator of the unknown elements of B_1, B_2 and C_1.

(c) Comment on the two estimators derived above when the sub-system is a single structural equation.

(Reference: Godfrey and Wickens, 1977.)

Question 6.19

Consider the stochastic model

$$C_t = \alpha + \beta Y_t + u_t \qquad (t = 1, \ldots, T) \qquad (6.19.1)$$

$$Y_t = C_t + I_t \qquad (t = 1, \ldots, T) \qquad (6.19.2)$$

$$0 < \beta < 1$$

where Y_t is real net national income in period t, C_t real consumption in period t, and I_t real investment in period t. The disturbances $u_1, \ldots, u_T$ are independent random variables each of which is normally distributed with mean zero and variance σ^2. The quantities $I_1, \ldots, I_T$ are non-random and satisfy

$$\sum_{t=1}^{T} (I_t - \bar{I})^2 = 1$$

where $\bar{I} = \Sigma_{t=1}^{T} I_t / T$.

(a) Derive the exact finite sample frequency function of the maximum likelihood estimator of the marginal propensity to consume, β, in the above model.

(b) Show that this distribution has no integral moments of any order.

(c) What do you know of the distribution of the ordinary least squares estimator of β?

Question 6.20

In the model

$$y_{1t} = b_{12}y_{2t} + c_{11}x_{1t} + u_{1t} \tag{6.20.1}$$

$$y_{2t} = c_{21}x_{1t} + c_{22}x_{2t} + c_{23}x_{3t} + c_{24}x_{4t} + u_{2t} \qquad (t = 1, \ldots, T) \tag{6.20.2}$$

the y_{it} are endogenous variables, the x_{it} are non-random exogenous variables and the u_{it} are serially independent random disturbances with zero mean and covariance matrix

$$\begin{bmatrix} \sigma^2 & \sigma^2 \\ \sigma^2 & 2\sigma^2 \end{bmatrix}.$$

If $(\hat{b}_{12}, \hat{c}_{11})$ denotes the two-stage least squares estimator of (b_{12}, c_{11}), and the sample second moment matrix of the exogenous variables is the identity matrix, show that Nagar's approximation to the bias of the two-stage least squares estimator is given by

$$E \begin{bmatrix} \hat{b}_{12} - b_{12} \\ \hat{c}_{11} - c_{11} \end{bmatrix} = \sigma^2 T^{-1} (c_{22}^2 + c_{23}^2 + c_{24}^2)^{-1} \begin{bmatrix} 1 \\ -c_{21} \end{bmatrix} + O(T^{-2})$$

Question 6.21

In the model

$$y_{1t} = by_{2t} + c_{11}x_{1t} + u_{1t} \tag{6.21.1}$$

$$y_{2t} = \sum_{j=1}^{m} c_{2j} x_{jt} + u_{2t} \qquad (t = 1, \ldots, T) \tag{6.21.2}$$

the y_{it} are endogenous variables, the x_{it} are non-random exogenous variables and the u_{it} are serially independent normally distributed disturbances with zero mean and covariance matrix

$$\begin{bmatrix} \sigma^2 & \sigma^2 \\ \sigma^2 & 2\sigma^2 \end{bmatrix}.$$

If b_{2SLS} and b_{LIML} denote the two-stage least squares and limited information maximum likelihood estimators of b respectively, and if

$$\lambda^2 = \sigma^2 \Big/ \left(\sum_{j=1}^{m} c_{2j}^2 \right) \tag{6.21.3}$$

it is known that

$$P[T^{1/2}(b_{2SLS} - b) \leqslant x] = I\left(\frac{x}{\lambda}\right) + i\left(\frac{x}{\lambda}\right)\left\{ \frac{\lambda}{T^{1/2}} \left[\left(\frac{x}{\lambda}\right)^2 - (m-2) \right] \right.$$

$$+ \frac{\lambda^2}{2T} \left[-(m-2)(m-3)\left(\frac{x}{\lambda}\right) + (2m-3)\left(\frac{x}{\lambda}\right)^3 - \left(\frac{x}{\lambda}\right)^5 \right] \right\} + O(T^{-3/2}) \tag{6.21.4}$$

and

$$P[T^{1/2}(b_{LIML} - b) \leqslant x] = I\left(\frac{x}{\lambda}\right) + i\left(\frac{x}{\lambda}\right)\left\{ \frac{\lambda}{T^{1/2}} \left(\frac{x}{\lambda}\right)^2 \right.$$

$$+ \frac{\lambda^2}{2T} \left[-(m-2)\left(\frac{x}{\lambda}\right) + \left(\frac{x}{\lambda}\right)^3 - \left(\frac{x}{\lambda}\right)^5 \right] \right\} + O(T^{-3/2}). \tag{6.21.5}$$

where $I(x) = \int_{-\infty}^{x} i(y)dy$ and $i(y) = (2\pi)^{-1/2} \exp(-y^2/2)$.

Compare the concentration of these two estimators of b by considering the probability [up to $O(T^{-1})$] that each estimator lies in an interval symmetric about the true value. Show that if $2 < m \leqslant 4$ then the two-stage least squares estimator is the more concentrated about the true value up to this order of approximation.

(Reference: Anderson, 1974.)

Question 6.22

Consider the model

$$y_{1t} = \alpha y_{2t}^2 + u_{1t} \tag{6.22.1}$$

$$y_{2t} = \beta + u_{2t} \tag{6.22.2}$$

where the $y_{it}(i = 1, 2)$ are endogenous variables and the $u_{it}(i = 1, 2)$ are serially independent, normally distributed disturbances with zero means and covariance matrix

$$\begin{bmatrix} \sigma^2 & \sigma^2 \\ \sigma^2 & 2\sigma^2 \end{bmatrix}$$

for all t.

(a) Find the limit in probability of the ordinary least squares estimator of α.

(b) Suggest a method of obtaining a consistent estimator of α and verify that your estimator is consistent.

(c) Find the variance of the limiting distribution of $\sqrt{T}(\alpha^* - \alpha)$ where α^* is your estimator from Part (b).

Question 6.23

Two theories that have been advanced to explain the net capital inflow $\dot{K}$ into the United States from Britain over the period 1871–1914 are:

    A. the 'pull' hypothesis which directly relates $\dot{K}_t$ to investment in US railroads, I^{US};

    B. the 'push' hypothesis which inversely relates $\dot{K}_t$ to British investment at home, I^{GB}.

Attempts to test these hypotheses have led to the following estimates:

$$(\text{OLS})\dot{K}_t = \text{const.} + \underset{(0.127)}{1.019 I^{US}_{t-1}} : \bar{R}^2 = 0.624 \tag{6.23.1}$$

$$(\text{OLS})\dot{K}_t = \text{const.} - \underset{(0.242)}{0.073 I^{US}_{t-1}} - \underset{(0.628)}{9.206 I^{GB}_t} : \bar{R}^2 = 0.739 \tag{6.23.2}$$

$$(\text{OLS})\dot{K}_t = \text{const.} - \underset{(0.151)}{0.232 I^{US}_{t-1}} - \underset{(1.533)}{9.079 I^{GB}_t}$$
$$+ \underset{(0.307)}{2.239 M^{US}_{t-1}} : \bar{R}^2 = 0.900 \tag{6.23.3}$$

$$(\text{2SLS})\dot{K}_t = \text{const.} + \underset{(0.185)}{0.967 I^{US}_{t-1}} + \underset{(1.120)}{1.203 I^{GB}_t} + \underset{(0.557)}{2.281 M^{US}_{t-1}} \tag{6.23.4}$$

where M^{US} denotes US imports, the figure in parentheses below each estimate is its standard error, OLS denotes the ordinary least squares method of estimation and 2SLS the two-stage least squares method.

    On the basis of these results compare the two theories. Suggest possible explanations for the differences between these estimates.

(Reference: G.N. von Tunzelmann 1968)

(University of Essex BA examinations, 1976.)

Question 6.24

From classical utility theory, the supply function of labour for husbands (m) and wives (f) can be written as

$$L_i = L_i(W_m, W_f, Y) \qquad (i = m, f) \tag{6.24.1}$$

where L_i is the supply of labour in hours, W_i is the wage rate and Y is family non-labour income. An approximation to (6.24.1) is

$$\Delta L_{ik} = s_{im}\Delta W_{mk} + s_{if}\Delta W_{fk} + b_i\Delta F_k + \sum_{j=1}^{J} c_{ij}X_{jk} + \epsilon_{ik}$$

$$(i = m, f; k = 1, .., K) \tag{6.24.2}$$

where Δ denotes deviations about the mean (e.g. $\Delta L_{ik} = L_{ik} - \bar{L}_i$), F_k is average family income, the X_{jk} are other variables and ϵ_{ik} is a disturbance term. ΔL and ΔF are treated as endogenous, while ΔW and the X's are exogenous variables. The s_{ij} are interpreted as Slutsky substitution effects. Tables 6.24.1 and 6.24.2 give the 3SLS estimates of certain coefficients of (6.24.2) and an estimate of the covariance matrix of these estimates.

(a) Treating (6.24.1) rather like a system of demand equations, show how (6.24.2) can be derived from (6.24.1) by totally differentiating (6.24.1), using the Slutsky decomposition

$$\frac{\partial L_i}{\partial W_j} = s_{ij} + L_j \frac{\partial L_i}{\partial Y} \quad \text{for} \quad i, j = m, f \tag{6.24.3}$$

and the approximation $dx = \Delta x$.
(b) Assuming that $\bar{L}_m = 0.979$ and $\bar{L}_f = 0.341$ are the sample means of L_m and L_f, test the following hypotheses and interpret your results

(i) $s_{ii} > 0$
(ii) $s_{mf} = s_{fm}$
(iii) $\partial L_i / \partial Y < 0$
(iv) $\partial L_i / \partial W_i < 0$

(Reference: O. Ashenfelter and J. Heckman, 1974.)

Table 6.24.1 3SLS estimates of certain coefficients of (6.24.2)

Labour supply of:	Coefficients of: ΔW_m	ΔW_f	ΔF
husbands	0.110	0.139	−0.112
wives	−0.081	0.972	−0.594

Table 6.24.2 An estimate of the covariance matrix of these estimated coefficients

	s_{mm}	s_{mf}	b_m	s_{ff}	s_{fm}	b_f
s_{mm}	0.184	0.217	−0.265	0.249	0.217	−0.304
s_{mf}		0.454	−0.419	0.588	0.454	−0.672
b_m			0.451	−0.516	−0.419	0.609
s_{ff}				7.461	0.588	−4.279
s_{fm}					0.454	−0.672
b_f						3.131

Note 1 This covariance matrix is in fact that for the restricted labour supply model (with $s_{mf} = s_{fm}$). The covariance matrix for the unrestricted model ought to be used but is not published. This change incorrectly alters many of the conclusions in the original study.

Note 2 For ease of reading the covariance matrix has been multiplied by 100.

2. SUPPLEMENTARY QUESTIONS

Question 6.25

How is it possible to test a given set of structural equations for identification?

The following equations are a Cobb–Douglas production function and equations determining the amount of each input.

$$X_t = K_t^{0.7} L_t^{0.3} e^{u_t}$$

$$0.7 X_t / K_t = 0.5 (r_t / p_t) e^{v_{1t}}$$

$$0.3 X_t / L_t = 0.6 (w_t / p_t) e^{v_{2t}}$$

where X_t is the output, K_t is capital, L_t is labour, p_t is the price of output, r_t is the return on capital and w_t is the wage rate.

Express this as a set of linear equations in the logarithms of the variables, and discuss the identification of each equation. Is it necessary to specify which variables are taken to be exogenous to determine identification?

(University of London BSc (Econ) examinations, 1965.)

Question 6.26

Assess the identifiability of the equations of the following models:

(1) $\quad c_t = \alpha_1 y_t + \alpha_2 r_{t-1} + u_{1t}$

$\qquad i_t = \beta_1 y_t + \beta_2 r_{t-1} + u_{2t}$

$\qquad y_t = c_t + i_t$

endogenous variables: y_t, c_t, i_t; exogenous variables: r_t.

(2) $\quad m_t = \gamma_1 r_t + \gamma_2 m_{t-1} + v_{1t}$

$\qquad r_t = \delta_1 m_t + \delta_2 m_{t-1} + \delta_3 y_t + v_{2t}$

endogenous variables: m_t, r_t; exogenous variables: y_t.

Obtain the reduced form equation for y_t in model (1), and the reduced form equation for r_t in model (2).

Assess the identifiability of a two-equation model comprising the reduced form equation for y_t in model (1) (an 'I–S curve') and the reduced form equation for r_t in model (2) (an 'L–M curve'). Given time series data on y, r, and m, how would you estimate this model? How is the estimation of the second equation of this model changed if it is assumed that the u's and v's are mutually uncorrelated?

(University of London MSc examinations, 1970.)

Question 6.27

A sample of 21 observations corresponding to the simple income determination model

$$C = \alpha + \beta Y$$

$$Y = C + I$$

gave the following data:

$$\sum_t (C_t - \bar{C})(Y_t - \bar{Y}) = 9, \qquad \sum_t (Y_t - \bar{Y})^2 = 12,$$

$$\sum_t (I_t - \bar{I})^2 = 1, \qquad \sum_t (C_t - \bar{C})(I_t - \bar{I}) = 2,$$

$$\sum_t (Y_t - \bar{Y})(I_t - \bar{I}) = 3.$$

(a) Estimate β by (i) regressing C on Y; (ii) indirect least squares; (iii) using I as an instrumental variable.

(b) What aspects of these estimation procedures are illustrated by your answers?

(Adapted from University of Essex MA examinations, 1974.)

Question 6.28

In the model

$$q_t = \alpha + \beta p_t + u_t \qquad \text{(demand equation)}$$

$$q_t = \gamma + \delta(p_t + s_t) + v_t \qquad \text{(supply equation)}$$

where q_t is the amount of commodity produced and sold in year t, p_t is the average price of commodity in year t and s_t is the rate of subsidy in year t. u_t and v_t are random disturbances which are serially independent and are distributed with zero means and finite second moments. The variable s_t is taken to be non-random and exogenous and its sample variance may be assumed to tend to a positive limit as the sample size T tends to infinity.
(a) Which of the parameters α, β, γ and δ are identifiable?
(b) Obtain consistent estimates of the identifiable parameters from the sample means $\bar{p} = 4$, $\bar{q} = 5$ and $\bar{s} = \frac{1}{3}$ and the following sample moments:

	p	q	s
p	6	1	0
q	1	5	2
s	0	2	4

Question 6.29

In the model

$$y_{1t} = b_{12} y_{2t} + b_{13} y_{3t} + c_{11} x_{1t} + c_{12} x_{2t} + u_{1t}$$

$$y_{2t} = b_{21} y_{1t} + b_{23} y_{3t} + u_{2t}$$

$$y_{3t} = b_{31} y_{1t} + b_{32} y_{2t} + u_{3t}$$

the y_{it} are endogenous variables, the x_{it} are exogenous variables and the u_{it} are serially independent random disturbances with zero means and non-singular covariance matrix.
(a) Verify that no equation in the above model is identified.
(b) If it is known, in addition, that

$$c_{11} + c_{12} = 1$$

verify that the parameters c_{11} and c_{12} are now identifiable.
(Reference: Rothenberg, 1971.)

Question 6.30

In the model

$$y_{1t} + b_{12}y_{2t} + c_{11}x_{2t} + c_{12}x_{2t} + c_{13}x_{3t} = u_{1t}$$
$$b_{21}y_{1t} + y_{2t} + c_{23}x_{3t} = u_{2t}$$
$$b_{31}y_{1t} + b_{32}y_{2t} + y_{3t} + c_{31}x_{1t} = u_{3t}$$

the $y_{it}(i = 1, 2, 3)$ are endogenous variables, the $x_{it}(i = 1, 2, 3)$ are exogenous variables and the $u_{it}(i = 1, 2, 3)$ are random disturbances. It is assumed that there are no a priori restrictions on the covariance matrix of the disturbances but their mean values are known to be zero.
(a) Consider the identifiability of each equation in the model.
(b) Is the model overidentified? Comment on your answer.

(University of Essex BA examinations, 1976.)

Question 6.31

In the model

$$y_{1t} = b_{12}y_{2t} + c_{11}x_{1t} + u_{1t}$$
$$y_{2t} = b_{21}y_{1t} + c_{21}x_{1t} + u_{2t}$$

the y_{it} are endogenous variables, the x_{it} are exogenous variables and the u_{it} are serially independent random disturbances that are identically distributed with zero means and non-singular covariance matrix for all t. It is known that the parameters in this model satisfy the cross equation restrictions

$$b_{12} + c_{21} = 0$$

and

$$c_{11} + b_{21} = 1$$

(a) Discuss the identifiability of the parameters in the above model.
(b) Consider, in particular, the identifiability of the structure in which $b_{12} = 1, b_{21} = -1, c_{11} = 2$ and $c_{21} = -1$.

Question 6.32

By using the method of two-stage least squares find an approximate 5 per cent confidence interval for the parameter b_{12} in the following model:

$$y_{1t} = b_{12}y_{2t} + u_{1t}$$
$$y_{2t} = b_{21}y_{1t} + c_{21}x_{1t} + c_{22}x_{2t} + u_{2t}$$

where the x_{it} are predetermined variables and the u_{it} are random disturbances. The sample moment matrix, computed from 100 observations is as follows:

	y_1	y_2	x_1	x_2
y_1	10	20	2	3
y_2	20	50	4	8
x_1	2	4	5	2
x_2	3	8	2	10

(Adapted from University of Auckland MA, MCom examinations, 1968.)

Question 6.33

One equation of a two-equation simultaneous equations model has the form

$$y_1 = by_2 + X_1 c + u$$

where y_1 and y_2 are T component observation vectors on two endogenous variables, X_1 is a $T \times m_1$ matrix of observations on m_1 exogenous variables, b is a scalar parameter, c is a vector of parameters and u is a disturbance vector. The matrix of observations on all exogenous variables that occur in the model is denoted by X.

Show that the two-stage least squares estimator of b can be written in the form

$$\hat{b} = \frac{y_2' Q y_1}{y_2' Q y_2}$$

where

$$Q = X(X'X)^{-1}X' - X_1(X_1'X_1)^{-1}X_1,$$

and the ordinary least squares estimator of b can be written in the form

$$b^* = \frac{y_2' R y_1}{y_2' R y_2} = \frac{y_2' Q y_1 + y_2' P y_1}{y_2' Q y_2 + y_2' P y_2}$$

where

$$R = I - X_1(X_1'X_1)^{-1}X_1,$$

and

$$P = I - X(X'X)^{-1}X'.$$

Question 6.34

In order to obtain consistent estimates of the parameter of an over-identified structural equation by simple application of the instrumental variable method, an investigator arbitrarily chooses the required number of instruments from those available. Compare this approach to that of two-stage least squares, in particular showing that it is in general less efficient.

(University of London BSc(Econ) examinations, 1976.)

Question 6.35

Show how it is possible to obtain efficient instrumental variable estimates in the case where there are more instrumental variables than unknown coefficients, and show that this is equivalent to using estimates of the systematic parts of the endogenous variables as instrumental variables, or to applying least squares to these estimated systematic parts. Extend this to the case where there are general linear constraints on the coefficients of the equation. If a complete model is estimated by instrumental variables, would there be any point in iterating by estimating the reduced form of the model from preliminary estimates of the structural form?

(University of London MSc(Econ) examinations, 1977.)

Question 6.36

Explain how, if the number of instrumental variables is larger than the number of unknown coefficients, efficient estimators may be obtained. Explain how you would modify your estimators if (i) the instrumental variable set is multicollinear, (ii) the instrumental variables are not adequate to identify the equation to be estimated.

(Adapted from University of London MSc(Econ) examinations, 1976.)

Question 6.37

It is hypothesised that the following single structural equation is subject to structural change such that

$$y_t = Y_{1t}\beta_1 + Y_{2t}\beta_2 + X_{1t}\gamma_1 + X_{2t}\gamma_2 + u_t, \quad \text{for} \quad t = 1, \ldots, T_1$$

and

$$y_t = Y_{1t}\beta_1 + Y_{2t}\beta_3 + X_{1t}\gamma_1 + X_{2t}\gamma_3 + u_t,$$
$$\text{for} \quad t = T_1 + 1, \ldots, T_1 + T_2,$$

where the complete set of predetermined variables is $X'_t = (X_{1t}X_{2t}X_{3t})$.
(a) Describe suitable estimators for the cases where
   (i) $\beta_2 = \beta_3$, $\gamma_2 \neq \gamma_3$, and
   (ii) $\beta_2 \neq \beta_3$, $\gamma_2 = \gamma_3$.

(b) Explain how you would test the null hypothesis $H_0 : \beta_2 = \beta_3, \gamma_2 = \gamma_3$ against each of the alternatives in (i) and (ii).

(Reference: A.P. Barten and Lise Salvas Bronsard, 1970.)

Question 6.38

Consider the linear simultaneous equation system

$$Y_t = B(Y_t - \hat{V}_t) + CX_t + U_t + B\hat{V}_t \tag{6.38.1}$$

where Y_t is a $p \times 1$ vector of endogenous variables, X_t is a $q \times 1$ vector of predetermined variables, U_t is a $p \times 1$ vector of serially independent structural disturbances with mean zero and covariance matrix Σ and $\hat{V}$ is a $p \times 1$ matrix of residuals obtained from OLS on the reduced form.

(a) Obtain an expression for Φ, the covariance matrix of

$$U_t + B\hat{V}_t. \tag{6.38.2}$$

(b) Using a consistent estimator of Φ based on 2SLS estimates, write equation (6.38.1) in unrestricted vector notation and prove that the generalised least squares estimators of the resulting equation is the 3SLS estimator.

(Reference: A. Maravall, 1976)

Question 6.39

Give a proof of the asymptotic error variance matrix of the 3SLS estimators of the general simultaneous equation model (6.0.1) (i) subject to zero-one restrictions, (ii) subject to general linear restrictions. Discuss the efficiency of these estimators compared to other estimators.

(University of London MSc(Econ) examinations, 1976.)

Question 6.40

Show that if the set of equations (6.0.1) are each just identified then 3SLS estimates for that set are the same as indirect least squares estimates. Supposing that in the latter case extra constraints are applied to just one equation, demonstrate the relationship between 3SLS and 2SLS estimates of the coefficients of this equation. Generalise your result to the case where some subsets of equations are over-identified.

(University of London MSc(Econ) examinations, 1977.)

Question 6.41

With reference to the econometric model whose structural form is

$$By_t + Cx_t = u_t \qquad (t = 1, \ldots, T)$$

and whose reduced form is

$$y_t = Px_t + v_t \qquad (t = 1, \ldots, T)$$

let P^* be the matrix of regression coefficients of y_t on x_t and define

$$M_{vv}^* = T^{-1} \sum_{t=1}^{T} (y_t - P^* x_t)(y_t - P^* x_t)'$$

Then the minimum distance estimator P^{**} of P is the matrix that minimises

$$T^{-1} \sum_{t=1}^{T} (y_t - Px_t)' M_{vv}^{*-1} (y_t - Px_t)$$

subject to the *a priori* restrictions on the coefficient matrices B and C in the structural form.

   Examine the relationship between P^{**} and the full information maximum likelihood estimator $\hat{P}$ which is obtained by maximising the likelihood function that corresponds to the assumption that u_t is normally distributed with unknown covariance matrix.

(Adapted from University of Auckland MA, MCom examinations, 1970.)

Question 6.42

For the linear simultaneous equation system

$$By_t + Cx_t = u_t$$

where the u_t are independent $N(0, \Sigma)$, obtain the limiting distributions of the maximum likelihood estimators of the coefficients of
(a) the unrestricted reduced form
(b) the solved (or restricted) reduced form.
(c) Compare the covariance matrices of these distributions.
(d) Interpret your results.

Question 6.43

In the model

$$y_{1t} = c_{11}x_{1t} + c_{12}x_{2t} + u_{1t}$$
$$y_{2t} = b_{21}y_{2t} + u_{2t} \qquad\qquad (6.43.1)$$

the y_{it} are endogenous variables, the x_{it} are exogenous variables and the u_{it} are serially independent normally distributed disturbances with zero means and covariance matrix

$$\begin{bmatrix} \sigma^2 & \sigma^2 \\ \sigma^2 & 2\sigma^2 \end{bmatrix}$$

(a) Find a matrix whose elements are independent of the unknown parameters in the model (6.43.1), and which can transform (6.43.1) into a recursive system.

(b) Explain why the use of ordinary least squares on each equation of the transformed system will *not* lead to asymptotically efficient estimators.

Question 6.44

In the simultaneous equation model

$$b_{11}y_{1t} + b_{12}y_{2t} + c_{11}x_{1t} = u_{1t}$$
$$b_{21}y_{1t} + b_{22}y_{2t} + c_{21}x_{1t} = u_{2t}$$

the following *a priori* restrictions (which include normalisations) are available:

$$b_{11} = 1, \quad b_{12} = 1, \quad c_{11} = 1, \quad b_{22} = 1, \quad c_{21} = 0.$$

The x_{it} are non-random, $\begin{bmatrix} u_{1t} \\ u_{2t} \end{bmatrix}$ is independent of $\begin{bmatrix} u_{1s} \\ u_{2s} \end{bmatrix}$ for $t \neq s$, and

there are no restrictions on the covariance matrix of $\begin{bmatrix} u_{1t} \\ u_{2t} \end{bmatrix}$. The following

data on sample second order moments are available.

	y_1	y_2	x_1
y_1	9	−3	−2
y_2	−3	$\frac{23}{2}$	3
x_1	−2	3	2

(a) Find the restricted reduced form.

(b) Estimate the covariance matrix of the unrestricted reduced form errors.

(c) Thus compute an estimate of b_{21} which is consistent and asymptotically efficient in the class of minimum distance estimators and which uses all the *a priori* information available.

(d) Compare your estimate with that obtained if the restrictions on the first equation are ignored.

(University of Essex MA examinations, 1977.)

Question 6.45

(a) Show that if a complete system of n structural equations can be partitioned into n_1 over-identified equations and n_2 unrestricted reduced form equations $(n = n_1 + n_2)$ then the FIML estimates of the coefficients of the over-identified set of equations, obtained using the complete system, are identical to the sub-system LIML estimates of these coefficients.

(b) Explain how this result can be used to compute
    (i) single equation LIML estimates, and
    (ii) more efficient estimates of the coefficients of a model that is incomplete (in the sense that it has more endogenous variables than structural equations) than can be obtained using single equation LIML or 2SLS on each equation.

(Reference: Godfrey and Wickens, 1977. See also questions 6.16–18.)

Question 6.46

The ith equation of the system (6.0.1) is written as in (6.0.3):

$$y_i = Z_i \delta_i + u_i$$

where δ_i is a $k_i \times 1$ vector of unknown coefficients. The 2SLS estimator $\hat{\delta}_i$ of δ_i minimises

$$\lambda(\delta_i) = T^{-1} (y_i - Z_i \delta_i)' X(X'X)^{-1} X'(y_i - Z_i \delta_i)$$

and the LIML estimator δ_i^* minimises

$$\mu(\delta_i) = \lambda(\delta_i)/\theta(\delta_i)$$

where

$$\theta(\delta_i) = T^{-1} (y_i - Z_i \delta_i)'(y_i - Z_i \delta_i).$$

If $\lim_{T \to \infty} T^{-1} X'X$ tends to a finite non-singular matrix
(a) Find the $k_i \times 1$ vector $\partial \lambda / \partial \delta_i$ and the $k_i \times k_i$ matrix $\partial^2 \lambda / \partial \delta_i \partial \delta_i'$.
(b) Prove that $(\hat{\delta}_i - \delta_i^*)$ is $O_p(T^{-1})$ and interpret your result.

(Adapted from University of York MA examinations, 1977.)

Question 6.47

An econometric model having been constructed and estimated, predictions of the endogenous variables for given values of the predetermined variables are required. Outline the steps required to calculate the standard errors of such predictions based on (a) direct estimation of the reduced form, (b) consistent estimates of the structural form, and comment on the relative merits of the two approaches.

(University of London BSc(Econ) examinations, 1976.)

Question 6.48

In many of the advanced economies, policy-makers have available to them a number of different macroeconometric models. What methodological difficulties are involved in attempting to determine which model performs 'best'? Is it possible or desirable to use the competing models jointly?

(University of London MSc(Econ) examinations, 1977.)

Question 6.49

For the income—expenditure model

$$c_t = \beta y_t + u_t$$

$$y_t = c_t + a_t \qquad (t = 1, \ldots, T)$$

where the u_t are independent $N(0, \sigma^2)$ variables and a_t is non-random, obtain the finite sample distribution of the instrumental estimator of β given by $b = \Sigma a_t c_t / \Sigma a_t y_t$.

3. SOLUTIONS

Solution 6.1

Part (a) In this answer we shall not attempt to present as rigorous a treatment of the identification problem as we shall to later problems. Our purpose here is to provide an introduction to the problem.

Suppose we let $Q_t = D_t = S_t$, then the model can be written:

$$Q_t = \alpha_0 - \alpha_1 p_t + \alpha_2 y_t + u_{1t} \tag{6.1.1}$$

$$Q_t = \beta_0 + \beta_1 p_t + u_{2t}. \tag{6.1.2}$$

Now consider the equation,

$$Q_t = \delta_0 - \delta_1 p_t + \delta_2 y_t + e_t \tag{6.1.3}$$

where δ_0, δ_1 and δ_2 are arbitrary coefficients and e_t is an arbitrary disturbance. We may regard the identification problem as it applies to equation (6.1.1) as follows: from knowledge of δ_i can we infer the values of $\alpha_i (i = 0, 1, 2)$? The answer to this question is no, if it is possible to form an equation like (6.1.3) from a linear combination of all the equations of the model. Without loss of generality, consider, for example, the following weighted average of (6.1.1) and (6.1.2):

$$Q_t = [\lambda\alpha_0 + (1-\lambda)\beta_0] - [\lambda\alpha_1 - (1-\lambda)\beta_1]p_t + \lambda\alpha_2 y_t$$
$$+ [\lambda u_{1t} + (1-\lambda)u_{2t}] \qquad 0 < \lambda < 1. \qquad (6.1.4)$$

We can equate (6.1.3) with (6.1.4), interpret δ_i as the coefficients of (6.1.4) and set $e_t = \lambda u_{1t} + (1-\lambda)u_{2t}$. Equations (6.1.3) and (6.1.4) have the same variables as (6.1.1) but, unless $\lambda = 1$, the coefficients are different. It is possible, therefore, to form from (6.1.1) and (6.1.2) an equation that has the same variables as (6.1.1) but different coefficients. Thus, we cannot deduce the coefficients α_i solely from knowledge of the coefficients δ_i. Equation (6.1.1), therefore, is not identified.

We can also ask the same question about equation (6.1.2). From (6.1.4), it is clear that the only linear combination of (6.1.1) and (6.1.2) that has the same variables as (6.1.2) requires that $\lambda = 0$. In other words, there is no linear combination of (6.1.1) and (6.1.2) that looks like (6.1.2). Consequently, the coefficients $\delta_i(i = 0, 1)$ defined in

$$Q_t = \delta_0 + \delta_1 p_t + e_t \qquad (6.1.5)$$

must satisfy $\delta_0 = \beta_0$ and $\delta_1 = \beta_1$; from knowledge of δ_i we can, therefore, infer $\beta_i(i = 0, 1)$. Thus equation (6.1.2) is identified.

A more general statement of the identification problem requires the concepts of 'structure', 'model' and 'observational equivalence'. A 'structure' is defined as a complete numerical specification of the stochastic relationships between the endogenous and exogenous variables. A 'model' is a set of structures each of which satisfies the same *a priori* restrictions but does not necessarily have the same numerical values. The endogenous variables of a model possess a certain joint probability distribution which is conditional on the values of the exogenous variables. For any given random sample from this probability distribution, we can construct the corresponding likelihood function by evaluating the joint probability density function at the sample point. If two structures are consistent with this likelihood function, then these two structures are said to be 'observationally equivalent'. A structure of a model is said to be identified if there exists no other observationally equivalent structure.

In the present example equation (6.1.1) is not identified because any linear combination of (6.1.1) and (6.1.2) is observationally equivalent to (6.1.1). In contrast, there exists no observationally equivalent structural equation to (6.1.2).

The joint probability distribution of the endogenous variables is the same for the two structures consisting of equations (6.1.1—2) and of equations (6.1.2 and 4) if these two structures have the same reduced form equations. (A proof that two structures are observationally equivalent if they have the same reduced form is given in Malinvaud, 1970b, pp. 650–1, and in particular, Proposition 1, and Schmidt, 1976, pp. 130–1.) If we consider first the structure formed from equations (6.1.2–3) we can then take the two structures above as special cases. We have

$$
\begin{bmatrix} 1 & \delta_1 \\ 1 & -\beta_1 \end{bmatrix} \begin{bmatrix} Q_t \\ P_t \end{bmatrix} - \begin{bmatrix} \delta_0 & \delta_2 \\ \beta_0 & 0 \end{bmatrix} \begin{bmatrix} 1 \\ y_t \end{bmatrix} = \begin{bmatrix} e_t \\ u_{2t} \end{bmatrix}.
\tag{6.1.6}
$$

The reduced form of (6.1.6) is

$$
\begin{bmatrix} Q_t \\ P_t \end{bmatrix} = \frac{1}{\delta_1 + \beta_1} \begin{bmatrix} \beta_1 & \delta_1 \\ 1 & -1 \end{bmatrix} \begin{bmatrix} \delta_0 & \delta_2 \\ \beta_0 & 0 \end{bmatrix} \begin{bmatrix} 1 \\ y_t \end{bmatrix} + \frac{1}{\delta_1 + \beta_1} \begin{bmatrix} \beta_1 & \delta_1 \\ 1 & -1 \end{bmatrix} \begin{bmatrix} e_t \\ u_{2t} \end{bmatrix}
$$

$$
= \frac{1}{\delta_1 + \beta_1} \begin{bmatrix} \delta_0\beta_1 + \delta_1\beta_0 & \delta_2\beta_1 \\ \delta_0 - \beta_0 & \delta_2 \end{bmatrix} \begin{bmatrix} 1 \\ y_t \end{bmatrix} + \frac{1}{\delta_1 + \beta_1} \begin{bmatrix} \beta_1 & \delta_1 \\ 1 & -1 \end{bmatrix} \begin{bmatrix} e_t \\ u_{2t} \end{bmatrix}
\tag{6.1.7}
$$

Substituting in (6.1.7) that $\delta_i = \alpha_i$ $(i = 0, 1, 2)$ and $e_t = u_{1t}$, we obtain the reduced form of (6.1.1–2):

$$
\begin{bmatrix} Q_t \\ P_t \end{bmatrix} = \frac{1}{\delta_1 + \beta_1} \begin{bmatrix} \alpha_0\beta_1 + \alpha_1\beta_0 & \alpha_2\beta_1 \\ \alpha_0 - \beta_0 & \alpha_2 \end{bmatrix} \begin{bmatrix} 1 \\ y_t \end{bmatrix} + \frac{1}{\alpha_1 + \beta_1} \begin{bmatrix} \beta_1 & \alpha_1 \\ 1 & -1 \end{bmatrix} \begin{bmatrix} u_{1t} \\ u_{2t} \end{bmatrix}
\tag{6.1.8}
$$

Substituting in (6.1.7) that $\delta_0 = \lambda\alpha_0 + (1-\lambda)\beta_0$, $\delta_1 = \lambda\alpha_1 - (1-\lambda)\beta_1$, $\delta_2 = \lambda\alpha_2$ and $e_t = \lambda u_{1t} + (1-\lambda)u_{2t}$ we obtain the reduced form of (6.1.2 and 4):

$$
\begin{bmatrix} Q_t \\ P_t \end{bmatrix} = \frac{1}{\lambda\alpha_1 - (1-\lambda)\beta_1 + \beta_1} \begin{bmatrix} (\lambda\alpha_0 + (1-\lambda)\beta_0)\beta_1 + (\lambda\alpha_1 - (1-\lambda)\beta_1)\beta_0 & \lambda\alpha_2\beta_1 \\ \lambda\alpha_0 + (1-\lambda)\beta_0 - \beta_0 & \lambda\alpha_2 \end{bmatrix} \begin{bmatrix} 1 \\ y_t \end{bmatrix}
$$

$$
+ \frac{1}{\lambda\alpha_1 - (1-\lambda)\beta_1 + \beta_1} \begin{bmatrix} \beta_1 & \lambda\alpha_1 - (1-\lambda)\beta_1 \\ 1 & -1 \end{bmatrix} \begin{bmatrix} \lambda u_{1t} + (1-\lambda)u_{2t} \\ u_{2t} \end{bmatrix}
$$

$$
= \frac{1}{\lambda(\alpha_1 + \beta_1)} \begin{bmatrix} \lambda(\alpha_0\beta_1 + \alpha_1\beta_1) & \lambda\alpha_2\beta_1 \\ \lambda(\alpha_0 - \beta_0) & \lambda\alpha_2 \end{bmatrix} \begin{bmatrix} 1 \\ y_t \end{bmatrix} + \frac{1}{\lambda(\alpha_1 + \beta_1)} \begin{bmatrix} \beta_1 & \lambda\alpha_1 - (1-\lambda)\beta_1 \\ 1 & -1 \end{bmatrix}
$$

$$
\cdot \begin{bmatrix} \lambda & 1-\lambda \\ 0 & 1 \end{bmatrix} \begin{bmatrix} u_{1t} \\ u_{2t} \end{bmatrix}
$$

$$
= \frac{1}{\alpha_1 + \beta_1} \begin{bmatrix} \alpha_0\beta_1 + \alpha_1\beta_1 & \alpha_2\beta_1 \\ \alpha_0 - \beta_0 & \alpha_2 \end{bmatrix} \begin{bmatrix} 1 \\ y_t \end{bmatrix} + \frac{1}{\lambda(\alpha_1 + \beta_1)} \begin{bmatrix} \lambda\beta_1 & \lambda\alpha_1 \\ \lambda & -1 \end{bmatrix} \begin{bmatrix} u_{1t} \\ u_{2t} \end{bmatrix}
$$

$$= \frac{1}{\alpha_1 + \beta_1} \begin{bmatrix} \alpha_0 \beta_1 + \alpha_1 \beta_1 & \alpha_2 \beta_1 \\ \alpha_0 - \beta_0 & \alpha_2 \end{bmatrix} \begin{bmatrix} 1 \\ y_t \end{bmatrix} + \frac{1}{\alpha_1 + \beta_1} \begin{bmatrix} \beta_1 & \alpha_1 \\ 1 & -1 \end{bmatrix} \begin{bmatrix} u_{1t} \\ u_{2t} \end{bmatrix},$$

which is identical to (6.1.8). Thus the two structures have the same reduced form and hence are observationally equivalent.

It is important to appreciate that the identification problem arises logically prior to estimation. If an equation is not identified, there is no point in trying to estimate it because, although it might be possible to obtain estimates of the coefficients of an equation that has the same variables as the equation we are interested in, the lack of identification of that equation implies that these estimates tell us nothing about the true coefficients of the equation of interest.

Part (b) We are asked to evaluate $\operatorname{plim}_{T \to \infty} (b_1 - \beta_1)$, where b_1 is the OLS estimator of β_1. Now

$$b_1 = \frac{\Sigma(p_t - \bar{p})(Q_t - \bar{Q})}{\Sigma(p_t - \bar{p})^2}$$

$$= \beta_1 + \frac{\Sigma(p_t - \bar{p})u_{2t}}{\Sigma(p_t - \bar{p})^2} \, .$$

Hence

$$\operatorname*{plim}_{T \to \infty} b_1 = \beta_1 + \frac{\operatorname{cov}(p, u_2)}{\operatorname{var}(p)}. \tag{6.1.9}$$

As p is determined in the market it is an endogenous variable. Random shifts in the supply function, due to u_2, affect p and imply that $\operatorname{cov}(p, u_2)$ is non-zero. In order to evaluate $\operatorname{cov}(p, u_2)$ we use the reduced form equation of p. This is given in (6.1.8) as

$$p_t = \frac{(\alpha_0 - \beta_0)}{\alpha_1 + \beta_1} + \frac{\alpha_2}{\alpha_1 + \beta_1} y_t + \frac{(u_{1t} - u_{2t})}{\alpha_1 + \beta_1}. \tag{6.1.10}$$

Since y_t is non-random, we can show from (6.1.10) that,

$$\operatorname{cov}(p, u_2) = \operatorname{cov}\left[u_{2t}, \frac{(u_{1t} - u_{2t})}{\alpha_1 + \beta_1}\right]$$

$$= \frac{\sigma_{12} - \sigma_2^2}{\alpha_1 + \beta_1} \tag{6.1.11}$$

and

$$\operatorname{var}(p) = \operatorname{var}\left[\frac{u_{1t} - u_{2t}}{\alpha_1 + \beta_1}\right]$$

$$= \frac{\sigma_1^2 + \sigma_2^2 - 2\sigma_{12}}{(\alpha_1 + \beta_1)^2}. \tag{6.1.12}$$

Substituting (6.1.11) and (6.1.12) into (6.1.9) we obtain the asymptotic bias

$$\text{plim}(b_1 - \beta_1) = (\alpha_1 + \beta_1) \cdot \frac{\sigma_{12} - \sigma_2^2}{\sigma_1^2 + \sigma_2^2 - 2\sigma_{12}} . \tag{6.1.13}$$

From (6.1.9) we see that the source of this asymptotic bias is the non-zero covariance between p and u_2. This non-zero covariance is the result of the fact that p is an endogenous variable. Random shifts in the supply function (6.1.2), due to u_2, simultaneously influence price and output. Consequently this asymptotic bias is known as simultaneous equation bias.

Part (c) If $\sigma_{12} = 0$, (6.1.13) becomes

$$\text{plim}(b_1 - \beta_1) = -\frac{(\alpha_1 + \beta_1)\sigma_2^2}{\sigma_1^2 + \sigma_2^2} \tag{6.1.14}$$

We expect α_1 and β_1 to be non-negative, hence (6.1.14) is non-positive. That is, b_1 is biased downwards; our estimate of β_1 is too small. The absolute size of this bias depends on the relative magnitudes of σ_1^2 and σ_2^2 and on the slopes of the demand and supply functions. It is greater the larger is σ_2^2 relative to σ_1^2 and the larger the absolute slopes of the two functions, namely α_1 and β_1.

Solution 6.2

Part (a) First we shall show how the *a priori* restrictions on the structural equations can be expressed and then we shall consider whether or not these restrictions are sufficient to identify the structural model. We can rewrite the simultaneous equation system

$$By_t + Cx_t = u_t \qquad (t = 1, \ldots, T) \tag{6.2.1}$$

where B is $n \times n$ and C is $n \times m$, as

$$Aw_t = u_t \tag{6.2.2}$$

where $A = (B \vdots C)$ is an $n \times (m + n)$ matrix and $w_t' = (y_t', x_t')$. The ith equation of (6.2.2) is written

$$a_i'w_t = u_{it} \tag{6.2.3}$$

where a_i' is the ith row of A and u_{it} is the ith element of u_t.

Suppose there are k_i linear homogeneous restrictions on the ith equation. These can be written

$$a_i'\Phi_i = 0 \tag{6.2.4}$$

where Φ_i is an $(m + n) \times k_i$ matrix of restrictions. For example, consider the first equation of the model. The coefficients of y_{2t}, y_{3t} and x_{2t} are restricted to be zero, implying that we have three restrictions: $b_{12} = b_{13} = c_{12} = 0$. In this case $a'_1 = (b_{11}, b_{12}, b_{13}, c_{11}, c_{12})$ and

$$\Phi_1 = \begin{bmatrix} 0 & 0 & 0 \\ 1 & 0 & 0 \\ 0 & 1 & 0 \\ 0 & 0 & 0 \\ 0 & 0 & 1 \end{bmatrix}$$

and so equation (6.2.4) becomes

$$(b_{11}, b_{12}, b_{13}, c_{11}, c_{12}) \begin{bmatrix} 0 & 0 & 0 \\ 1 & 0 & 0 \\ 0 & 1 & 0 \\ 0 & 0 & 0 \\ 0 & 0 & 1 \end{bmatrix} = (0 \quad 0 \quad 0) \qquad (6.2.5)$$

or,

$$(b_{12}, b_{13}, c_{12}) = (0 \quad 0 \quad 0).$$

Thus for each of the above restrictions the restriction matrix requires one column. The elements of this column are chosen so that the appropriate element of a_1 is selected. This element is then set to zero in the corresponding element of the vector on the right hand side of (6.2.4).

In the answer to Question (6.1) the identification problem was related to the joint probability distribution of the endogenous variables in the structural form of the model and then to the likelihood function. Now we wish to show exactly what this relationship is. We shall then derive the rank and order conditions which are necessary for identifiability.

Suppose the disturbances u_t defined in (6.2.1) have the joint probability density function $f(u_t)$, then the endogenous variables y_t have a joint probability density function conditional on x_t given by

$$f(y_t \mid x_t) = |\det(B)| f(u_t)$$

where $|\det(B)|$, the absolute value of the determinant of B, is the Jacobian of the transformation. If the u_t are serially independent, the likelihood function obtained from an independent random sample of size T is

$$L = \prod_{t=1}^{T} f(y_t \mid x_t) = |\det(B)|^T f(u_1) \ldots f(u_T). \qquad (6.2.6)$$

Consider now the structural model

$$H(By_t + Cx_t) = Hu_t = e_t \qquad (6.2.7)$$

where H is an $n \times n$ non-singular matrix. The joint probability density function of e_t is given by

$$f(e_t) = |\det(H^{-1})| f(u_t)$$

and hence the likelihood function of (6.2.7) is

$$\begin{aligned}
L^* &= |\det(HB)|^T f(e_1) \ldots f(e_T) \\
&= |\det(HB)|^T |\det(H^{-1})|^T f(u_1) \ldots f(u_T) \\
&= |\det(B)|^T f(u_1) \ldots f(u_T)
\end{aligned}$$

which is identical to (6.2.6). In other words, the linear combination (6.2.7) of the original structural model (6.2.1) has the same likelihood function as (6.2.1) and hence is observationally equivalent to (6.2.1).

If the entire structure (6.2.1) is to be identifiable then we must exclude all structures such as (6.2.7) except those in which H is the identity matrix. If we are concerned with a single equation (say the ith) then we must exclude all structures, such as (6.2.7), except those in which HA has the same ith row as A, i.e. all matrices H except those which have an ith row with unity in the ith position and zeros elsewhere.

A necessary and sufficient condition for this to be so is the following well-known rank condition. For a proof of this result see Malinvaud (1970b, pp. 656–660), Fisher (1966) and Schmidt (1976, p. 134).

Rank Condition A necessary and sufficient condition for the identifiability of the ith equation is that the rank of $A\Phi_i$ is $n-1$.

Order Condition A necessary (but not sufficient) condition is that k_i, the rank of Φ_i, satisfies $k_i \geqslant n-1$, where k_i is the number of restrictions and hence the number of columns of Φ_i.

For the case of zero restrictions on A, the rank condition is equivalent to requiring that A_i^*, the matrix of coefficients formed by deleting from A all columns corresponding to the variables included in the ith equation, should have rank $n-1$. To see this, re-order the variables in w_t such that

$$\Phi_i = \begin{bmatrix} 0 \\ I_{k_i} \end{bmatrix}$$ and partition A conformably. Thus

$$A\Phi_i = (A_0 \vdots A_i^*)\begin{bmatrix} 0 \\ I_{k_i} \end{bmatrix} = A_i^*$$

where A_i^* is an $n \times k_i$ matrix with a zero ith row. It follows that rank $(A\Phi_i) = $ rank (A_i^*) which we set out to prove. In other words, for the identifiability of the ith equation we must not be able to form another equation from a linear combination of the remaining $n-1$ equations that excludes the same variables as are excluded from the ith equation. The order condition can be derived for this case by noting that max $\{\text{rank}(A_i^*)\}$ = min $\{k_i, n-1\}$. Therefore, in order that rank $(A\Phi_i) = n-1$, we require $k_i \geqslant n-1$, that is, we require at least $n-1$ (linear) restrictions. If $k_i < n-1$ then the ith *equation* is said to be *under-identified*, if $k_i = n-1$ and the rank condition is satisfied, it is said to be *just identified*, and if $k_i > n-1$ and the rank condition is satisfied, it is said to be *over-identified*. In Part (b) we will discuss the concept of an over-identified model as distinct from an over-identified equation.

(i) To establish the identifiability of the first equation of the model we note first that the restriction matrix Φ_1, defined in equation (6.2.5), is formed from three zero restrictions. As $n-1=2$, the order condition is satisfied by the first equation. The rank condition applies to the matrix

$$A\Phi_1 = \begin{bmatrix} b_{11} & 0 & 0 & c_{11} & 0 \\ b_{21} & b_{22} & 0 & c_{21} & 0 \\ 0 & b_{32} & b_{33} & c_{31} & c_{32} \end{bmatrix} \begin{bmatrix} 0 & 0 & 0 \\ 1 & 0 & 0 \\ 0 & 1 & 0 \\ 0 & 0 & 0 \\ 0 & 0 & 1 \end{bmatrix}$$

$$= \begin{bmatrix} 0 & 0 & 0 \\ b_{22} & 0 & 0 \\ b_{32} & b_{33} & c_{32} \end{bmatrix} = A_1^*$$

The rank of A_1^* is 2 if it has at least one non-zero, 2×2 minor. A_1^* has two such minors, they are

$$\begin{vmatrix} b_{22} & 0 \\ b_{23} & b_{33} \end{vmatrix} \quad \text{and} \quad \begin{vmatrix} b_{22} & 0 \\ b_{23} & c_{32} \end{vmatrix}$$

The first minor is non-zero if $b_{22}, b_{33} \neq 0$, the second minor is non-zero if $b_{22}, c_{32} \neq 0$. But due to normalisation, $b_{22} = b_{33} = 1$, hence the rank condition is satisfied for the first equation. As the number of restrictions on the first equation is $k_1 = 3$, which is greater than $n-1=2$, this equation is over-identified.

We proceed similarly to establish the identifiability conditions for the second and third equations. For the second equation as $k_2 = 2$ the order condition is satisfied. Now

$$\Phi_2 = \begin{bmatrix} 0 & 0 \\ 0 & 0 \\ 1 & 0 \\ 0 & 0 \\ 0 & 1 \end{bmatrix} \quad \text{and} \quad A\Phi_2 = A_2^* = \begin{bmatrix} 0 & 0 \\ 0 & 0 \\ b_{33} & c_{32} \end{bmatrix}.$$

hence the rank of A_2^* is unity which is less than $n - 1 = 2$. The second equation, therefore, is not identified despite satisfying the order condition. There is only one restriction for the third equation, implying that neither the order nor the rank condition is satisfied. The third equation, therefore, is said to be under-identified.

(ii) If $c_{31} = 0$ an extra restriction is imposed on the third equation, which now satisfies the order condition. We can obtain

$$\Phi_3 = \begin{bmatrix} 1 & 0 \\ 0 & 0 \\ 0 & 0 \\ 0 & 1 \\ 0 & 0 \end{bmatrix} \quad \text{and} \quad A\Phi_3 = A_3^* = \begin{bmatrix} b_{11} & c_{11} \\ b_{21} & c_{21} \\ 0 & 0 \end{bmatrix}.$$

Since $b_{11} = 1$, the rank of A_2^* is 2 if $c_{21} - c_{11}b_{21} \neq 0$. Hence the third equation is now just identified if $c_{21} - c_{11}b_{21} \neq 0$. This additional restriction does affect the identifiability of the first and second equations as their order conditions and A_1^* and A_2^* are unaltered.

(iii) The restriction $b_{21} + c_{21} = 0$ is imposed on the second equation. We now have three restrictions on the second equation. The restriction matrix Φ_2 can be written

$$\Phi_2 = \begin{bmatrix} 0 & 0 & 1 \\ 0 & 0 & 0 \\ 1 & 0 & 0 \\ 0 & 0 & 1 \\ 0 & 1 & 0 \end{bmatrix} \quad \text{and hence} \quad A\Phi_2 = A_2^* = \begin{bmatrix} 0 & 0 & b_{11}+c_{11} \\ 0 & 0 & 0 \\ b_{33} & c_{32} & c_{31} \end{bmatrix}.$$

Since $b_{11}, b_{33} = 1$, the rank of A_2^* is 2 if $c_{11} \neq -1$ and the rank condition is satisfied. The second equation, therefore, is now over-identified. The identifiability of the first and third equations is unchanged.

Part (b) We can also consider the identifiability of a whole structural *model* as opposed to the individual structural equations (see, in particular, Malinvaud, 1970b, pp. 650–654). The structural form of a *model* is said to be identifiable if and only if no other structural form has the same reduced form. A structural *model* is said to be over-identified if it places restrictions on the reduced form. It should be noted that an over-identified model in the above sense does not necessarily imply that every structural equation in the model is identified in the sense of Part (a). We can illustrate this by considering the reduced form of the present structural model.

The reduced form coefficient matrix of the present structural model is obtained by partitioning the matrix of structural coefficients conformably with the endogenous and exogenous variables. Thus $A = [B \vdots C]$, where B is the matrix of structural coefficients of the endogenous variables and C is the matrix of structural coefficients of the exogenous variables. Using the normalisation rule $b_{ii} = 1$ for all i, the reduced form coefficient matrix is

$$P = -B^{-1}C$$

$$= -\begin{bmatrix} 1 & 0 & 0 \\ b_{21} & 1 & 0 \\ 0 & b_{32} & 1 \end{bmatrix}^{-1} \begin{bmatrix} c_{11} & 0 \\ c_{21} & 0 \\ c_{31} & c_{32} \end{bmatrix} = -\begin{bmatrix} 1 & 0 & 0 \\ -b_{21} & 1 & 0 \\ b_{21}b_{32} & -b_{32} & 1 \end{bmatrix} \begin{bmatrix} c_{11} & 0 \\ c_{21} & 0 \\ c_{31} & c_{32} \end{bmatrix}$$

$$= -\begin{bmatrix} c_{11} & 0 \\ -b_{21}c_{11} + c_{21} & 0 \\ b_{21}b_{32}c_{11} - b_{32}c_{21} + c_{31} & c_{32} \end{bmatrix}$$

We notice that P possesses two zero restrictions, therefore, the *model* is said to be over-identified. We can now ask if we can deduce any of the structural coefficients from knowledge of P. Clearly, if we know P then we know c_{11} and c_{32}. But c_{11} is the only unrestricted coefficient in the first structural equation, hence knowledge of c_{11} implies the identifiability of the first structural equation. However, without imposing further restrictions on P, we cannot identify the second and third structural equations.

In case (ii), $c_{31} = 0$. We notice, however, that we still cannot determine the structural coefficients of equations two and three uniquely without further information. In case (iii), $b_{21} + c_{21} = 0$ and hence we can now infer the coefficients of the second structural equation uniquely from knowledge of P as well as those of the first equation. However, we still cannot identify the third structural equation without further information.

These results illustrate our earlier remarks. They show that restrictions on the structural coefficients imply restrictions on the reduced form coefficients but a given set of restrictions on the reduced form coefficients are not necessarily sufficient to permit the identification of a particular structural equation.

Remark Some additional comments on the over-identification of a model may be helpful at this point. Recall that *a model is over-identified* when the *a priori* restrictions on the structural form of the model imply restrictions on the reduced form of the model. In most cases these restrictions involve the coefficients of the variables in the model. If there are n equations in a model and there are more than $n - 1$ linearly independent restrictions on the coefficients in one equation of this model (in our notation this will mean that Φ_i has $k_i \geqslant n$ columns for some i and has full rank) then the model will be over-identified. A full statement of this result together with the assumptions under which this is also a necessary condition for over-identification is given by Malinvaud (1970b, pp. 663). Sometimes, as we have seen in Part (a), we talk of *an equation being over-identified* when there are more than the $n - 1$ restrictions on its coefficients that are needed for identification. But this use of the term 'over-identification' should be carefully distinguished. For, it excludes those cases in which the reduced form coefficient matrix can be restricted when there are only $n - 1$ restrictions on each equation. (The interested reader is referred to Malinvaud, 1970b, pp. 661, for an example).

Part (c) (i) Whilst in practice the order condition is usually easy to verify, the rank condition is not, especially if we have a large system of equations or if the system is non-linear. In these cases frequently the rank condition is not checked before estimation. Nevertheless, we can sometimes receive signals about non-identification during estimation. If a system is under-identified then the information matrix of the system is singular at the true values of the parameters (Rothenberg 1971). Failure of the FIML estimator to converge may be the result of a singular information matrix and hence an indicator of under-identification. But, owing to sampling error, convergence may still be achieved even for an under-identified model.

(ii) From the previous discussion it is evident that identifiability *implies* the presence of restrictions on the parameter space. These restrictions are necessary to be able to infer a particular structure from a body of data. If more than one structure is consistent with the same set of data then we do not have identifiability. Restrictions should not be imposed on the data in order to achieve identification for such identifiability would be illusory. In order to safeguard against this it is desirable to test the identifying restrictions. Unfortunately, however, such tests can only be carried out on over-identifying restrictions and not on just identifying restrictions (see Fisher, 1966).

Solution 6.3

Part (a) Without loss of generality we can ignore the normalisation rule as in Question (6.2). There is one restriction on the first equation which therefore satisfies the order condition. For the rank condition we require that the rank of

$$
A\phi_1 = \begin{bmatrix} b_{11} & b_{12} & c_{11} & 0 \\ b_{21} & b_{22} & c_{21} & c_{22} \end{bmatrix} \begin{bmatrix} 0 \\ 0 \\ 0 \\ 1 \end{bmatrix} = \begin{bmatrix} 0 \\ c_{22} \end{bmatrix}
$$

equal unity. (The notation corresponds to that used in Question 6.2). Thus if $c_{22} \neq 0$, the first equation is just identified. There are no restrictions on the coefficients of the second equation, therefore this equation is under-identified.

Part (b) The restriction $b_{21} + c_{21} = 1$ is known as an inhomogeneous linear restriction (Fisher, 1966, pp. 56–61). A set of k_i inhomogeneous linear restrictions on the ith equation can be written

$$A_i \psi_i = \lambda_i \tag{6.3.1}$$

where A_i is the ith row of A, ψ_i is the $(m + n) \times k_i$ restriction matrix and λ_i is a k_i row vector of known constants with at least one non-zero element. In the present case (6.3.1) becomes

$$
(b_{21} \quad b_{22} \quad c_{21} \quad c_{22}) \begin{bmatrix} 1 \\ 0 \\ 1 \\ 0 \end{bmatrix} = 1. \tag{6.3.2}
$$

There are two ways of dealing with an inhomogeneous restriction. Either we can convert it to a homogeneous restriction plus a normalisation rule; in the present case this would imply the restrictions

$$b_{21} + c_{22} = b_{22} \quad \text{and} \quad b_{22} = 1.$$

Or, we can use a more general result. In the former case we apply the rank and order conditions for homogeneous linear restrictions. In the more general result the rank condition is that rank $(A\psi_i) = n$ and the order condition that rank $(\psi_i) \geqslant n$. (See Fisher 1966.)

In the above model the identification of the first equation remains unchanged. Applying the first method to the second equation we obtain the homogeneous restriction matrix

$$\phi_2 = \begin{bmatrix} 1 \\ -1 \\ 1 \\ 0 \end{bmatrix} \quad \text{and} \quad A\phi_2 = \begin{bmatrix} b_{11} - b_{12} + c_{11} \\ 0 \end{bmatrix}.$$

Provided $b_{11} + c_{11} \neq b_{12}$, therefore, the second equation is just identified. Applying the more general method we obtain

$$A_2 \begin{bmatrix} 0 & 1 \\ 1 & -1 \\ 0 & 1 \\ 0 & 0 \end{bmatrix} = (1 \quad 0)$$

which satisfies the order condition for inhomogeneous restrictions. Now

$$A\psi_2 = \begin{bmatrix} b_{12} & b_{11} - b_{12} + c_{11} \\ b_{22} & 0 \end{bmatrix}. \tag{6.3.3}$$

But as $b_{22} = 1$, the rank $(A\psi_2) = 2$ if $b_{11} + c_{11} \neq b_{12}$, which is the condition for just-identification obtained using the first method.

Part (c) Restrictions on the covariance matrix of disturbances can imply restrictions on the structural coefficients (see Fisher, 1966, Johnston, 1972, pp. 365–372, Rothenberg, 1971 and Wegge, 1965). To see this, consider the reduced form of a structural model such as (6.0.1):

$$y_t = Px_t + v_t \tag{6.3.4}$$

where $P = -B^{-1}C$, $v_t = B^{-1}u_t$, $E(v_t) = 0$ and $E(v_t v_t') = \Omega$. But

$$E(v_t v_t') = E(B^{-1} u_t u_t' B^{-1}{}') = B^{-1} \Sigma B^{-1}{}'.$$

where $E(u_t u_t') = \Sigma$ is the covariance matrix of the structural disturbances. Hence

$$B\Omega B' = \Sigma. \tag{6.3.5}$$

Equation (6.3.5) provides a set of non-linear restrictions on the elements of B. Economic theory usually provides restrictions for the structural coefficients and only very occasionally can it be expected to provide restrictions on the elements of Σ. Using the restrictions on Σ in the present case, (6.3.5) can be written

$$\begin{bmatrix} b_{11} & b_{12} \\ b_{21} & b_{22} \end{bmatrix} \begin{bmatrix} \omega_{11} & \omega_{12} \\ \omega_{21} & \omega_{22} \end{bmatrix} \begin{bmatrix} b_{11} & b_{21} \\ b_{12} & b_{22} \end{bmatrix} = \begin{bmatrix} \sigma_{11} & 0 \\ 0 & \sigma_{22} \end{bmatrix} \tag{6.3.6}$$

or

$$\left[\begin{array}{c} b_{11}^2 \omega_{11} + b_{11} b_{12} (\omega_{21} + \omega_{12}) + b_{12}^2 \omega_{22} \\ \hline b_{21} b_{11} \omega_{11} + b_{21} b_{12} \omega_{21} + b_{22} b_{11} \omega_{12} + b_{22} b_{12} \omega_{22} \end{array} \right.$$

$$\left. \begin{array}{c} b_{21} b_{11} \omega_{11} + b_{21} b_{12} \omega_{21} + b_{22} b_{11} \omega_{12} + b_{22} b_{12} \omega_{22} \\ \hline b_{21}^2 \omega_{11} + b_{21} b_{22} (\omega_{21} + \omega_{12}) + b_{22}^2 \omega_{22} \end{array} \right]$$

$$= \begin{bmatrix} \sigma_{11} & 0 \\ 0 & \sigma_{22} \end{bmatrix} \tag{6.3.7}$$

From the normalisation rule $b_{ii} = 1$ $(i = 1, 2)$, we can obtain from (6.3.7) the non-linear restriction

$$b_{21} \omega_{11} + b_{21} b_{12} \omega_{21} + \omega_{12} + b_{12} \omega_{22} = 0 \tag{6.3.8}$$

or

$$b_{21} = -\frac{\omega_{12} + b_{12} \omega_{22}}{\omega_{11} + b_{12} \omega_{21}} = \mu. \tag{6.3.9}$$

Since b_{12} is identified in the first equation, we can interpret (6.3.9) as an inhomogeneous restriction on the second equation with μ treated as a known (or estimable) constant. The inhomogeneous restriction on the second equation becomes

$$A_2 \begin{bmatrix} 0 & 1 \\ 1 & 0 \\ 0 & 0 \\ 0 & 0 \end{bmatrix} = (1 \quad \mu). \tag{6.3.10}$$

This satisfies the order condition. Now

$$A \psi_2 = \begin{bmatrix} b_{12} & b_{11} \\ b_{22} & b_{21} \end{bmatrix}$$

and rank $(A \psi_2) = 2$ if $b_{11} b_{22} - b_{12} b_{21} \neq 0$. If this condition holds, the second equation is now identified. The identification of the first equation is unaltered.

Solution 6.4

Part (a) Since the restrictions (6.4.3–4) involve parameters from both equations we cannot appeal to the usual rank and order conditions to examine the identifiability of the parameters in this model (compare Solution 6.2). However, we can treat the model as a whole and apply the rank and order conditions developed by Wegge (1966) and Rothenberg (1971). An alternative approach in the present case is to solve for the reduced form and examine directly the correspondence between the structural and reduced form parameters in the light of the prior restrictions (6.4.3–4). We shall consider both these approaches.

In the notation of (6.0.1) we have

$$B = \begin{bmatrix} b_{11} & -b_{12} \\ -b_{21} & b_{22} \end{bmatrix}, \quad C = \begin{bmatrix} -c_{11} \\ -c_{21} \end{bmatrix}$$

and the complete set of restrictions (including normalisations) is

$$b_{11} - 1 = 0$$
$$b_{12} + b_{21} - 1 = 0$$
$$b_{22} - 1 = 0$$
$$c_{11} - c_{21} = 0$$

which we can write as the system of equations

$$\psi(B, C) = 0$$

or

$$\psi(b, c) = 0 \tag{6.4.5}$$

where $b = \text{vec}(B)$, $c = \text{vec}(C)$. From (6.4.5) we can form the matrices of derivatives

$$\Psi_b = \frac{\partial \psi}{\partial b'} = \begin{bmatrix} 1 & 0 & 0 & 0 \\ 0 & 1 & 1 & 0 \\ 0 & 0 & 0 & 1 \\ 0 & 0 & 0 & 0 \end{bmatrix}$$

and

$$\psi_c = \frac{\partial \psi}{\partial c'} = \begin{bmatrix} 0 & 0 \\ 0 & 0 \\ 0 & 0 \\ 1 & -1 \end{bmatrix}$$

If we now let $\alpha' = (b, c)$, it follows directly from the results in Wegge

(1966) and Rothenberg (1971; in particular, Theorem 9 p. 588) that the parameter vector α is identifiable if and only if the matrix

$$W^* = \Psi_b (I_2 \otimes B') + \Psi_c (I_2 \otimes C') \tag{6.4.6}$$

has rank = 4 (the number of equations in the model squared), where W^* is evaluated at the true value of the parameter vector.

We find that

$$W^* = \begin{bmatrix} 1 & 0 & 0 & 0 \\ 0 & 1 & 1 & 0 \\ 0 & 0 & 0 & 1 \\ 0 & 0 & 0 & 0 \end{bmatrix} \begin{bmatrix} b_{11} & -b_{21} & 0 & 0 \\ -b_{12} & b_{22} & 0 & 0 \\ 0 & 0 & b_{11} & -b_{21} \\ 0 & 0 & -b_{12} & b_{22} \end{bmatrix}$$

$$+ \begin{bmatrix} 0 & 0 \\ 0 & 0 \\ 0 & 0 \\ 1 & -1 \end{bmatrix} \begin{bmatrix} -c_{11} & -c_{21} & 0 & 0 \\ 0 & 0 & -c_{11} & -c_{21} \end{bmatrix}$$

$$= \begin{bmatrix} b_{11} & -b_{21} & 0 & 0 \\ -b_{12} & b_{22} & b_{11} & -b_{21} \\ 0 & 0 & -b_{12} & b_{22} \\ -c_{11} & -c_{21} & c_{11} & c_{21} \end{bmatrix} \tag{6.4.7}$$

and, using the fact that $b_{11} = b_{22} = 1$ and $c_{11} = c_{21}$, this matrix becomes

$$\begin{bmatrix} 1 & -b_{21} & \vdots & 0 & 0 \\ -b_{12} & 1 & \vdots & 1 & -b_{21} \\ \cdots & \cdots & \vdots & \cdots & \cdots \\ 0 & 0 & \vdots & -b_{12} & 1 \\ -c_{11} & -c_{11} & \vdots & c_{11} & c_{11} \end{bmatrix}$$

Evaluating the determinant of this matrix according to the indicated partition (for the determinant of a partitioned matrix see, for example, Johnston, 1972, p. 95) we obtain

$$\begin{vmatrix} 1 & -b_{21} \\ -b_{12} & 1 \end{vmatrix} \det \left\{ \begin{bmatrix} -b_{12} & 1 \\ c_{11} & c_{11} \end{bmatrix} - \begin{bmatrix} 0 & 0 \\ -c_{11} & -c_{11} \end{bmatrix} \begin{bmatrix} 1 & -b_{21} \\ -b_{12} & 1 \end{bmatrix}^{-1} \begin{bmatrix} 0 & 0 \\ 1 & -b_{21} \end{bmatrix} \right\}$$

which is non-zero provided both factors are non-zero. From the first factor we have the condition

$$d = 1 - b_{12}b_{21} \neq 0 \tag{6.4.8}$$

and from the second (assuming (6.4.8) holds) we obtain

$$\det \left\{ \begin{bmatrix} -b_{12} & 1 \\ c_{11} & c_{11} \end{bmatrix} + \frac{1}{d} \begin{bmatrix} 0 & 0 \\ c_{11} & c_{11} \end{bmatrix} \begin{bmatrix} 1 & b_{21} \\ b_{12} & 1 \end{bmatrix} \begin{bmatrix} 0 & 0 \\ 1 & -b_{21} \end{bmatrix} \right\} \neq 0$$

or

$$\begin{vmatrix} -b_{12} & 1 \\ c_{11} + d^{-1}c_{11}(1 + b_{21}) & c_{11} - d^{-1}b_{21}C_{11}(1 + b_{21}) \end{vmatrix} \neq 0$$

from which we obtain the second condition:

$$c_{11}(1 + b_{12}) + c_{11}(1 + b_{21}) \neq 0$$

or

$$c_{11}(2 + b_{12} + b_{21}) \neq 0. \tag{6.4.9}$$

In view of (6.4.3), (6.4.9) implies that

$$c_{11} \neq 0 \tag{6.4.10}$$

Hence, W^* has full rank $(= 4)$ provided (6.4.8) and (6.4.10) hold; and it follows that all structures of the model are identifiable except for those in which either $1 - b_{12}b_{21} = 0$ or $c_{11} = 0$.

Each of these conditions has a simple interpretation. When $1 - b_{12}b_{21} = 0$, the coefficient matrix B is singular and the model does not provide a unique solution for the endogenous variables.

Secondly, when $c_{11} = 0$, we see that the model contains no exogenous variables so that the reduced form of (6.4.1–2), in this case, is just

$$\begin{bmatrix} y_{2t} \\ y_{2t} \end{bmatrix} = \begin{bmatrix} 1 & -b_{12} \\ -b_{21} & 1 \end{bmatrix}^{-1} \begin{bmatrix} u_{1t} \\ u_{2t} \end{bmatrix} = \frac{1}{1 - b_{12}b_{21}} \begin{bmatrix} u_{1t} + b_{12}u_{2t} \\ u_{2t} + b_{21}u_{1t} \end{bmatrix}.$$

The mean value of this vector is zero for all values of t and its covariance matrix V, which comprises three distinct elements, will depend on the values of b_{12}, b_{21}, and Σ, the covariance matrix of (u_{1t}, u_{2t}). Taking into account the restriction (6.4.3) and the three distinct elements in the covariance matrix Σ we will then obtain from the relation

$$V = \begin{bmatrix} 1 & -b_{12} \\ -b_{21} & 1 \end{bmatrix}^{-1} \Sigma \begin{bmatrix} 1 & -b_{21} \\ -b_{12} & 1 \end{bmatrix}^{-1}.$$

three distinct equations in four unknowns. We will, in general, not be able to identify the parameters b_{12} and b_{21}.

Remark 1 Since the restrictions (6.4.5) are linear in the elements of B and C and are independent of the elements of the covariance matrix of the disturbances (u_{1t}, u_{2t}) the above results are globally true. By this we mean that, if a parameter is identifiable, then it is identifiable in the entire parameter space. This concept of global identification (which we have, in fact, implicitly used in our earlier solutions of 6.1 to 6.3) should be distinguished from that of local identification, by which term we mean that a parameter is identifiable when we confine ourselves to a region of a particular value (and, therefore, not necessarily to the entire parameter space). The reader is referred to the elegant paper of Rothenberg (1971) for a complete discussion of these points.

Remark 2   Rather than use the above method of dealing with a complete system of equations, we can in this simple two-equation case readily use the correspondence between the structural form and reduced form parameters to examine identifiability. The reduced form of the system (6.4.1—2) is given by

$$\begin{bmatrix} y_{1t} \\ y_{2t} \end{bmatrix} = \frac{1}{1-b_{12}b_{21}} \begin{bmatrix} 1 & b_{12} \\ b_{21} & 1 \end{bmatrix} \begin{bmatrix} c_{11} \\ c_{11} \end{bmatrix} x_{1t} + \frac{1}{1-b_{12}b_{21}} \begin{bmatrix} u_{1t}+b_{12}u_{2t} \\ u_{2t}+b_{21}u_{1t} \end{bmatrix}$$

$$= \begin{bmatrix} \pi_1 \\ \pi_2 \end{bmatrix} x_{1t} + \begin{bmatrix} v_{1t} \\ v_{2t} \end{bmatrix}$$

say, where

$$\pi_1 = \frac{c_{11}(1+b_{12})}{1-b_{12}b_{21}} \quad \text{and} \quad \pi_2 = \frac{c_{11}(1+b_{21})}{1-b_{12}b_{21}}. \tag{6.4.11}$$

Note that the existence of the reduced form requires our earlier condition (6.4.8) or $1-b_{12}b_{21} \neq 0$. From (6.4.11) we now have the relation

$$\frac{\pi_1}{\pi_2} = \frac{1+b_{12}}{1+b_{21}}$$

provided $c_{11} \neq 0$. And since from (6.4.3)

$$b_{21} = 1-b_{12} \tag{6.4.12}$$

it follows that

$$b_{12} = \frac{2\pi_1/\pi_2 - 1}{\pi_1/\pi_2 + 1}$$

we can then readily obtain b_{21} and c_{11} from (6.4.12) and (6.4.11) respectively. Thus, the structural parameters can be identified in the reduced form provided our earlier conditions (6.4.8) and (6.4.10) hold.

Part (b)   When we consider the particular structure in which $b_{12} = -1$,

$b_{21} = 2$, $c_{11} = 1$ and $c_{21} = 1$, we need only check that conditions (6.4.8) and (6.4.10) hold. It is clear that they do in fact hold for this structure and it follows that this structure is identifiable.

From the point of view of the reduced form, from (6.4.10), we have in this case

$$\pi_1 = \frac{c_{11}(1 + b_{12})}{1 - b_{12}b_{21}} = 0$$

and

$$\pi_2 = \frac{c_{11}(1 + b_{21})}{1 - b_{12}b_{21}} = \frac{c_{11}(1 + b_{21})}{1 + b_{21}} = c_{11} = 1.$$

Then, with $\pi_2 \neq 0$ it follows immediately from the form of the functions (6.4.11) that $c_{11} \neq 0$ so that $b_{12} = -1$. We then have $c_{11} = \pi_2$ as above.

Solution 6.5

Part (a) The matrix of structural coefficients in this model has the form

$$A = \begin{bmatrix} 1 & -b_{12} & 0 & c_{11} & 0 \\ 0 & 1 & -b_{23} & 0 & c_{22} \\ -b_{31} & 0 & 1 & 0 & c_{32} \end{bmatrix}$$

and using Φ_i to denote the matrix of restrictions on the ith equation (as in Solution 6.2) we have

$$A\Phi_1 = \begin{bmatrix} 0 & 0 \\ -b_{23} & c_{22} \\ 1 & c_{32} \end{bmatrix}, \quad A\Phi_2 = \begin{bmatrix} 1 & c_{11} \\ 0 & 0 \\ -b_{31} & 0 \end{bmatrix}$$

and

$$A\Phi_3 = \begin{bmatrix} -b_{12} & c_{11} \\ 1 & 0 \\ 0 & 0 \end{bmatrix}.$$

Thus,

$$\text{rank} (A\Phi_1) = 2 \qquad \text{unless either } -b_{23} = c_{22}/c_{32} \quad \text{when} \quad c_{32} \neq 0$$
$$\text{or } c_{22} = 0 \quad \text{when} \quad c_{32} = 0.$$
$$\text{rank} (A\Phi_2) = 2 \qquad \text{unless } b_{31} = 0 \quad \text{or} \quad c_{11} = 0$$
$$\text{rank} (A\Phi_3) = 2 \qquad \text{unless } c_{11} = 0.$$

Part (b) To consider the identifiability of the given structure we substitute the particular parameter values into the matrices $A\Phi_i (i = 1, 2, 3)$ above. We have

$$A\Phi_1 = \begin{bmatrix} 0 & 0 \\ -2 & 6 \\ 1 & -3 \end{bmatrix}, \quad A\Phi_2 = \begin{bmatrix} 1 & 5 \\ 0 & 0 \\ -4 & 0 \end{bmatrix}$$

and

$$A\Phi_3 = \begin{bmatrix} -1 & 5 \\ 1 & 0 \\ 0 & 0 \end{bmatrix}.$$

It follows that $A\Phi_2$ and $A\Phi_3$ have rank 2 but $A\Phi_1$ has rank 1 (the second row is -2 times the third row or $-b_{23} = c_{22}/c_{32}$). Thus, the second and third equations are identified but the first is not in this particular structure.

Solution 6.6

Part (a) We can write the structural equations of the given model in the form

$$y_i = Z_i \delta_i + u_i \tag{6.6.1}$$

where y_i denotes the vector of observations of the ith endogenous variable, Z_i the matrix of observations of the included right hand endogenous variables and exogenous variables, u_i the corresponding vector of disturbances and δ_i the vector of unknown parameters. If X is the matrix of observations of all the exogenous variables in the system then the two-stage least squares estimator of δ_i is just (Theil, 1971, p. 497; Johnston, 1972, p. 396; Goldberger, 1964, p. 348):

$$\delta_i^* = [Z_i'X(X'X)^{-1}X'Z_i]^{-1} [Z_i'X(X'X)^{-1}X'y_i]$$

$$= \left[\left(\frac{Z_i'X}{T} \right) \left(\frac{X'X}{T} \right)^{-1} \left(\frac{X'Z_i}{T} \right) \right]^{-1} \left[\left(\frac{Z_i'X}{T} \right) \left(\frac{X'X}{T} \right)^{-1} \left(\frac{X'y_i}{T} \right) \right]. \tag{6.6.2}$$

In this expression, the matrices $Z_i'X/T$, $X'X/T$ and $X'y_i/T$ have elements which are the sample second moments (taken about the origin) of the data. Using the sample moment matrix given in the question we can evaluate the above moment matrices and then use these to compute δ_i^* from (6.6.2). Thus

$$\frac{Z_1'X}{T} = \frac{1}{T}\begin{bmatrix} y_{21} & \cdots & y_{2T} \\ x_{11} & \cdots & x_{1T} \end{bmatrix} \begin{bmatrix} x_{11} & x_{21} & x_{31} \\ \cdot & \cdot & \cdot \\ \cdot & \cdot & \cdot \\ \cdot & \cdot & \cdot \\ x_{1T} & x_{2T} & x_{3T} \end{bmatrix}$$

$$= \begin{bmatrix} T^{-1}\sum_{t=1}^{T} y_{2t}x_{1t} & T^{-1}\sum_{t=1}^{T} y_{2t}x_{2t} & T^{-1}\sum_{t=1}^{T} y_{2t}x_{3t} \\ T^{-1}\sum_{t=1}^{T} x_{1t}^2 & T^{-1}\sum_{t=1}^{T} x_{1t}x_{2t} & T^{-1}\sum_{t=1}^{T} x_{1t}x_{3t} \end{bmatrix}$$

$$= \begin{bmatrix} -20 & 50 & 80 \\ 200 & 0 & 0 \end{bmatrix},$$

$$\frac{X'X}{T} = \frac{1}{T}\begin{bmatrix} x_{11} & \cdots & x_{1T} \\ x_{21} & \cdots & x_{2T} \\ x_{31} & \cdots & x_{3T} \end{bmatrix} \begin{bmatrix} x_{11} & x_{21} & x_{31} \\ \cdot & \cdot & \cdot \\ \cdot & \cdot & \cdot \\ \cdot & \cdot & \cdot \\ x_{1T} & x_{2T} & x_{3T} \end{bmatrix}$$

$$= \begin{bmatrix} T^{-1}\sum_{t=1}^{T} x_{1t}^2 & T^{-1}\sum_{t=1}^{T} x_{1t}x_{2t} & T^{-1}\sum_{t=1}^{T} x_{1t}x_{3t} \\ T^{-1}\sum_{t=1}^{T} x_{2t}x_{1t} & T^{-1}\sum_{t=1}^{T} x_{2t}^2 & T^{-1}\sum_{t=1}^{T} x_{2t}x_{3t} \\ T^{-1}\sum_{t=1}^{T} x_{2t}x_{1t} & T^{-1}\sum_{t=1}^{T} x_{3t}x_{2t} & T^{-1}\sum_{t=1}^{T} x_{3t}^2 \end{bmatrix}$$

$$= \begin{bmatrix} 200 & 0 & 0 \\ 0 & 250 & 0 \\ 0 & 0 & 400 \end{bmatrix}$$

and

$$\frac{X'y_1}{T} = \frac{1}{T}\begin{bmatrix} x_{11} & \cdots & x_{1T} \\ x_{21} & \cdots & x_{2T} \\ x_{31} & \cdots & x_{3T} \end{bmatrix} \begin{bmatrix} y_{11} \\ \cdot \\ \cdot \\ \cdot \\ y_{1T} \end{bmatrix}$$

$$= \begin{bmatrix} T^{-1} \sum x_{1t} y_{1t} \\ \\ T^{-1} \sum x_{2t} y_{1t} \\ \\ T^{-1} \sum x_{3t} y_{1t} \end{bmatrix} = \begin{bmatrix} 30 \\ 35 \\ 40 \end{bmatrix}.$$

We now find that

$$\left(\frac{Z_1' X}{T} \right) \left(\frac{X'X}{T} \right)^{-1} = \begin{bmatrix} -\frac{1}{10} & \frac{1}{5} & \frac{1}{5} \\ 1 & 0 & 0 \end{bmatrix},$$

$$\left(\frac{Z_1' X}{T} \right) \left(\frac{X'X}{T} \right)^{-1} \left(\frac{X'Z_1}{T} \right) = \begin{bmatrix} 24 & -20 \\ -20 & 200 \end{bmatrix},$$

$$\left[\left(\frac{Z_1' X}{T} \right) \left(\frac{X'X}{T} \right)^{-1} \left(\frac{X'Z_1}{T} \right) \right]^{-1} = \frac{1}{4,400} \begin{bmatrix} 200 & 20 \\ 20 & 24 \end{bmatrix}$$

and

$$\left(\frac{Z_1' X}{T} \right) \left(\frac{X'X}{T} \right)^{-1} \left(\frac{X'y_1}{T} \right) = \begin{bmatrix} 12 \\ 30 \end{bmatrix}$$

so that

$$\delta_1^* = \begin{bmatrix} b_{12}^* \\ c_{11}^* \end{bmatrix} = \frac{1}{4,400} \begin{bmatrix} 200 & 20 \\ 20 & 24 \end{bmatrix} \begin{bmatrix} 12 \\ 30 \end{bmatrix}$$

$$= \frac{1}{4,400} \begin{bmatrix} 3,000 \\ 960 \end{bmatrix} = \begin{bmatrix} 0.6818 \\ 0.2182 \end{bmatrix}.$$

Part (b) If we are interested only in a consistent estimate of $\delta_1' = (\beta_{12}, \gamma_{11})$, we do not need to calculate δ_1^*. We could, alternatively, use either x_2 or x_3 as an instrument for y_2 on the right side of the first equation of the model. If we were to use x_2, say, we would have the normal equations

$$Q' y_1 = Q' Z_1 \hat{\delta}_1$$

where

$$Q' = \begin{bmatrix} x_{21} & \cdots & x_{2T} \\ x_{11} & \cdots & x_{1T} \end{bmatrix}.$$

This leads us to the estimate

$$\hat{\delta}_1 = \begin{bmatrix} \hat{b}_{12} \\ \hat{c}_{11} \end{bmatrix} = \begin{bmatrix} T^{-1} \sum_{t=1}^{T} x_{2t} y_{2t} & T^{-1} \sum_{t=1}^{T} x_{2t} x_{1t} \\ T^{-1} \sum_{t=1}^{T} x_{1t} y_{2t} & T^{-1} \sum_{t=1}^{T} x_{1t}^2 \end{bmatrix}^{-1}$$

$$\times \begin{bmatrix} T^{-1} \sum_{t=1}^{T} x_{2t} y_{1t} \\ T^{-1} \sum_{t=1}^{T} x_{1t} y_{1t} \end{bmatrix}$$

$$= \begin{bmatrix} 50 & 0 \\ -20 & 200 \end{bmatrix}^{-1} \begin{bmatrix} 35 \\ 30 \end{bmatrix}$$

$$= \frac{1}{10000} \begin{bmatrix} 200 & 0 \\ 20 & 50 \end{bmatrix} \begin{bmatrix} 35 \\ 30 \end{bmatrix} = \begin{bmatrix} 0.7000 \\ 0.2200 \end{bmatrix}.$$

The two methods lead to estimates which differ only at the second decimal place. But note that the two-stage least squares method has greater asymptotic efficiency (see, for instance, Malinvaud, 1970b, pp. 715–716 and Solution 6.7).

Solution 6.7

Part (a) The instrumental variable estimator of δ is given by (see Theil, 1971, p. 451 and Malinvaud, 1970b, pp. 395–400)

$$d = [Z'X(X'X)^{-1} X'Z]^{-1} Z'X(X'X)^{-1} X'y. \tag{6.7.2}$$

We know that the limiting distribution of $\sqrt{T}(d - \delta)$ is $N(0, V)$ where

$$V = \sigma^2 (M_{zx} M_{xx}^{-1} M_{xz})^{-1}, \tag{6.7.3}$$

$\text{plim}_{T \to \infty} X'Z/T = M_{xz}$ is assumed to be of full rank and $M_{zx} = M'_{xz}$ (see Theil, 1971, p. 497).

For $k = p = 1$, we have $d = X'y/X'Z$ and

$$V = \sigma^2 M_{xx}/M_{xz} = \sigma^2/(M_{zz} r_{xz}^2) \tag{6.7.4}$$

where $r_{xz}^2 = M_{xz}^2/(M_{xx} M_{zz})$ is the large sample correlation between X and Z. It follows that as r_{xz}^2 increases, V decreases.

Part (b) Using the instrumental variables X, the variance matrix of the limiting distribution of $\sqrt{T}(d - \delta)$ is

$$V_x = \sigma^2 \plim_{T \to \infty} T[Z'X(X'X)^{-1}X'Z]^{-1}. \tag{6.7.5}$$

A corresponding expression can be obtained when $W = (X \vdots H)$ is the augmented matrix of instrumental variables. We denote the resulting covariance matrix V_w. We wish to compare V_w with V_x.

First we consider

$$W(W'W)^{-1}W' = W\begin{bmatrix} X'X & X'H \\ H'X & H'H \end{bmatrix}^{-1} W'$$

$$= W\begin{bmatrix} (X'X)^{-1} + (X'X)^{-1}X'H(H'QH)^{-1}H'X(X'X)^{-1} & \\ \hline - (H'QH)^{-1}H'X(X'X)^{-1} & \end{bmatrix}$$

$$\begin{bmatrix} - (X'X)^{-1}X'H(H'QH)^{-1} \\ \hline (H'QH)^{-1} \end{bmatrix} W' \tag{6.7.6}$$

where $Q = I - X(X'X)^{-1}X'$. Multiplying out the matrices in (6.7.6) we obtain

$$W(W'W)^{-1}W' = P + PBP - BP - PB + B$$

$$= P + QBQ \tag{6.7.7}$$

where $P = I - Q$ and $B = H(H'QH)^{-1}H'$. It follows that

$$V_w = \sigma^2 \plim T[Z'X(X'X)^{-1}X'Z + Z'QBQZ]^{-1} \tag{6.7.8}$$

and hence that

$$V_w^{-1} - V_x^{-1} = \sigma^{-2} \plim T^{-1}Z'QBQZ \tag{6.7.9}$$

which is positive semi-definite since B is positive semi-definite.

If A and B are symmetric, positive definite matrices and $A - B$ is positive semi-definite, then $B^{-1} - A^{-1}$ is positive definite. (See Goldberger, 1964, p. 38). Hence we may deduce from (6.7.9) that $V_x - V_w$ is positive semi-definite. If however, (6.7.9) is a null matrix then $V_x = V_w$.

To summarise, we have shown that using additional instrumental variables will lead to an estimator that is at least as efficient as the original instrumental variable estimator. No gain in efficiency occurs if (6.7.9) is a null matrix. A sufficient condition for this is that $QBQ = 0$. But $QBQ = QH(H'QH)^{-1}H'Q$, so that it is sufficient that $H'Q = 0$. In other words, if the additional instruments H are perfectly correlated with the existing instruments X there is no gain in efficiency.

Solution 6.8

Part (a) If we write the first equation of the model as $y_1 = Z_1 \delta_1 + u_1$ in the notation of (6.6.1) and the matrix of observations of the exogenous variables as X, then we obtain the two-stage least-squares estimate of α as follows (in this case $\delta_1 = -\alpha$):

$$
\begin{aligned}
-\alpha^* &= \left[\left(\frac{Z_1'X}{T} \right) \left(\frac{X'X}{T} \right)^{-1} \left(\frac{X'Z_1}{T} \right) \right]^{-1} \left[\left(\frac{Z_1'X}{T} \right) \left(\frac{X'X}{T} \right)^{-1} \left(\frac{X'y_1}{T} \right) \right] \\
&= \left[(10,\ 10) \begin{pmatrix} 5 & 5 \\ 5 & 25 \end{pmatrix}^{-1} \begin{pmatrix} 10 \\ 10 \end{pmatrix} \right]^{-1} \cdot \left[(10,\ 10) \begin{pmatrix} 5 & 5 \\ 5 & 25 \end{pmatrix}^{-1} \begin{pmatrix} 2 \\ 10 \end{pmatrix} \right] \\
&= \left[(1,\ 1) \begin{pmatrix} 25 & -5 \\ -5 & 5 \end{pmatrix} \begin{pmatrix} 1 \\ 1 \end{pmatrix} \right]^{-1} \left[(1,\ 1) \begin{pmatrix} 25 & -5 \\ -5 & 5 \end{pmatrix} \begin{pmatrix} 1/5 \\ 1 \end{pmatrix} \right] \\
&= \frac{4}{20}
\end{aligned}
$$

so that

$$\alpha^* = -0.2.$$

Part (b) To find an approximate 95% confidence interval for α we use the fact that, under certain conditions, $\sqrt{T}(\alpha^* - \alpha)$ has a limiting normal distribution with zero mean and variance given by the limit in probability of

$$
\sigma^2 \left[\left(\frac{Z_1'X}{T} \right) \left(\frac{X'X}{T} \right)^{-1} \left(\frac{X'Z_1}{T} \right) \right]^{-1} \tag{6.8.1}
$$

where $\sigma^2 = E(u_{1t}^2)$, the variance of disturbance on the first equation. A full statement of the theorem which establishes this result and the conditions under which it holds is given by Theil (1971, pp. 497–499).

We can use this result to obtain a confidence interval for α which holds approximately in large samples. We must first estimate the variance (6.8.1). We can use

$$
s^2 \left[\left(\frac{Z_1'X}{T} \right) \left(\frac{X'X}{T} \right)^{-1} \left(\frac{X'Z_1}{T} \right) \right]^{-1}
$$

where

$$
\begin{aligned}
s^2 &= T^{-1}(y_1 - Z_1 \delta_1^*)'(y_1 - Z_1 \delta_1^*) \\
&= T^{-1} y_1' y_1 - 2T^{-1} y_1' Z_1 \delta_1^* + \delta_1^{*'} T^{-1} (Z_1' Z_1) \delta_1^*
\end{aligned}
$$

is an estimate of σ^2 based on the residuals $u_1^* = y_1 - Z_1 \delta_1^*$ from the two-stage least squares regression. From the data given and the estimate $\delta_1^* = -\alpha^* = -0.20$ we have

$$
\begin{aligned}
s^2 &= 10 - 2(6)(-0.20) + (-0.20)^2 40 \\
&= 10 + 2.4 + 1.6 \\
&= 14.
\end{aligned}
$$

We now assume that $\sqrt{T}(\alpha^* - \alpha)$ is approximately distributed as normal with zero mean and variance

$$
s^2 \left[\left(\frac{Z_1' X}{T} \right) \left(\frac{X'X}{T} \right)^{-1} \left(\frac{X'Z_1}{T} \right) \right]^{-1} = \frac{14}{20}
$$

so that α^* is approximately normal with mean α and variance

$$
\frac{1}{T} \left(\frac{14}{20} \right) = 0.014
$$

when $T = 50$. An approximate 95% confidence interval for α is therefore

$$
\alpha^* \pm 1.96\sqrt{0.014}
$$

or $-0.20 \pm 1.96(0.118)$

or $(-0.432, \ 0.032)$

Since this interval contains the origin we note that, at the 5% level, α^* is not significantly different from zero.

Solution 6.9

Part (a) The reduced form estimator of y_1 is

$$
\hat{y}_1 = X(X'X)^{-1} X' y_1 \tag{6.9.2}
$$

where X is the matrix of observations on the predetermined variables. The 2SLS estimators of b and c are

$$
\begin{bmatrix} \hat{b} \\ \hat{c} \end{bmatrix} = [Z'X(X'X)^{-1} X'Z]^{-1} Z'X(X'X)^{-1} X' y_1 \tag{6.9.3}
$$

where $Z = (y_2 \vdots x_1)$. Replacing y_1 by $\hat{y}_1$ leaves (6.9.3) unaltered as $X(X'X)^{-1} X'$ is idempotent.

Part (b) We now denote the 2SLS estimator of b obtained with y_1 as the dependent variable by $\hat{b}_1$, and define $\hat{Z} = X(X'X)^{-1} X'Z$. But since

$X(X'X)^{-1}X'y_2 = \hat{y}_2$ and $X(X'X)^{-1}X'x_1 = x_1$, $\hat{Z} = (\hat{y}_2 \vdots x_1)$ and hence from (6.9.3) we have

$$\begin{bmatrix} \hat{b}_1 \\ \hat{c}_1 \end{bmatrix} = (\hat{Z}'\hat{Z})^{-1}\hat{Z}'\hat{y}_1$$

$$= \begin{bmatrix} \hat{y}_2'\hat{y}_2 & \hat{y}_2'x_1 \\ x_1'\hat{y}_2 & x_1'x_1 \end{bmatrix}^{-1} \begin{bmatrix} \hat{y}_2'\hat{y}_1 \\ x_1'\hat{y}_1 \end{bmatrix}$$

$$= \frac{1}{(\hat{y}_2'\hat{y}_2)(x_1'x_1) - (x_1'\hat{y}_2)^2} \begin{bmatrix} x_1'x_1 & -\hat{y}_2'x_1 \\ -x_1'\hat{y}_2 & \hat{y}_2'\hat{y}_2 \end{bmatrix} \begin{bmatrix} \hat{y}_2'\hat{y}_1 \\ x_1'\hat{y}_1 \end{bmatrix}.$$

Hence

$$\hat{b}_1 = \frac{(\hat{y}_2'\hat{y}_1)(x_1'x_1) - (\hat{y}_1'x_1)(\hat{y}_2'x_1)}{(\hat{y}_2'\hat{y}_2)(x_1'x_1) - (x_1'\hat{y}_2)^2}. \tag{6.9.4}$$

Rewriting (6.9.1) with y_2 as the dependent variable we have

$$y_2 = \frac{1}{b}y_1 - \frac{c}{b}x_1 - \frac{1}{b}u. \tag{6.9.5}$$

Therefore, $\hat{b}_2$ as defined in the question is the reciprocal of the 2SLS estimator of $1/b$. The formula for $\hat{b}_2$ can be written by inspection from (6.9.4). It is

$$b_2 = \frac{(\hat{y}_1'\hat{y}_1)(x_1'x_1) - (x_1'\hat{y}_1)^2}{(\hat{y}_2'\hat{y}_1)(x_1'x_1) - (\hat{y}_1'x_1)(\hat{y}_2'x_1)}. \tag{6.9.6}$$

From (6.9.4) and (6.9.6) we obtain

$$\frac{\hat{b}_1}{\hat{b}_2} = \frac{[(\hat{y}_2'\hat{y}_1)(x_1'x_1) - (\hat{y}_1'x_1)(\hat{y}_2'x_1)]^2}{[(\hat{y}_1'\hat{y}_1)(x_1'x_1) - (x_1'\hat{y}_1)^2][(\hat{y}_2'\hat{y}_2)(x_1'x_1) - (x_1'\hat{y}_2)^2]}$$

$$= \left\{ \frac{\hat{y}_2'\hat{y}_1}{[(\hat{y}_2'\hat{y}_2)(\hat{y}_1'\hat{y}_1)]^{1/2}} - \frac{(\hat{y}_1'x_1)(\hat{y}_2'x_1)}{[(\hat{y}_2'\hat{y}_2)(\hat{y}_1'\hat{y}_1)]^{1/2}(x_1'x_1)} \right\}^2 \Big/$$

$$\left[1 - \frac{(x_1'\hat{y}_1)^2}{(\hat{y}_1'\hat{y}_1)(x_1'x_1)} \right] \left[1 - \frac{(x_1'\hat{y}_2)^2}{(\hat{y}_2'\hat{y}_2)(x_1'x_1)} \right]$$

$$= \frac{(r_{12} - r_{1x}r_{2x})^2}{(1 - r_{1x}^2)(1 - r_{2x}^2)} \tag{6.9.7}$$

where r_{12}, r_{1x} and r_{2x} are the sample correlations between $\hat{y}_1$ and $\hat{y}_2$, $\hat{y}_1$ and x_1, and $\hat{y}_2$ and x_1, respectively. But (6.9.7) can also be interpreted as

$r_{12.x}^2$, the squared partial correlation of $\hat{y}_1$ and $\hat{y}_2$ given x_1. Hence

$$\frac{\hat{b}_1}{\hat{b}_2} = r_{12.x}^2 \leqslant 1. \tag{6.9.8}$$

Solution 6.10

Part (a) To find the limit in probability of the ordinary least squares estimator of δ we must first find the limit in probability of the sample moments of the data that involve the two endogenous variables. Using the true values of the coefficients, the model (6.10.1—2) is, in vector form,

$$\begin{bmatrix} 1 & -1 \\ -2 & 1 \end{bmatrix} \begin{bmatrix} y_{1t} \\ y_{2t} \end{bmatrix} = \begin{bmatrix} 0 & 2 & 0 \\ 3 & 0 & 1 \end{bmatrix} \begin{bmatrix} x_{1t} \\ x_{2t} \\ x_{3t} \end{bmatrix} + \begin{bmatrix} u_{1t} \\ u_{2t} \end{bmatrix}$$

and the reduced form is

$$\begin{bmatrix} y_{1t} \\ y_{2t} \end{bmatrix} = \begin{bmatrix} 1 & -1 \\ -2 & 1 \end{bmatrix}^{-1} \begin{bmatrix} 0 & 2 & 0 \\ 3 & 0 & 1 \end{bmatrix} \begin{bmatrix} x_{1t} \\ x_{2t} \\ x_{3t} \end{bmatrix} + \begin{bmatrix} 1 & -1 \\ -2 & 1 \end{bmatrix}^{-1} \begin{bmatrix} u_{1t} \\ u_{2t} \end{bmatrix}$$

$$= -\begin{bmatrix} 3 & 2 & 1 \\ 3 & 4 & 1 \end{bmatrix} \begin{bmatrix} x_{1t} \\ x_{2t} \\ x_{3t} \end{bmatrix} - \begin{bmatrix} 1 & 1 \\ 2 & 1 \end{bmatrix} \begin{bmatrix} u_{1t} \\ u_{2t} \end{bmatrix}. \tag{6.10.3}$$

We know that

$$\operatorname*{plim}_{T \to \infty} T^{-1} \sum_{t=1}^{T} x_{it} u_{jt} = 0 \qquad (i = 1, 2, 3; \quad j = 1, 2) \tag{6.10.4}$$

since the limit of the matrix $T^{-1} \Sigma_{t=1}^{T} x_t x_t'$ is given and finite and the u_{jt} have finite second moments, which are also given [(6.10.4) can be established by using Tchebycheff's theorem — see Cramér, 1946, pp. 182–3, and Solution 2.15 above].

Writing $y_t' = (y_{1t}, y_{2t})$ and $u_t' = (u_{1t}, u_{2t})$, we obtain from (6.10.3), (6.10.4) and the given limit of $T^{-1} \Sigma_{t=1}^{T} x_t x_t'$

$$\operatorname*{plim}_{T \to \infty} T^{-1} \sum_{t=1}^{T} y_t x_t' = -\begin{bmatrix} 3 & 2 & 1 \\ 3 & 4 & 1 \end{bmatrix} \begin{bmatrix} 1 & 1 & 0 \\ 1 & 2 & 0 \\ 0 & 0 & 1 \end{bmatrix}$$

$$= -\begin{bmatrix} 5 & 7 & 1 \\ 7 & 11 & 1 \end{bmatrix},$$

and

$$\operatorname*{plim}_{T \to \infty} T^{-1} \sum_{t=1}^{T} y_t y_t' = \begin{bmatrix} 3 & 2 & 1 \\ 3 & 4 & 1 \end{bmatrix} \lim_{T \to \infty} \left(T^{-1} \sum_{t=1}^{T} x_t x_t' \right) \begin{bmatrix} 3 & 3 \\ 2 & 4 \\ 1 & 1 \end{bmatrix}$$

$$+ \begin{bmatrix} 1 & 1 \\ 2 & 1 \end{bmatrix} \left(\operatorname*{plim}_{T \to \infty} T^{-1} \sum_{t=1}^{T} u_t u_t' \right) \begin{bmatrix} 1 & 2 \\ 1 & 1 \end{bmatrix}. \quad (6.10.5)$$

But $\{u_t\}$ is a sequence of independent, identically distributed random vectors with covariance matrix

$$E(u_t u_t') = \begin{bmatrix} 5 & 1 \\ 1 & 1 \end{bmatrix}$$

so that

$$\operatorname*{plim}_{T \to \infty} T^{-1} \sum_{t=1}^{T} u_t u_t' = E(u_t u_t') = \begin{bmatrix} 5 & 1 \\ 1 & 1 \end{bmatrix} \quad (6.10.6)$$

by the law of large numbers (in particular, by Khintchine's theorem — see Cramér, 1946, pp. 253–254 and p. 346, and Solution 2.15).

Hence from (6.10.4) and (6.10.5) we have

$$\operatorname*{plim}_{T \to \infty} T^{-1} \sum_{t=1}^{T} y_t y_t' = \begin{bmatrix} 3 & 2 & 1 \\ 3 & 4 & 1 \end{bmatrix} \begin{bmatrix} 1 & 1 & 0 \\ 1 & 2 & 0 \\ 0 & 0 & 1 \end{bmatrix} \begin{bmatrix} 3 & 3 \\ 2 & 4 \\ 1 & 1 \end{bmatrix}$$

$$+ \begin{bmatrix} 1 & 1 \\ 2 & 1 \end{bmatrix} \begin{bmatrix} 5 & 1 \\ 1 & 1 \end{bmatrix} \begin{bmatrix} 1 & 2 \\ 1 & 1 \end{bmatrix}$$

$$= \begin{bmatrix} 30 & 44 \\ 44 & 66 \end{bmatrix} + \begin{bmatrix} 8 & 14 \\ 14 & 25 \end{bmatrix}$$

$$= \begin{bmatrix} 38 & 58 \\ 58 & 91 \end{bmatrix}$$

The complete limit matrix of second moments is, therefore, as follows:

	y_1	y_2	x_1	x_2	x_3
y_1	38	58	-5	-7	-1
y_2	58	91	-7	-11	-1
x_1	-5	-7	1	1	0
x_2	-7	-11	1	2	0
x_3	-1	-1	0	0	1

We now write the first equation of (6.10.1) in the vector form

$$y_1 = Z_1 \delta + u_1$$

where

$$Z_1 = \begin{bmatrix} y_{21} & \cdots & y_{2T} \\ x_{21} & \cdots & x_{2T} \end{bmatrix},$$

$$y_1' = [y_{11}, \ldots , y_{1T}]$$

and

$$u_1' = [u_1, \ldots , u_{1T}]$$

so that the ordinary least squares estimator of δ is given by $\hat{\delta} = (Z_1' Z_1)^{-1} Z_1' y_1$. Then

$$\underset{T \to \infty}{\text{plim}} \; \hat{\delta} = (\underset{T \to \infty}{\text{plim}} \; Z_1' Z_1 / T)^{-1} \, (\underset{T \to \infty}{\text{plim}} \; Z_1' y_1 / T)$$

$$= \begin{bmatrix} 91 & -11 \\ -11 & 2 \end{bmatrix}^{-1} \begin{bmatrix} 58 \\ -7 \end{bmatrix}$$

$$= \frac{1}{61} \begin{bmatrix} 2 & 11 \\ 11 & 91 \end{bmatrix} \begin{bmatrix} 58 \\ 17 \end{bmatrix} = \begin{bmatrix} 39/61 \\ 1/61 \end{bmatrix}$$

We notice that this limit in probability is *not* equal to the true vector of parameters $(1, 2)$. As an exercise, the reader may like to check by similar calculations that the limit in probability of the two-stage least-squares estimator *is* equal to the true value of the parameter vector.

Part (b) If δ^* is the two-stage least-squares estimator of δ, then the covariance matrix of the limiting distribution of $\sqrt{T}(\delta^* - \delta)$ is given by (c.f. Theil, 1971, p. 497)

$$\sigma_1^2 \left[\plim_{T \to \infty} \left(\frac{Z_1' X}{T} \right) \left(\frac{X'X}{T} \right)^{-1} \left(\frac{X'Z_1}{T} \right) \right]^{-1} \tag{6.10.6}$$

where X is the matrix of observations of all the exogenous variables. In the present case, (6.10.6) becomes

$$5 \left\{ \begin{bmatrix} -7 & -11 & -1 \\ 1 & 2 & 0 \end{bmatrix} \begin{bmatrix} 1 & 1 & 0 \\ 1 & 2 & 0 \\ 0 & 0 & 1 \end{bmatrix}^{-1} \begin{bmatrix} -7 & 1 \\ -11 & 2 \end{bmatrix} \right\}^{-1}$$

$$= 5 \left\{ \begin{bmatrix} -7 & -11 & -1 \\ 1 & 2 & 0 \end{bmatrix} \begin{bmatrix} 2 & -1 & 0 \\ -1 & 1 & 0 \\ 0 & 0 & 1 \end{bmatrix} \begin{bmatrix} -7 & 1 \\ -11 & 2 \\ -1 & 0 \end{bmatrix} \right\}^{-1}$$

$$= 5 \begin{bmatrix} 66 & -11 \\ -11 & 2 \end{bmatrix}^{-1} = \begin{bmatrix} 0.909 & 5 \\ 5 & 30 \end{bmatrix}.$$

Part (c) With the new parameter values the model (6.10.1–2) is now

$$y_{1t} = b_{12} y_{2t} + u_{1t} \tag{6.10.8}$$

$$y_{2t} = c_{21} x_{1t} + u_{2t} \tag{6.10.9}$$

with $b_{12} = 1$, $c_{21} = 3$ and, as before,

$$E(u_{1t}^2) = 5, \quad E(u_{1t} u_{2t}) = 1, \quad E(u_{2t}^2) = 1.$$

We write the first equation (6.10.8) as

$$y_1 = b_{12} y_2 + u_1$$

where $y_1' = (y_{11}, \ldots, y_{1T})$, $y_2' = (y_{21}, \ldots, y_{2T})$ and $u_1' = (u_{11}, \ldots, u_{1T})$ and then

$$\hat{b}_{12} = \frac{y_2' y_1}{y_2' y_2} = b_{12} + \frac{y_2' u_1}{y_2' y_2}$$

Setting $y_2' = (y_{21}, \ldots, y_{2T})$, $x_1' = (x_1, \ldots, x_T)$ and $u_2' = (u_{21}, \ldots, u_{2T})$ we now obtain

$$\hat{b}_{12} = b_{12} + c_{21} \frac{x_1' u_1}{y_2' y_2} + \frac{u_2' u_1}{y_2' y_2} \tag{6.10.10}$$

and taking limits in probability we have

$$\bar{b}_{12} = \plim_{T \to \infty} \hat{b}_{12} = b_{12} + c_{21} \left(\plim_{T \to \infty} \frac{y_2' y_2}{T} \right)^{-1} \left(\plim_{T \to \infty} \frac{x_1' u_1}{T} \right)$$

$$+ \left(\plim_{T \to \infty} \frac{y_2' y_2}{T} \right)^{-1} \left(\plim_{T \to \infty} \frac{u_2' u_1}{T} \right) \qquad (6.10.11)$$

The second term on the right side of (6.10.11) is zero since $\plim_{T \to \infty} (x_1' u_1)/T = 0$, $\plim_{T \to \infty} (x_1' u_2)/T = 0$ and

$$\plim_{T \to \infty} \frac{y_2' y_2}{T} = c_{21}^2 \lim_{T \to \infty} \frac{x_1' x_1}{T} + \plim_{T \to \infty} \frac{u_2' u_2}{T}$$

$$= 9(1) + E(u_{2t}^2)$$

$$= 9 + 1$$

$$= 10$$

from the given data. We also have

$$\plim_{T \to \infty} \left(\frac{u_2' u_1}{T} \right) = E(u_{1t} u_{2t}) = 1$$

so that (6.10.11) becomes

$$\bar{b}_{12} = b_{12} + \left(\frac{1}{10} \right) 1 = 1.10 .$$

As T becomes large the distribution of $\hat{b}_{12}$ becomes centred on $\bar{b}_{12}$ so we consider

$$\hat{b}_{12} - \bar{b}_{12} = c_{21} \left(\frac{x_1' u_1}{y_2' y_2} \right) + \frac{u_2' u_1}{y_2' y_2} - \left(\plim_{T \to \infty} \frac{y_2' y_2}{T} \right)^{-1} \left(\plim_{T \to \infty} \frac{u_2' u_1}{T} \right)$$

$$= c_{21} \left(\frac{y_2' y_2}{T} \right)^{-1} \left(\frac{x_1' u_1}{T} \right) + \left(\frac{y_2' y_2}{T} \right)^{-1} \left[\frac{u_2' u_1}{T} - \plim_{T \to \infty} \left(\frac{u_2' u_1}{T} \right) \right]$$

$$+ \plim_{T \to \infty} \left(\frac{u_2' u_1}{T} \right) \left[\left(\frac{y_2' y_2}{T} \right)^{-1} - \plim_{T \to \infty} \left(\frac{y_2' y_2}{T} \right)^{-1} \right]$$

from (6.10.10) and (6.10.11). We can now write

$$\sqrt{T}(\hat{b}_{12} - \bar{b}_{12}) = c_{21} \left(\frac{y_2' y_2}{T} \right)^{-1} \left(\frac{x_1' u_1}{\sqrt{T}} \right)$$

$$+ \left(\frac{y_2' y_2}{T}\right)^{-1} \sqrt{T} \left[\left(\frac{u_2' u_1}{T}\right) - \plim_{T \to \infty} \left(\frac{u_2' u_1}{T}\right)\right]$$

$$+ \plim_{T \to \infty} \left(\frac{u_2' u_1}{T}\right) \sqrt{T} \left[\left(\frac{y_2' y_2}{T}\right)^{-1} - \plim_{T \to \infty} \left(\frac{y_2' y_2}{T}\right)^{-1}\right]$$

which has the same limiting distribution as $T \to \infty$ as

$$\frac{3}{10} \left(\frac{x_1' u_1}{\sqrt{T}}\right) + \frac{\sqrt{T}}{10} \left[\frac{u_2' u_1}{T} - E(u_{2t} u_{1t})\right]$$

$$+ \sqrt{T} \left[\left(\frac{y_2' y_2}{T}\right)^{-1} - \plim_{T \to \infty} \left(\frac{y_2' y_2}{T}\right)^{-1}\right]. \qquad (6.10.12)$$

We know (see Solution 2.16 above) that the first term of (6.10.12) has a limiting normal distribution as $T \to \infty$. The second and third terms of (6.10.12) also have limiting normal distributions as $T \to \infty$: the second term because $u_2' u_1 / T$ is a sample second moment of the disturbances and the standardised statistic

$$\sqrt{T} \left[\frac{u_2' u_1}{T} - E(u_{2t} u_{1t})\right]$$

has a limiting normal distribution as $T \to \infty$ provided *moments of the fourth order* of u_{1t} and u_{2t} exist — in fact the variance of the limiting distribution will depend on these fourth order moments (see Cramér, 1946, pp. 363–366); the third term of (6.10.12) also has a limiting normal distribution as $T \to \infty$ because $(y_2' y_2 / T)^{-1}$ is a simple and smooth function of the sample moment $y_2' y_2 / T$ and it is true that such functions of sample moments are asymptotically normal (see, once again, Cramér, 1946, pp. 366–367).

Since all terms of (6.10.12) have limiting normal distributions, it follows that (6.10.12) has a limiting normal distribution itself, being in the limit a linear combination of normally distributed variables. Since each component of (6.10.12) has a limiting distribution centred on the origin, the limiting distribution of $\sqrt{T}(\hat{b}_{12} - \bar{b}_{12})$ will have zero mean. Its variance is more difficult to compute. In the first place, as we have noted above the variance of the limiting distribution of

$$\sqrt{T} \left[\frac{u_2' u_1}{T} - E(u_{2t} u_{1t})\right]$$

will depend on the fourth order moments of the disturbances (as well as the second moments). The same will also be true of the variance of the limiting distribution of the third term of (6.10.12). But the given data in our problem do not include these fourth order moments (and, for that matter, do not even specify that they exist). In the second place we need to take into account the covariance between the terms of (6.10.12) in deriving the variance of the limiting distribution of $\sqrt{T}(\hat{b}_{12} - \bar{b}_{12})$; and these covariances will themselves involve moments of the disturbances of higher order than the second. These difficulties mean that we cannot, with the given data, find the variance of the limiting distribution of

$$\sqrt{T}(\hat{b}_{12} - \bar{b}_{12})$$

But, on the assumption that the fourth order moments of the disturbances do exist, we can assert that this limiting distribution will be normal.

Remark It is worthwhile to notice that, whereas the existence of the limiting normal distribution of $\sqrt{T}(\hat{b}_{12} - \bar{b}_{12})$ depends on finite fourth order moments of the disturbances, the corresponding limiting normal distribution of the two-stage least-squares estimator is established on the basis of finite second order moments of the disturbances (when the disturbances are independently and identically distributed for all t — see Theil, 1971, pp. 499).

Solution 6.11

We write the reduced form equation for y_t as

$$y_t = \pi_0 + \pi_1 I_t + v_t$$

where

$$\pi_0 = \frac{\alpha}{1 - \beta}, \quad \pi_1 = \frac{1}{1 - \beta} \quad \text{and} \quad v_t = \frac{u_t}{1 - \beta}.$$

The indirect least squares estimates of α and β are given by

$$\hat{\alpha} = \pi_0^*/\pi_1^* \qquad \hat{\beta} = 1 - 1/\pi_1^*$$

where π_0^* and π_1^* are the ordinary least squares estimates of π_0 and π_1 from the regression of Y_t on I_t. We note that, under the assumptions given, the vector

$$\sqrt{T} \begin{bmatrix} \pi_0^* - \pi_0 \\ \pi_1^* - \pi_1 \end{bmatrix}$$

has a limiting normal distribution as $T \to \infty$ (see Solution 2.16) with zero mean and covariance matrix

$$\sigma_v^2 \left\{ \lim_{T \to \infty} T^{-1} \sum_{t=1}^{T} \begin{bmatrix} 1 & I_t \\ I_t & I_t^2 \end{bmatrix} \right\}^{-1} \tag{6.11.1}$$

where $\sigma_v^2 = \sigma^2 / (1 - \beta)^2$. We let

$$m_{\text{I}} = \lim_{T \to \infty} T^{-1} \sum_{t=1}^{T} I_t$$

$$m_{\text{II}} = \lim_{T \to \infty} T^{-1} \sum_{t=1}^{T} I_t^2$$

and

$$m^2 = m_{\text{II}} - m_{\text{I}}^2$$

so that (6.11.1) is just

$$\frac{\sigma^2}{(1 - \beta)^2} \begin{bmatrix} 1 & m_{\text{I}} \\ m_{\text{I}} & m_{\text{II}} \end{bmatrix}^{-1} = \frac{\sigma^2}{(1 - \beta)^2} (m_{\text{II}} - m_{\text{I}}^2)^{-1} \begin{bmatrix} m_{\text{II}} & -m_{\text{I}} \\ -m_{\text{I}} & 1 \end{bmatrix}$$

$$= \frac{\sigma^2}{m^2 (1 - \beta)^2} \begin{bmatrix} m_{\text{II}} & -m_{\text{I}} \\ -m_{\text{I}} & 1 \end{bmatrix}.$$

To find the limiting distribution of $(\hat{\alpha}, \hat{\beta})$ we note that

$$\begin{bmatrix} \hat{\alpha} \\ \hat{\beta} \end{bmatrix} - \begin{bmatrix} \alpha \\ \beta \end{bmatrix} = \begin{bmatrix} \pi_0^* / \pi_1^* \\ (\pi_1^* - 1)/\pi_1^* \end{bmatrix} - \begin{bmatrix} \pi_0 / \pi_1 \\ (\pi_1 - 1)/\pi_1 \end{bmatrix}$$

$$= f(\pi_0^*, \pi_1^*) - f(\pi_0, \pi_1),$$

say, where $f(\ .\ )$ is the vector of the two functions defining the individual components. Now $f(\ .\ )$ is continuously differentiable to the second order so that

$$\sqrt{T} \left\{ \begin{bmatrix} \hat{\alpha} \\ \hat{\beta} \end{bmatrix} - \begin{bmatrix} \alpha \\ \beta \end{bmatrix} \right\} \tag{6.11.2}$$

has the same limiting distribution when $T \to \infty$ as (see, for instance, Dhrymes, 1970, pp. 112–113, or Theil, 1971, pp. 373–374)

$$\begin{bmatrix} \dfrac{\partial f(\pi_0, \pi_1)}{\partial \pi_0} & \dfrac{\partial f(\pi_0, \pi_1)}{\partial \pi_1} \end{bmatrix} \begin{bmatrix} \sqrt{T}(\pi_0^* - \pi_0) \\ \sqrt{T}(\pi_1^* - \pi_1) \end{bmatrix}$$

$$= H(\pi_0, \pi_1) \begin{bmatrix} \sqrt{T}(\pi_0^* - \pi_0) \\ \sqrt{T}(\pi_1^* - \pi_1) \end{bmatrix}$$

say.

We find that

$$H(\pi_0, \pi_1) = \begin{bmatrix} 1/\pi_1 & -\pi_0/\pi_1^2 \\ 0 & 1/\pi_1^2 \end{bmatrix} = \begin{bmatrix} 1-\beta & -\alpha(1-\beta) \\ 0 & (1-\beta)^2 \end{bmatrix}$$

so that the limiting distribution of (6.11.2) is normal with zero mean and covariance matrix

$$H(\pi_0, \pi_1) \frac{\sigma^2}{m^2(1-\beta)^2} \begin{bmatrix} m_{II} & -m_I \\ -m_I & 1 \end{bmatrix} H'(\pi_0, \pi_1)$$

$$= \frac{\sigma^2}{m^2(1-\beta)^2} \left[\begin{array}{c|c} (1-\beta)m_{II} + \alpha(1-\beta)m_I & -(1-\beta)m_I - \alpha(1-\beta) \\ \hline -(1-\beta)^2 m_I & (1-\beta)^2 \end{array} \right]$$

$$\times \begin{bmatrix} 1-\beta & 0 \\ -\alpha(1-\beta) & (1-\beta)^2 \end{bmatrix}$$

$$= \frac{\sigma^2}{m^2(1-\beta)^2} \left[\begin{array}{c|c} (1-\beta)^2(m_{II} + 2\alpha m_I + \alpha^2) & -(1-\beta)^3(m_I + \alpha) \\ \hline -(1-\beta)^3(m_I + \alpha) & (1-\beta)^4 \end{array} \right]$$

In particular, therefore, $\sqrt{T}(\hat{\beta} - \beta)$ has a limiting normal distribution with zero mean and variance $\sigma^2(1-\beta)^2/m^2$; and $\sqrt{T}(\hat{\alpha} - \alpha)$ has a limiting normal distribution with zero mean and variance $\sigma^2 m^{-2}(m_{II} + 2\alpha m_I + \alpha^2)$ $= \sigma^2 m^{-2}(m^2 + (m_I + \alpha)^2)$.

Solution 6.12

Part (a) We write the first equation of the given model in the form

$$Y_\Delta b_\Delta + X_\Delta c_\Delta = u_1 \tag{6.12.1}$$

where

$$Y_\Delta' = \begin{bmatrix} y_{11} & \cdots & y_{1T} \\ y_{21} & \cdots & y_{2T} \end{bmatrix}, \quad b_\Delta = \begin{bmatrix} 1 \\ b_{12} \end{bmatrix}$$

$$X_\Delta' = [x_{11} \quad \cdots \quad x_{1T}], \quad c_\Delta = c_{11}$$

(Our notation here is similar to that in Johnston, 1972, pp. 384–387 and that originally used by Koopmans and Hood, 1953). Then the limited information maximum likelihood estimates of b_{12} and c_{11} are obtained by the following steps (see Johnston, 1972, pp. 387 or, with some modification of the algebra, Malinvaud, 1970b, p. 597):

(1) Find the smallest root $\hat{\lambda}$ of the determinantal equation

$$| W^*_{\Delta\Delta} - \lambda W_{\Delta\Delta} | = 0 \qquad (6.12.2)$$

where

$$W^*_{\Delta\Delta} = \frac{Y'_\Delta Y_\Delta}{T} - \left(\frac{Y'_\Delta X_\Delta}{T}\right)\left(\frac{X'_\Delta X_\Delta}{T}\right)^{-1}\left(\frac{X'_\Delta Y_\Delta}{T}\right)$$

$$W_{\Delta\Delta} = \frac{Y'_\Delta Y_\Delta}{T} - \left(\frac{Y'_\Delta X}{T}\right)\left(\frac{X'X}{T}\right)^{-1}\left(\frac{X'Y_\Delta}{T}\right)$$

and

$$X' = \begin{bmatrix} x_{11} & \cdots & x_{1T} \\ x_{21} & \cdots & x_{2T} \\ x_{31} & \cdots & x_{3T} \end{bmatrix}.$$

(2) Find $\hat{b}_\Delta$ by solving the system

$$(W^*_{\Delta\Delta} - \hat{\lambda} W_{\Delta\Delta})\hat{b}_\Delta = 0 \qquad (6.12.3)$$

and setting the first element of $\hat{b}_\Delta$ equal to unity so that

$$\hat{b}_\Delta = \begin{bmatrix} 1 \\ \hat{b}_{12} \end{bmatrix}.$$

(This is merely the imposition of the normalisation rule we have adapted for the first equation).

(3) Find $\hat{c}_\Delta$ from the equation

$$\hat{c}_\Delta = -(X'_\Delta X_\Delta)^{-1} X'_\Delta Y_\Delta \hat{b}_\Delta$$

$$= -\left(\frac{X'_\Delta X_\Delta}{T}\right)^{-1}\left(\frac{X'_\Delta Y_\Delta}{T}\right)\hat{b}_\Delta \qquad (6.12.4)$$

Remark In the above we have defined $W^*_{\Delta\Delta}$ and $W_{\Delta\Delta}$ in terms of sample moments about the origin. We notice that

$$W^*_{\Delta\Delta} = T^{-1}[Y'_\Delta Y_\Delta - (Y'_\Delta X_\Delta)(X'_\Delta X_\Delta)^{-1} X'_\Delta Y_\Delta] = T^{-1} E^*_{\Delta\Delta}$$

say, and

$$W_{\Delta\Delta} = T^{-1}[Y'_\Delta Y_\Delta - Y'_\Delta X(X'X)^{-1} X'Y_\Delta] = T^{-1} E_{\Delta\Delta},$$

say, so that

$$| W^*_{\Delta\Delta} - \lambda W_{\Delta\Delta} | = 0$$

is equivalent to

$$\left(\frac{1}{T}\right)^2 |E_{\Delta\Delta}^* - \lambda E_{\Delta\Delta}| = 0$$

or

$$|E_{\Delta\Delta}^* - \lambda E_{\Delta\Delta}| = 0.$$

The factor $1/T^2$ in the above arises because, in the present case, the matrices $E_{\Delta\Delta}^*$ and $E_{\Delta\Delta}$ are 2×2 matrices and we are taking the factor $1/T$ outside the determinant.

From the given data we can compute

$$W_{\Delta\Delta}^* = \begin{bmatrix} 14 & 6 \\ 6 & 10 \end{bmatrix} - \begin{bmatrix} 2 \\ 2 \end{bmatrix} \times 1 \times [2, \ 2]$$

$$= \begin{bmatrix} 10 & 2 \\ 2 & 6 \end{bmatrix}$$

$$W_{\Delta\Delta} = \begin{bmatrix} 14 & 6 \\ 6 & 10 \end{bmatrix} - \begin{bmatrix} 2 & 3 & 0 \\ 2 & 1 & 0 \end{bmatrix} \begin{bmatrix} 1 & 0 & 0 \\ 0 & 1 & 0 \\ 0 & 0 & 1 \end{bmatrix} \begin{bmatrix} 2 & 2 \\ 3 & 1 \\ 0 & 0 \end{bmatrix}$$

$$= \begin{bmatrix} 1 & -1 \\ -1 & 5 \end{bmatrix}$$

Equation (6.12.2) is now

$$\det \left\{ \begin{bmatrix} 10 & 2 \\ 2 & 6 \end{bmatrix} - \lambda \begin{bmatrix} 1 & -1 \\ -1 & 5 \end{bmatrix} \right\} = 0$$

or

$$\det \begin{bmatrix} 10 - \lambda & 2 + \lambda \\ 2 + \lambda & 6 - 5\lambda \end{bmatrix} = 0$$

or

$$(10 - \lambda)(6 - 5\lambda) - (2 + \lambda)^2 = 0$$

and, simplifying, we obtain

$$4\lambda^2 - 60\lambda + 56 = 0$$

so that

$$(\lambda - 14)(\lambda - 1) = 0$$

and

$$\lambda = 1 \quad \text{or} \quad 14$$

Thus $\hat{\lambda} = 1$ is the smallest root. From equation (6.8a.2) we now have

$$\left\{ \begin{bmatrix} 10 & 2 \\ 2 & 6 \end{bmatrix} - \begin{bmatrix} 1 & -1 \\ -1 & 5 \end{bmatrix} \right\} \hat{b}_\Delta = 0$$

or

$$\begin{bmatrix} 9 & 3 \\ 3 & 1 \end{bmatrix} \begin{bmatrix} 1 \\ \hat{b}_{12} \end{bmatrix} = 0$$

that is

$$9 + 3\hat{b}_{12} = 0$$

or

$$\hat{b}_{12} = -3.$$

From equation (6.12.4) we find

$$\hat{c}_{11} = \hat{c}_\Delta = -1 \times (2, 2) \begin{pmatrix} 1 \\ -3 \end{pmatrix} = -(2 - 6) = 4$$

Hence the limited information maximum likelihood estimates of b_{12} and c_{11} are

$$\hat{b}_{12} = -3, \quad \hat{c}_{11} = 4.$$

Remark We notice that $\hat{\lambda} = 1$ so that in the present case the limited information estimates are just the k class estimates with $k = 1$ (see Theil, 1971, pp. 504). But when $k = 1$, the k class estimates correspond to the two-stage least-squares estimates. We can verify this directly in the present case by computing the two-stage least-squares estimates of b_{12} and c_{11} and by checking that these estimates are the same as those obtained above.

Part (b) One test of the over-identifying restrictions on the first equation is based on the smallest root $\hat{\lambda}$ of the determinantal equation (6.12.1) above. It is known that as $T \to \infty$ the statistic $T(\hat{\lambda} - 1)$ has a limiting χ^2 distribution with degrees of freedom equal to the degree of over-identification of the equation (see Theil, 1971, p. 507). In this case the degree of over-identification is $2 - 1 = 1$, the number of excluded exogenous variables less one.

From our computations in Part (a) we know that $\hat{\lambda} = 1$, so that the test statistic is

$$T(\hat{\lambda} - 1) = 0$$

which is less than the upper tail critical value

$$\chi_1^2(0.005) = 3.84$$

at the 5% level of significance and we would not reject the hypothesis that the over-identifying restrictions are correct on the basis of this test.

Basmann (1960b) (see also Theil, 1971, pp. 507–508) has suggested an alternative statistic for testing the over-identifying restrictions in a single equation. We write the single equation complete with T observations as

$$Y_\Delta b_\Delta + X_\Delta c_\Delta = u_1$$

where in the general case Y_Δ is $T \times (n_\Delta + 1)$ and X_Δ is $T \times m_\Delta$ so that there are $n_\Delta + 1$ included endogenous variables and m_Δ included exogenous variables. We let X be the $T \times m$ matrix of observations of all m exogenous variables in the model. Then Basmann suggests that we use the test statistic

$$F = \frac{T - m}{m - m_\Delta - n_\Delta} \frac{\hat{b}_\Delta' Y_\Delta' [X(X'X)^{-1} X' - X_\Delta (X_\Delta' X_\Delta)^{-1} X_\Delta'] Y_\Delta \hat{b}_\Delta}{\hat{b}_\Delta' Y_\Delta' [I - X(X'X)^{-1} X'] Y_\Delta \hat{b}_\Delta}.$$

When the over-identifying restrictions are correctly imposed (note that they number, in this case, $m - m_\Delta - n_\Delta = [n - (n_\Delta + 1) + m - m_\Delta - (n - 1)]$, F has approximately an F distribution with $m - m_\Delta - n_\Delta$ and $T - m$ degrees of freedom. We would reject the hypothesis that the restrictions were imposed correctly if the calculated F value exceeded the critical value $F_{m - m_\Delta - n_\Delta, T - m}$ (0.05) at the 5% level of significance.

In our example we have

$$T - m = 23 - 3 = 20$$

$$m - m_\Delta - n_\Delta = 3 - 1 - 1 = 1$$

$$T^{-1} \hat{b}_\Delta' Y_\Delta' X(X'X)^{-1} X' Y_\Delta \hat{b}_\Delta - T^{-1} \hat{b}_\Delta' Y_\Delta' X_\Delta (X_\Delta' X_\Delta)^{-1} X_\Delta' Y_\Delta b_\Delta$$

$$= \hat{b}_\Delta' (W_{\Delta\Delta}^* - W_{\Delta\Delta}) \hat{b}_\Delta$$

$$= (1, \, -3) \left\{ \begin{bmatrix} 10 & 2 \\ 2 & 6 \end{bmatrix} - \begin{bmatrix} 1 & -1 \\ -1 & 5 \end{bmatrix} \right\} \begin{pmatrix} 1 \\ -3 \end{pmatrix}$$

$$= (1, \, -3) \begin{pmatrix} 9 & 3 \\ 3 & 1 \end{pmatrix} \begin{pmatrix} 1 \\ -3 \end{pmatrix} = 0$$

and

$$T^{-1} \hat{b}_\Delta' Y_\Delta' [1 - X(X'X)^{-1} X'] Y_\Delta \hat{b}_\Delta$$

$$= \hat{b}_\Delta' W_{\Delta\Delta} \hat{b}_\Delta$$

$$= (1, \, -3) \begin{bmatrix} 1 & -1 \\ -1 & 5 \end{bmatrix} \begin{pmatrix} 1 \\ -3 \end{pmatrix} = 52.$$

It follows that $F = 0$ and since $F_{1,20}(0.05) = 4.35$, we do not reject the hypothesis that the over-identifying restrictions are correctly imposed.

Remark It is no coincidence that, in this particular case, both test statistics are zero. For the limited information estimate $\hat{b}_\Delta$ is constructed so that it minimises the 'variance ratio' (c.f. Johnston, 1972, p. 386)

$$\lambda = \frac{b'_\Delta W^*_{\Delta\Delta} b_\Delta}{b'_\Delta W_{\Delta\Delta} b_\Delta}$$

$$= \frac{b'_\Delta Y'_\Delta [I - X_\Delta (X'_\Delta X_\Delta)^{-1} X'_\Delta] Y_\Delta b_\Delta}{b'_\Delta Y'_\Delta [I - X(X'X)^{-1} X'] Y_\Delta b_\Delta}$$

The numerator is just the residual sum of squares from the regression of $Y_\Delta b_\Delta$ on X_Δ and the denominator is the residual sum of squares from the regression of $Y_\Delta b_\Delta$ on X. Since X contains more columns than X_Δ, the second regression will lead to a smaller residual sum of squares than the first. Hence $\lambda \geqslant 1$. The vector $\hat{b}_\Delta$ is calculated in such a way that the difference between these residual sums of squares is as small as possible (or, more precisely, λ is as close to unity as possible). We then get

$$\hat{\lambda} = \frac{\hat{b}'_\Delta W^*_{\Delta\Delta} \hat{b}_\Delta}{\hat{b}'_\Delta W_{\Delta\Delta} \hat{b}_\Delta}$$

and

$$\hat{\lambda} - 1 = \frac{\hat{b}'_\Delta W^*_{\Delta\Delta} \hat{b}_\Delta - \hat{b}'_\Delta W_{\Delta\Delta} \hat{b}_\Delta}{\hat{b}'_\Delta W_{\Delta\Delta} \hat{b}_\Delta}$$

can be regarded as a measure of the extent to which the extra variables in X (over and above those in X_Δ) are capable of reducing the residual sum of squares.

If the specification is correct and the over-identifying restrictions are correctly imposed then we would expect $\hat{\lambda} - 1$ to be small since by hypothesis, the extra variables in X do not enter as explanatory variables in this equation. When the specification is incorrect we might expect $\hat{\lambda} - 1$ to be larger, indicating that the extra variables are capable of reducing the residual sum of squares significantly.

In the present case, $\hat{\lambda}$ attains its minimum of unity. The extra variables in X cannot contribute to a reduction in the residual sum of squares and as a result both test statistics (which are based on the extent of this reduction in the residual sum of squares) are zero.

Solution 6.13

Consider the system of n linear simultaneous equations

$$By_t + Cx_t = u_t \qquad (t = 1, \ldots, T) \qquad (6.13.1)$$

where u_t is an independent $N(0, \Sigma)$. We can write (6.13.1) more compactly as

$$BY' + CX' = U' \tag{6.13.2}$$

where $Y' = [y_1, \ldots, y_T]$, $X' = [x_1, \ldots, x_T]$ and $U' = (u_1, \ldots, u_T)$; or, as

$$AW' = U' \tag{6.13.3}$$

where $A = (B \vdots C)$ and $W = (Y \vdots X)$.

The joint density function of the structural errors U is

$$f(U; \Sigma) = (2\pi)^{nT/2} \, |\, \Sigma^{-1}\, |^{T/2} \exp[-\tfrac{1}{2} \operatorname{tr}(U'U\Sigma^{-1})],$$

hence the log likelihood function of (6.13.3) is (see also Dhrymes, 1970, pp. 322–323)

$$\ln L = \text{const} + T \ln |B| + \tfrac{1}{2} T \ln |\Sigma^{-1}| - \tfrac{1}{2} \operatorname{tr}(AW'WA'\Sigma^{-1}). \tag{6.13.4}$$

For convenience we assume that (6.13.1) is identified by zero-one restrictions, implying that some of the elements of A are zero, and Σ is unrestricted. We require the FIML estimators of the unrestricted elements of A and Σ. Differentiating the log likelihood function with respect to the *unknown* (or unrestricted) elements of A and Σ^{-1} we obtain

$$\frac{\partial \ln L}{\partial B} = T\hat{B}'^{-1} - \hat{\Sigma}^{-1}\hat{A}W'Y \underset{R}{=} 0 \tag{6.13.5}$$

$$\frac{\partial \ln L}{\partial C} = -\hat{\Sigma}^{-1}\hat{A}W'X \underset{R}{=} 0 \tag{6.13.6}$$

$$\frac{\partial \ln L}{\partial \sigma_{ij}} = (T\hat{\Sigma}^{-1} - \hat{\Sigma}^{-1}\hat{A}W'W\hat{A}'\hat{\Sigma}^{-1})_{ij} = 0 \quad \text{for} \quad i \neq j$$

$$= \tfrac{1}{2}(T\hat{\Sigma}^{-1} - \hat{\Sigma}^{-1}\hat{A}W'W\hat{A}'\hat{\Sigma}^{-1})_{ii} = 0 \quad \text{for} \quad i = j \tag{6.13.7}$$

where $\underset{R}{=}$ denotes that the equality sign holds only for unrestricted elements of B and C. Because Σ is unrestricted (6.13.7) has the usual equality sign. From (6.13.7) we obtain

$$T\hat{\Sigma}^{-1} - \hat{\Sigma}^{-1}\hat{A}W'W\hat{A}'\hat{\Sigma}^{-1} = 0$$

or, post-multiplying by $\hat{\Sigma}\hat{B}'^{-1}$, we can derive

$$T\hat{B}'^{-1} - \hat{\Sigma}^{-1}\hat{A}W'W\hat{A}'\hat{B}'^{-1} = 0 \tag{6.13.8}$$

But $\hat{B}^{-1}\hat{A} = [I \vdots -\hat{P}]$ as

$$\hat{P} = -\hat{B}^{-1}\hat{C} \tag{6.13.9}$$

are estimated reduced form coefficients satisfying the (constrained) reduced form

$$Y = X\hat{P}' + \hat{V} = \bar{Y} + \hat{V} \tag{6.13.10}$$

where $\hat{V} = U\hat{B}'^{-1}$ and $\bar{Y}$ is the predicted value of Y. Hence, $W\hat{A}'\hat{B}'^{-1} = Y - X\hat{P}'$. Substituting this into (6.13.8) we find that

$$T\hat{B}'^{-1} - \hat{\Sigma}^{-1}\hat{A}W'Y = \hat{\Sigma}^{-1}\hat{A}W'X\hat{P}'. \tag{6.13.11}$$

Equation (6.13.5) states that the left-hand side of (6.13.11) is zero for unrestricted elements of B. Thus

$$\hat{\Sigma}^{-1}\hat{A}W'X\hat{P}' \underset{R}{=} 0. \tag{6.13.12}$$

Combining (6.13.6) and (6.13.12) we obtain

$$\hat{\Sigma}^{-1}\hat{A}W'X(\hat{P}' \vdots I) \underset{R}{=} 0 \tag{6.13.13}$$

or

$$\hat{\Sigma}^{-1}\hat{A}W'\bar{W} \underset{R}{=} 0 \tag{6.13.14}$$

where, from (6.13.10),

$$\bar{W} = X[\hat{P}' \vdots I] = [X\hat{P}' \vdots X] = [\bar{Y} \vdots X]$$

We wish now to write (6.13.14) in unrestricted form. To do so we must obtain (6.13.2) in unrestricted form. The ith equation of (6.13.2) can be written in unrestricted form as

$$y_i = Y_i b_i + X_i c_i + u_i \qquad (i = 1, \ldots, n) \tag{6.13.15}$$

where b_i and c_i are the unrestricted coefficients in the ith equation and, hence, in the ith columns of $-B'$ and $-C'$, respectively, y_i, Y_i and X_i are the variables appearing with non-zero coefficients in the ith equation. Assuming that the normalisation rule is $b_{ii} = 1$, y_i is the ith column of Y, u_i is the ith column of U and Y_i and X_i are the columns of Y and X, respectively, corresponding to the unrestricted coefficients of the ith equation, (6.13.15) can also be written as

$$y_i = Z_i \delta_i + u_i \tag{6.13.16}$$

where $\delta_i = (b_i', c_i')'$ and $Z_i = (Y_i \vdots X_i)$. The complete system can then be written in unrestricted form as

$$y = Z\delta + u \tag{6.13.17}$$

where $y = \overline{\text{vec}}(Y) = (y_1', \ldots, y_n')'$, $u = \overline{\text{vec}}(U) = (u_1', \ldots, u_n')'$, $\delta = (\delta_1' \ . \ . \ \delta_n')'$ and

$$Z = \begin{bmatrix} Z_1 & 0 & \cdots & 0 \\ 0 & Z_2 & \cdots & 0 \\ \cdot & & & \cdot \\ \cdot & & & \cdot \\ \cdot & & & \cdot \\ 0 & & \cdots & Z_n \end{bmatrix}$$

(See Appendix A for a discussion of vec and $\overline{vec}$ notation.) We shall also require

$$\overline{Z} = \begin{bmatrix} \overline{Z}_1 & 0 & \cdots & 0 \\ 0 & \overline{Z}_2 & \cdots & 0 \\ \cdot & & & \cdot \\ \cdot & & & \cdot \\ \cdot & & & \cdot \\ 0 & & \cdots & \overline{Z}_n \end{bmatrix}$$

where $\overline{Z}_i = [\overline{Y}_i \vdots X_i]$, $(i = 1, \ldots, n)$; in other words, $\overline{Z}_i$ is obtained from Z_i through replacing Y_i by its predicted value from the restricted reduced form (6.13.10). Transposing (6.13.14) and vectorising using the result in Appendix A, that $\overline{vec}\,(ABC) = (C' \otimes A)\,\overline{vec}\,(B)$, we obtain

$$\overline{vec}\,(\overline{W}'W\hat{A}'\hat{\Sigma}^{-1}) = (\hat{\Sigma}^{-1} \otimes \overline{W}')\,\overline{vec}\,(W\hat{A}') \tag{6.13.18}$$

$$= (I \otimes \overline{W})'(\Sigma^{-1} \otimes I)\,\overline{vec}\,(W\hat{A}') \underset{R}{=} 0. \tag{6.13.19}$$

But $\overline{vec}\,(W\hat{A}') = \overline{vec}\,(\hat{U}) = \hat{u} = y - Z\hat{\delta}$. Moreover, when we delete rows of $(I \otimes \overline{W})'$ corresponding to unrestricted elements of A, we see that $(I \otimes \overline{W})$ reduces to the matrix $(-Z)$. We can, therefore, write (6.13.19) unrestrictedly as

$$-\overline{Z}'(\hat{\Sigma}^{-1} \otimes I)(y - Z\hat{\delta}) = 0. \tag{6.13.20}$$

Thus the FIML estimator of δ satisfies

$$\hat{\delta} = [\overline{Z}'(\hat{\Sigma}^{-1} \otimes I)Z]^{-1}\,\overline{Z}'(\hat{\Sigma}^{-1} \otimes I)y. \tag{6.13.21}$$

To obtain the FIML estimator of Σ we solve (6.13.7) to get

$$\hat{\Sigma} = T^{-1}\hat{A}W'W\hat{A}'. \tag{6.13.22}$$

The FIML estimators of δ and Σ can be obtained by using an iteration based on (6.13.21) and (6.13.22). Starting with *any* consistent estimators of δ and Σ we construct $\hat{P}$ defined by (6.13.9), then $\overline{Y}$ from (6.13.10) and hence $\overline{Z}$. With this estimate of $\overline{Z}$ and the initial estimate of Σ we solve (6.13.21) to obtain a new estimate of δ. A new estimate of Σ is obtained by substituting this estimate of δ in (6.13.22). We can now go through this process again starting with these new estimates of δ and Σ. Iteration is continued until convergence is achieved. The resulting estimates of δ and Σ will be the FIML estimates. It should be noted, however, that convergence is not guaranteed by this procedure.

Part (b) An instrumental variable interpretation of FIML follows immediately from (6.13.21). Defining the set of instrumental variables

$$H = (\hat{\Sigma}^{-1} \otimes I_T)\bar{Z} \tag{6.1.23}$$

we can rewrite (6.13.21) as

$$\hat{\delta} = (H'Z)^{-1}H'y \tag{6.13.24}$$

which has the familiar form of an instrumental variable estimator. It is clear, therefore, that FIML can be interpreted as an iterated instrumental variable estimator where we revise the matrix of instruments at each iteration.

Part (c) Suppose that our initial estimator of Σ is derived from (6.13.22) using 2SLS estimates of A and that we obtain our initial estimator $\bar{Y}$ from unrestricted estimates of Π. Thus our starting value of $\bar{Y}$ would be

$$\bar{Y} = X(X'X)^{-1}X'Y$$

implying that

$$\bar{Z}_i = [X(X'X)^{-1}X'Y_i \vdots X_i]$$
$$= X(X'X)^{-1}X'Z_i$$

and hence that

$$\bar{Z} = [I \otimes X(X'X)^{-1}X']Z. \tag{6.13.25}$$

Substituting from (6.13.25) into (6.13.21) we obtain the 3SLS estimator:

$$\hat{\delta}_{3SLS} = \{Z'[\hat{\Sigma}^{-1} \otimes X(X'X)^{-1}X']Z\}^{-1}Z'[\hat{\Sigma}^{-1} \otimes X(X'X)^{-1}X']y. \tag{6.13.26}$$

Thus the 3SLS estimator is the first iteration of the FIML estimator provided the above starting values are used. It can be interpreted, therefore, as a non-iterated instrumental variable estimator in which the instrumental variables are

$$H = [\hat{\Sigma}^{-1} \otimes X(X'X)^{-1}X']Z. \tag{6.13.27}$$

Part (d) The limiting distribution of the FIML estimator is obtained by substituting for y from (6.13.17) in (6.13.21). After some slight rearranging we obtain

$$T^{1/2}(\hat{\delta} - \delta) = [T^{-1}\bar{Z}'(\hat{\Sigma}^{-1} \otimes I)Z]^{-1}T^{-1/2}\bar{Z}'(\hat{\Sigma}^{-1} \otimes I)u. \tag{6.13.28}$$

The limiting distribution of $T^{1/2}(\hat{\delta} - \delta)$ is the same as that of

$$[\text{plim } T^{-1} \bar{Z}'(\hat{\Sigma}^{-1} \otimes I)Z]^{-1} T^{-1/2} \bar{Z}'(\hat{\Sigma} \otimes I_T)u \qquad (6.13.29)$$

assuming that the matrix in square brackets in (6.13.29) exists and is non-singular. Under this assumption the limiting distribution of $T^{-1/2} \bar{Z}'(\hat{\Sigma} \oplus I_T)u$ can be shown to be $N\{0, \text{plim } [T^{-1} \bar{Z}'(\hat{\Sigma} \oplus I_T)\bar{Z}]\}$ when $T^{-1/2} X'u$ has a limiting normal distribution. But, since $\hat{\Sigma}$ is consistent for Σ, and in view of (6.13.25),

$$\text{plim } T^{-1} \{\bar{Z}'(\hat{\Sigma}^{-1} \otimes I_T)\bar{Z} - Z'[\hat{\Sigma}^{-1} \otimes X(X'X)^{-1}X']Z\} = 0.$$

Thus $T^{1/2}(\hat{\delta} - \delta)$ has a limiting $N(0, V_{\text{FIML}})$ where

$$V_{\text{FIML}} = \{\text{plim } T^{-1} Z'[\Sigma^{-1} \otimes X(X'X)^{-1}X']Z\}^{-1}. \qquad (6.13.30)$$

By a similar argument we can show that the limiting distribution of $T^{1/2}(\hat{\delta}_{3\text{SLS}} - \delta)$ is $N(0, V_{\text{FIML}})$. Thus, 3SLS is asymptotically as efficient as FIML. For further discussion on FIML, see Dhrymes (1970, pp. 304–327), Schmidt (1976, pp. 216–236), Rothenberg (1973, pp. 79–81) and Hendry (1976).

Solution 6.14

Part (a) The 3SLS estimator has been derived in Solution (6.13). In the notation of (6.13) we have

$$\hat{\delta}_{3\text{SLS}} = \{Z'[\Sigma^{-1} \otimes X(X'X)^{-1}X']Z\}^{-1} Z'[\Sigma^{-1} \otimes X(X'X)^{-1}X']y \qquad (6.14.1)$$

where Σ^{-1} is calculated from 2SLS residuals.

Equation (6.14.1) can also be written as

$$\hat{\delta}_{3\text{SLS}} = \begin{bmatrix} \hat{\sigma}^{11} Z_1' X(X'X)^{-1}X'Z_1 & \cdots & \hat{\sigma}^{1n} Z_1' X(X'X)^{-1}X'Z_n \\ & \cdots & \\ \hat{\sigma}^{n1} Z_n' X(X'X)^{-1}X'Z_1 & \cdots & \hat{\sigma}^{nn} Z_n' X(X'X)^{-1}X'Z_n \end{bmatrix}^{-1}$$

$$\times \begin{bmatrix} \sum \hat{\sigma}^{1i} Z_1' X(X'X)^{-1}X'y_i \\ \cdots \\ \sum \hat{\sigma}^{ni} Z_n' X(X'X)^{-1}X'y_i \end{bmatrix} \qquad (6.14.2)$$

(i) If Σ is diagonal (6.14.2) simplifies to

$$\hat{\delta}_{3\text{SLS}} = \begin{bmatrix} \hat{\sigma}^{11} Z_1' X(X'X)^{-1}X'Z_1 & \cdots & 0 \\ & \cdots & \\ 0 & & \hat{\sigma}^{nn} Z_n' X(X'X)^{-1}X'Z_n \end{bmatrix}$$

$$\begin{bmatrix} \hat{\sigma}^{11} Z_1' X(X'X)^{-1} X'y_1 \\ \vdots \\ \hat{\sigma}^{nn} Z_n' X(X'X)^{-1} X'y_n \end{bmatrix}$$

$$= \begin{bmatrix} [Z_1' X(X'X)^{-1} X'Z_1]^{-1} Z_1' X(X'X)^{-1} X'y_1 \\ \cdots \\ [Z_n' X(X'X)^{-1} X'Z_n]^{-1} Z_n' X(X'X)^{-1} X'y_n \end{bmatrix} \qquad (6.14.3)$$

In other words, if Σ is diagonal, 3SLS is equivalent to applying 2SLS to each equation separately.

(ii) Equation (6.12.1) can be written as

$$\hat{\delta}_{3SLS} = \{ Z'(I \otimes X)[\hat{\Sigma}^{-1} \otimes (X'X)^{-1}](I \otimes X)'Z \}^{-1} Z'(I \otimes X)$$
$$\cdot [\hat{\Sigma}^{-1} \otimes (X'X)^{-1}](I \otimes X)'y. \qquad (6.14.4)$$

If the ith equation is just identified, k_i the number of linear restrictions on that equation satisfies $k_i = n - 1$, where n is the number of equations (see Solution 6.2). $Z_i = [Y_i \vdots X_i]$ is the matrix of observations on the variables corresponding to the unrestricted coefficients in the ith equation and hence is a $T \times (n + m - k_i - 1)$ matrix, implying that $X'Z_i$ is an $m \times (n + m - k_i - 1)$ matrix. If the ith equation is just identified $X'Z_i$ is an $m \times m$ square matrix. If each is identified $(I \otimes X)'Z$ is an $nm \times nm$ (non-singular) square matrix. Hence (6.14.4) simplifies to

$$\hat{\delta}_{3SLS} = [(I \otimes X')Z]^{-1}(I \otimes X')y \qquad (6.14.5)$$

which is the interpretation of an instrumental variable estimator with instrument matrix $I \otimes X$. Equation (6.14.5) can also be written as

$$\hat{\delta}_{3SLS} = \begin{bmatrix} (X'Z_1)^{-1} X'y_1 \\ \vdots \\ (X'Z_n)^{-1} X'y_n \end{bmatrix} = \begin{bmatrix} [Z_1' X(X'X)^{-1} X'Z_1]^{-1} Z_1' X(X'X)^{-1}X'y_1 \\ \cdots \\ [Z_n' X(X'X)^{-1} X'Z_n]^{-1} Z_n' X(X'X)^{-1}X'y_n \end{bmatrix}$$

$$(6.14.6)$$

Thus, if each equation is just-identified, the 3SLS estimator is equivalent to applying 2SLS (or indirect least squares) to each equation separately.

Part (b) Suppose we partition the complete system of equations

$$y = Z\delta + u \qquad (6.14.7)$$

into two subsets, the first of which has m_1 equations and the second m_2 just-identified equations, then (6.14.7) can be written as

$$\begin{pmatrix} y_1 \\ y_2 \end{pmatrix} = \begin{pmatrix} Z_1 & 0 \\ 0 & Z_2 \end{pmatrix} \begin{pmatrix} \delta_1 \\ \delta_2 \end{pmatrix} + \begin{pmatrix} u_1 \\ u_2 \end{pmatrix} \qquad (6.14.8)$$

From the result of Part (ii) above we can note that $(I_{m_2} \otimes X')Z_2$ is an $nm_2 \times nm_2$, non-singular, square matrix. The 3SLS estimator of δ can be expressed as

$$\begin{pmatrix} \hat{\delta}_1 \\ \hat{\delta}_2 \end{pmatrix} = \left[\begin{pmatrix} Z_1 & 0 \\ 0 & Z_2 \end{pmatrix}' [\hat{\Sigma}^{-1} \otimes X(X'X)^{-1}X'] \begin{pmatrix} Z_1 & 0 \\ 0 & Z_2 \end{pmatrix} \right]^{-1}$$

$$\left[\begin{pmatrix} Z_1 & 0 \\ 0 & Z_2 \end{pmatrix}' [\hat{\Sigma}^{-1} \otimes X(X'X)^{-1}X'] \begin{pmatrix} y_1 \\ y_2 \end{pmatrix} \right] \qquad (6.14.9)$$

or as

$$\begin{pmatrix} \hat{\delta}_1 \\ \hat{\delta}_2 \end{pmatrix} = \left[\begin{pmatrix} \bar{Z}_1 & 0 \\ 0 & \bar{Z}_2 \end{pmatrix}' (\hat{\Sigma}^{-1} \otimes I) \begin{pmatrix} \bar{Z}_1 & 0 \\ 0 & \bar{Z}_2 \end{pmatrix} \right]^{-1} \begin{pmatrix} \bar{Z}_1 & 0 \\ 0 & \bar{Z}_2 \end{pmatrix}' (\hat{\Sigma}^{-1} \otimes I) \begin{pmatrix} y_1 \\ y_2 \end{pmatrix}$$

$$(6.14.10)$$

where $\bar{Z}_i = [I_{m_i} \otimes X(X'X)^{-1}X'] Z_i$ for $i = 1, 2$. Introducing the partitioned matrix

$$\hat{\Sigma}^{-1} = \begin{bmatrix} \hat{\Sigma}^{11} & \hat{\Sigma}^{12} \\ \hat{\Sigma}^{21} & \hat{\Sigma}^{22} \end{bmatrix}$$

we obtain

$$\begin{bmatrix} \hat{\delta}_1 \\ \hat{\delta}_2 \end{bmatrix} = \begin{bmatrix} \bar{Z}_1'(\hat{\Sigma}^{11} \otimes I)\bar{Z}_1 & \bar{Z}_1'(\hat{\Sigma}^{12} \otimes I)\bar{Z}_2 \\ \bar{Z}_2'(\hat{\Sigma}^{21} \otimes I)\bar{Z}_1 & \bar{Z}_2'(\hat{\Sigma}^{22} \otimes I)\bar{Z}_2 \end{bmatrix}^{-1}$$

$$\begin{bmatrix} \bar{Z}_1'(\hat{\Sigma}^{11} \otimes I)y_1 + \bar{Z}_1'(\hat{\Sigma}^{12} \otimes I)y_2 \\ \bar{Z}_2'(\hat{\Sigma}^{21} \otimes I)y_1 + \bar{Z}_2'(\hat{\Sigma}^{22} \otimes I)y_2 \end{bmatrix} \qquad (6.14.11)$$

Using the result in Question (2.1) on the inverse of a partitioned matrix we can obtain

$$\hat{\delta}_1 = \{\bar{Z}_1'(\hat{\Sigma}^{11} \otimes I)\bar{Z}_1 - \bar{Z}_1'(\hat{\Sigma}^{12} \otimes I)\bar{Z}_2 [\bar{Z}_2'(\hat{\Sigma}^{22} \otimes I)\bar{Z}_2]^{-1}\bar{Z}_2'(\hat{\Sigma}^{21} \otimes I)\bar{Z}_1\}^{-1}$$

$$\left\{ \sum_{i=1}^{2} \bar{Z}_1'(\hat{\Sigma}^{1i} \otimes I)y_i - \sum_{i=1}^{2} \bar{Z}_1'(\hat{\Sigma}^{12} \otimes I)\bar{Z}_2 [\bar{Z}_2'(\hat{\Sigma}^{22} \otimes I)\bar{Z}_2]^{-1}\bar{Z}_2'(\hat{\Sigma}^{2i} \otimes I)y_i \right\}$$

$$(6.14.12)$$

By virtue of the fact that $(I_{m_2} \otimes X)'\bar{Z}_2$ is square, non-singular, and from the definition of $\bar{Z}_2$, we can show that

$$[\bar{Z}_2'(\hat{\Sigma}^{22} \otimes I)\bar{Z}_2]^{-1} = [(I \otimes X')Z_2]^{-1} [\hat{\Sigma}^{22} \otimes (X'X)^{-1}]^{-1} [Z_2'(I \otimes X)]$$

and hence that

$$\hat{\delta}_1 = \{\bar{Z}_1'(\hat{\Sigma}^{11} \otimes I)\bar{Z}_1 - \bar{Z}_1'[\hat{\Sigma}^{12}(\hat{\Sigma}^{22})^{-1}\hat{\Sigma}^{21} \otimes I]\bar{Z}_1\}^{-1}\{\bar{Z}_1'(\hat{\Sigma}^{11} \otimes I)y_1$$
$$- \bar{Z}_1'[\hat{\Sigma}^{12}(\hat{\Sigma}^{22})^{-1}\hat{\Sigma}^{21} \otimes I]y_1 + \bar{Z}_1'(\hat{\Sigma}^{12} \otimes I)y_2$$
$$- \bar{Z}_1'[\hat{\Sigma}^{12}(\hat{\Sigma}^{22})^{-1}\hat{\Sigma}^{22} \otimes I]y_2\}. \tag{6.14.13}$$

Using the result, $\hat{\Sigma}_{11}^{-1} = \hat{\Sigma}^{11} - \hat{\Sigma}^{12}(\hat{\Sigma}^{22})^{-1}\hat{\Sigma}^{21}$, which is derived from the inverse of a partitioned matrix, (6.14.13) becomes

$$\hat{\delta}_1 = [\bar{Z}_1'(\hat{\Sigma}_{11}^{-1} \otimes I)\bar{Z}_1]^{-1}\bar{Z}_1'(\hat{\Sigma}_{11}^{-1} \otimes I)y_1 \tag{6.14.14}$$

which is our required expression. We can interpret (6.14.14) as a 3SLS estimator applied to the sub-system of over-identified equations with the difference that we use all of the predetermined variables in the system as instruments and not just those appearing in the sub-system. The reader is referred to Court (1974) and Godfrey and Wickens (1977) for further discussion of this point. Also, see Dhrymes (1970, pp. 209–219) and Theil (1971, pp. 508–527) for further discussion of the 3SLS estimator and Question (6.18) for a discussion of sub-system LIML.

Solution 6.15

Part (a) We note that equations (6.15.1) and (6.15.2) are just-identified. Instead of obtaining the FIML estimates of the structural coefficients directly (as we will need to do later in Question 6.17 and as we have to do, in general, when we are dealing with a model containing over-identified structural equations) we can here obtain them indirectly from estimates of the reduced form coefficients. We use the following procedure:

(i) Calculate the coefficients in the unrestricted least squares regressions of y_{1t} on x_{1t} and x_{2t}, and y_{2t} on x_{1t} and x_{2t}.

(ii) Derive the FIML estimates of the coefficients of (6.15.1–2) by solving the equations which define the correspondence between the coefficients of (6.15.1–2) and the coefficients of the reduced form of (6.15.1–2) by substituting for these latter coefficients the estimates obtained in step (i).

To explain these steps in more detail we write (6.15.1–2) as

$$By_t + Cx_t = u_t \tag{6.15.3}$$

so that the reduced form is just

$$y_t = Px_t + v_t \tag{6.15.4}$$

where $P = -B^{-1}C$ and $v_t = B^{-1}u_t$. We have

$$P = \begin{bmatrix} p_{11} & p_{12} \\ p_{21} & p_{22} \end{bmatrix} = -\begin{bmatrix} 1 & b_{12} \\ b_{21} & 1 \end{bmatrix}^{-1} \begin{bmatrix} c_{11} & 0 \\ 0 & c_{22} \end{bmatrix}$$

$$= \frac{1}{b_{12}b_{21} - 1} \begin{bmatrix} 1 & -b_{12} \\ -b_{21} & 1 \end{bmatrix} \begin{bmatrix} c_{11} & 0 \\ 0 & c_{22} \end{bmatrix}$$

so that

$$\left. \begin{aligned} p_{11} &= c_{11}/(b_{12}b_{21} - 1) \\ p_{12} &= -b_{12}c_{22}/(b_{12}b_{21} - 1) \\ p_{21} &= -b_{21}c_{11}/(b_{12}b_{21} - 1) \\ p_{22} &= c_{22}/(b_{12}b_{21} - 1) \end{aligned} \right\} \qquad (6.15.5)$$

and hence

$$\left. \begin{aligned} b_{21} &= -p_{21}/p_{11} \\ b_{12} &= -p_{12}/p_{22} \\ b_{12}b_{21} - 1 &= (p_{12}p_{21} - p_{11}p_{22})/p_{11}p_{22} \\ c_{11} &= (p_{12}p_{21} - p_{11}p_{22})/p_{22} \\ c_{22} &= (p_{12}p_{21} - p_{11}p_{22})/p_{11} \end{aligned} \right\} \qquad (6.15.6)$$

The ordinary least squares estimates of the p_{ij} are given by (compare Solution 3.1)

$$P^{*\prime} = \begin{bmatrix} p_{11}^* & p_{21}^* \\ p_{12}^* & p_{22}^* \end{bmatrix} = (X'X)^{-1} X'Y$$

where $Y' = [y_1, \ldots, y_T]$ and $X' = [x_1, \ldots, x_T]$. We then obtain in step (ii) the following estimates of the coefficients in (6.15.1):

$$\left. \begin{aligned} \hat{b}_{21} &= -p_{21}^*/p_{11}^* \\ \hat{b}_{12} &= -p_{12}^*/p_{22}^* \\ \hat{c}_{11} &= (p_{12}^*p_{21}^* - p_{11}^*p_{22}^*)/p_{22}^* \\ \hat{c}_{22} &= (p_{12}^*p_{21}^* - p_{11}^*p_{22}^*)/p_{11}^* \end{aligned} \right\} . \qquad (6.15.7)$$

Part (b) To prove that the procedure in Part (a) does yield the FIML estimates of the coefficients of (6.15.1) we note first that P^* obtained in Part (a) is the maximum likelihood estimator of P. This follows because the matrix P is unrestricted and there are no restrictions on the covariance matrix of v_t (since the covariance matrix of u_t in (6.13.3) is also unrestricted) so that least squares regression on each equation of (6.15.4) leads to the maximum likelihood estimator of P (see, for instance, Goldberger, 1964, p. 211–212, or Malinvaud, 1970b, p. 174). We recall that, by assumption, u_t has the same bivariate normal distribution for all values of t.

We must now show that equations (6.15.7) yield the maximum likelihood estimates of b_{21}, b_{12}, c_{11} and c_{22}. But, equations (6.15.5) and (6.15.6) define a one-to-one correspondence between the coefficients of (6.15.1–2) and the elements of the matrix P. It follows, therefore, from the invariance property of maximum likelihood estimators (see, for instance, Goldberger, 1964, p. 131) that equations (6.15.7) define the maximum likelihood estimators of b_{21}, b_{12}, c_{11} and c_{22}.

Solution 6.16

We note first from the form of the model (6.16.1–2) that there are two exclusion restrictions on the first equation, no restrictions on the coefficients of the second equation and no restrictions on the covariance matrix of the disturbances (other than its non-singularity). It follows that all the *a priori* restrictions on the model are embodied in the specification of the first equation (and the coefficients of the second equation are not identifiable). Therefore, the full information maximum likelihood estimate of b_{12} is just the limited information maximum likelihood estimate of that parameter — there is no extra information in the second equation that can be used for estimation.

To find the limited information maximum likelihood estimate of b_{12} we proceed as in Solution 6.12. In the present case, we have (in the notation of Solution 6.12)

$$W^*_{\Delta\Delta} = \left(\frac{Y'_\Delta Y_\Delta}{T}\right) - \left(\frac{Y'_\Delta X_\Delta}{T}\right)^{-1}\left(\frac{X'_\Delta Y_\Delta}{T}\right) = \frac{Y'_\Delta Y_\Delta}{T} = \begin{bmatrix} 10 & 8 \\ 8 & 40 \end{bmatrix}$$

Since there are no included exogenous variables in (6.16.1) and $X_\Delta = 0$, we also have

$$W_{\Delta\Delta} = \left(\frac{Y'_\Delta Y_\Delta}{T}\right) - \left(\frac{Y'_\Delta X}{T}\right)\left(\frac{X'X}{T}\right)^{-1}\left(\frac{X'Y_\Delta}{T}\right)$$

$$= \begin{bmatrix} 10 & 8 \\ 8 & 40 \end{bmatrix} - \begin{bmatrix} 2 & 10 \\ 10 & 10 \end{bmatrix}\begin{bmatrix} 5 & 5 \\ 5 & 25 \end{bmatrix}^{-1}\begin{bmatrix} 2 & 10 \\ 10 & 10 \end{bmatrix}$$

$$= \begin{bmatrix} 10 & 8 \\ 8 & 40 \end{bmatrix} - \frac{1}{100} \begin{bmatrix} 2 & 10 \\ 10 & 10 \end{bmatrix} \begin{bmatrix} 25 & -5 \\ -5 & 5 \end{bmatrix} \begin{bmatrix} 2 & 10 \\ 10 & 10 \end{bmatrix}$$

$$= \begin{bmatrix} 10 & 8 \\ 8 & 40 \end{bmatrix} - \frac{1}{100} \begin{bmatrix} 400 & 400 \\ 400 & 2000 \end{bmatrix} = \begin{bmatrix} 6 & 4 \\ 4 & 20 \end{bmatrix}$$

We now solve the determinantal equation corresponding to (6.12.2) viz

$$\det \left\{ \begin{bmatrix} 10 & 8 \\ 8 & 40 \end{bmatrix} - \lambda \begin{bmatrix} 6 & 4 \\ 4 & 20 \end{bmatrix} \right\} = 0$$

or

$$\begin{vmatrix} 10 - 6\lambda & 8 - 4\lambda \\ 8 - 4\lambda & 40 - 20\lambda \end{vmatrix} = 0$$

and we obtain the following values of λ:

$$\lambda = \frac{21}{13}, 2 .$$

Selecting the smallest root $\hat{\lambda} = 21/13$ we now estimate b_{12} by solving

$$\left\{ \begin{bmatrix} 10 & 8 \\ 8 & 40 \end{bmatrix} - \frac{21}{13} \begin{bmatrix} 6 & 4 \\ 4 & 20 \end{bmatrix} \right\} \begin{bmatrix} 1 \\ -\hat{\beta}_{12} \end{bmatrix} = 0 .$$

The matrix in braces in the above expression has rank unity and the system reduces to the single equation

$$\begin{bmatrix} 5 - \frac{63}{13}, & 4 - \frac{42}{13} \end{bmatrix} \begin{bmatrix} 1 \\ -\hat{b}_{12} \end{bmatrix} = 0 .$$

We then find that

$$\hat{b}_{12} = \frac{65 - 63}{52 - 42} = \frac{2}{10} = 0.20 .$$

Thus, $\hat{b}_{12} = 0.20$ is the full information maximum likelihood estimate of b_{12} in this model from the given data.

Remark In our last two questions (6.15 and 6.16) we have encountered situations where the FIML estimates can be obtained by a procedure which involves simple calculations. These situations have arisen because of the special nature of the models specified in those questions. But they are examples of a more general result which is given in Question (6.18) and the reader is referred to Solution (6.18) for a detailed discussion of the issues involved.

Solution 6.17

Part (a) We write the model (6.17.1–2) in the form

$$\begin{bmatrix} 1 & -\alpha \\ 0 & 1 \end{bmatrix}\begin{bmatrix} y_{1t} \\ y_{2t} \end{bmatrix} + \begin{bmatrix} 0 & 0 \\ -\beta & -\gamma \end{bmatrix}\begin{bmatrix} x_{1t} \\ x_{2t} \end{bmatrix} = \begin{bmatrix} u_{1t} \\ u_{2t} \end{bmatrix}$$

or as

$$A z_t = u_t$$

where $z_t' = (y_{1t}, y_{2t}, x_{1t}, x_{2t})$, $u_t' = (u_{1t}, u_{2t})$.

$$A = \begin{bmatrix} 1 & -\alpha & 0 & 0 \\ 0 & 1 & -\beta & -\gamma \end{bmatrix}$$

and the covariance matrix of u_t is

$$\Sigma = \begin{bmatrix} \sigma^2 & \sigma^2 \\ \sigma^2 & 2\sigma^2 \end{bmatrix} = \sigma^2 \begin{bmatrix} 1 & 1 \\ 1 & 2 \end{bmatrix} = \sigma^2 \Sigma_0,$$

say. The FIML estimates of α, β, γ and σ^2 maximise the following log likelihood function (c.f. Goldberger, 1964, p. 353, Dhrymes, 1970, p. 322)

$$L(\alpha, \beta, \gamma, \sigma^2) = \text{const} - \tfrac{1}{2} T \ln (\det \Sigma) + T \ln |\det B|$$

$$- \tfrac{1}{2} T \operatorname{tr} \left(\Sigma^{-1} A \frac{Z'Z}{T} A' \right)$$

where

$$B = \begin{bmatrix} 1 & -\alpha \\ 0 & 1 \end{bmatrix},$$

and $Z' = [z_1, \ldots, z_T]$. We see that $\det B = 1$ and is independent of the parameters α, β and γ; and

$$\Sigma^{-1} = \frac{1}{\sigma^2} \begin{bmatrix} 2 & -1 \\ -1 & 1 \end{bmatrix} = \frac{1}{\sigma^2} \Sigma_0^{-1}$$

We now write $L(\alpha, \beta, \gamma, \sigma^2)$ as

$$\text{const} - \tfrac{1}{2} T \ln (\sigma^4) - \frac{T}{2\sigma^2} \operatorname{tr} \left[\Sigma_0^{-1} A \left(\frac{Z'Z}{T} \right) A' \right] \tag{6.17.3}$$

and find from the first order conditions (differentiating with respect to σ^2) that

$$-\frac{T}{\hat{\sigma}^2} + \frac{T}{2\hat{\sigma}^4} \operatorname{tr}\left[\Sigma_0^{-1} A\left(\frac{Z'Z}{T}\right)A'\right] = 0$$

so that

$$\sigma^2 = \frac{1}{2}\operatorname{tr}\left[\Sigma_0^{-1} A\left(\frac{Z'Z}{T}\right)A'\right] \tag{6.17.4}$$

It follows now from (6.17.3) and (6.17.4), that the FIML estimates of α, β and γ maximise the concentrated log likelihood function

$$L^*(\alpha, \beta, \gamma) = \operatorname{const} - \tfrac{1}{2}T \ln\left\{\frac{1}{2}\operatorname{tr}\left[\Sigma_0^{-1} A\left(\frac{Z'Z}{T}\right)A'\right]\right\}^2$$

$$= \operatorname{const} - T \ln\left\{\operatorname{tr}\left[\Sigma_0^{-1} A\left(\frac{Z'Z}{T}\right)A'\right]\right\}$$

Hence, the FIML estimates of α, β and γ minimise

$$\ln\left\{\operatorname{tr}\left[\Sigma_0^{-1} A\left(\frac{Z'Z}{T}\right)A'\right]\right\}$$

or equivalently

$$\operatorname{tr}\left[\Sigma_0^{-1} A\left(\frac{Z'Z}{T}\right)A'\right] \tag{6.17.5}$$

We now differentiate (6.17.5) with respect to α, β and γ and noting that, for instance,

$$\operatorname{tr}\left[\Sigma_0^{-1} \frac{\partial A}{\partial \alpha}\left(\frac{Z'Z}{T}\right)A' + \Sigma_0^{-1} A\left(\frac{Z'Z}{T}\right)\frac{\partial A'}{\partial \alpha}\right]$$

$$= 2\operatorname{tr}\left[\Sigma_0^{-1} \frac{\partial A}{\partial \alpha}\left(\frac{Z'Z}{T}\right)A'\right]$$

we have the first order conditions

$$\operatorname{tr}\left[\Sigma_0^{-1} \frac{\partial A}{\partial \alpha}\left(\frac{Z'Z}{T}\right)A'\right] = 0 \tag{6.17.6}$$

$$\text{tr}\left[\Sigma_0^{-1}\frac{\partial A}{\partial \beta}\left(\frac{Z'Z}{T}\right)A'\right] = 0 \tag{6.17.7}$$

$$\text{tr}\left[\Sigma_0^{-1}\frac{\partial A}{\partial \gamma}\left(\frac{Z'Z}{T}\right)A'\right] = 0 \tag{6.17.8}$$

We find

$$\frac{\partial A}{\partial \alpha} = \begin{bmatrix} 0 & -1 & 0 & 0 \\ 0 & 0 & 0 & 0 \end{bmatrix}$$

$$\frac{\partial A}{\partial \beta} = \begin{bmatrix} 0 & 0 & 0 & 0 \\ 0 & 0 & -1 & 0 \end{bmatrix}$$

$$\frac{\partial A}{\partial \gamma} = \begin{bmatrix} 0 & 0 & 0 & 0 \\ 0 & 0 & 0 & -1 \end{bmatrix}$$

and from the given data

$$\frac{Z'Z}{T} = \begin{bmatrix} 10 & 2 & 3 & 1 \\ 2 & 5 & 1 & 1 \\ 3 & 1 & 2 & 1 \\ 1 & 1 & 1 & 1 \end{bmatrix}$$

Hence (6.17.6) becomes

$$\text{tr}\left\{ \begin{bmatrix} 2 & -1 \\ -1 & 1 \end{bmatrix} \begin{bmatrix} 0 & -1 & 0 & 0 \\ 0 & 0 & 0 & 0 \end{bmatrix} \begin{bmatrix} 10 & 2 & 3 & 1 \\ 2 & 5 & 1 & 1 \\ 3 & 1 & 2 & 1 \\ 1 & 1 & 1 & 1 \end{bmatrix} \begin{bmatrix} 1 & 0 \\ -\alpha & 1 \\ 0 & -\beta \\ 0 & -\gamma \end{bmatrix} \right\} = 0$$

$$\text{tr}\left\{ \begin{bmatrix} 0 & -2 & 0 & 0 \\ 0 & 1 & 0 & 0 \end{bmatrix} \begin{bmatrix} 10 & 2 & 3 & 1 \\ 2 & 5 & 1 & 1 \\ 3 & 1 & 2 & 1 \\ 1 & 1 & 1 & 1 \end{bmatrix} \begin{bmatrix} 1 & 0 \\ -\alpha & 1 \\ 0 & -\beta \\ 0 & -\gamma \end{bmatrix} \right\} = 0$$

$$\text{tr}\left\{\begin{bmatrix} -4 & -10 & -2 & -2 \\ 2 & 5 & 1 & 1 \end{bmatrix}\begin{bmatrix} 1 & 0 \\ -\alpha & 1 \\ 0 & -\beta \\ 0 & -\gamma \end{bmatrix}\right\} = 0$$

or

$$(-4 + 10\alpha) + (5 - \beta - \gamma) = 0$$

or the linear equation

$$10\alpha - \beta - \gamma = -1 .\tag{6.17.9}$$

Similarly (6.17.7) becomes

$$\text{tr}\left\{\begin{bmatrix} 0 & 0 & 1 & 0 \\ 0 & 0 & -1 & 0 \end{bmatrix}\begin{bmatrix} 10 & 2 & 3 & 1 \\ 2 & 5 & 1 & 1 \\ 3 & 1 & 2 & 1 \\ 1 & 1 & 1 & 1 \end{bmatrix}\begin{bmatrix} 1 & 0 \\ -\alpha & 1 \\ 0 & -\beta \\ 0 & -\gamma \end{bmatrix}\right\} = 0$$

$$\text{tr}\left\{\begin{bmatrix} 3 & 1 & 2 & 1 \\ -3 & -1 & -2 & -1 \end{bmatrix}\begin{bmatrix} 1 & 0 \\ -\alpha & 1 \\ 0 & -\beta \\ 0 & -\gamma \end{bmatrix}\right\} = 0$$

i.e.

$$(3 - \alpha) + (-1 + 2\beta + \gamma) = 0$$

or

$$-\alpha + 2\beta + \gamma = -2 .\tag{6.17.10}$$

Finally, (6.17.8) becomes

$$\text{tr}\left\{\begin{bmatrix} 0 & 0 & 0 & 1 \\ 0 & 0 & 0 & -1 \end{bmatrix}\begin{bmatrix} 10 & 2 & 3 & 1 \\ 2 & 5 & 1 & 1 \\ 3 & 1 & 2 & 1 \\ 1 & 1 & 1 & 1 \end{bmatrix}\begin{bmatrix} 1 & 0 \\ -\alpha & 1 \\ 0 & -\beta \\ 0 & -\gamma \end{bmatrix}\right\} = 0$$

$$\operatorname{tr}\left\{\begin{bmatrix} 1 & 1 & 1 & 1 \\ -1 & -1 & -1 & -1 \end{bmatrix}\begin{bmatrix} 1 & 0 \\ -\alpha & 1 \\ 0 & -\beta \\ 0 & -\gamma \end{bmatrix}\right\} = 0$$

i.e.

$$(1 - \alpha) + (-1 + \beta + \gamma) = 0$$

or

$$-\alpha + \beta + \gamma = 0 . \tag{6.17.11}$$

From (6.17.9) and (6.17.11) we find

$$9\alpha = -1 \quad \text{or} \quad \alpha = -\tfrac{1}{9} \tag{6.17.12}$$

and from (6.17.10) and (6.17.11) we find

$$\beta = -2 \tag{6.17.13}$$

so that, from (6.17.11) and with the above values of α and β, we obtain

$$\gamma = 1\tfrac{8}{9} . \tag{6.17.14}$$

(6.19.12–14) give us the FIML estimates of α, β and γ.

Part (b) If the sample second moment matrix of the x_{it} converges as the sample size $T \to \infty$ to a finite non-singular matrix then the FIML estimates obtained in Part (a) wlll be asymptotically efficient (in the sense we discussed in Solution 3.7). When there are *no* restrictions on the covariance matrix of the structural form disturbances, we know that asymptotically efficient estimates of the structural coefficients can be obtained by the method of three-stage least squares (3SLS). Indeed the 3SLS estimator and the FIML estimator have the same asymptotic distribution in this case (Sargan, 1964, and see also Schmidt, 1976, pp. 224–231 and Solution 6.13). But, when there are restrictions on the covariance matrix of the structural form disturbances this result no longer holds and the 3SLS estimator is no longer asymptotically efficient. This is true even if the covariance matrix is known and this knowledge is utilised in the construction of the 3SLS estimator (by using in the formula for the 3SLS estimator the true covariance matrix instead of the estimator based on the residuals from a 2SLS regression). The fact that the 3SLS pro-cedure does not yield asymptotically efficient estimates in cases where the covariance matrix of the structural disturbances is restricted has been discussed by several authors; and the reader is recommended to consult the excellent discussion in Rothenberg (1973, pp. 73–77) and the recent treatment by Schmidt (1976, pp. 231–233). In the present example we see that the covariance matrix of the structural disturbances is just

$$\Sigma = \sigma^2 \begin{bmatrix} 1 & 1 \\ 1 & 2 \end{bmatrix} = \sigma^2 \Sigma_0$$

and is known up to the scalar coefficient σ^2. Although we can utilise Σ directly in the computation of the 3SLS estimates as we have indicated above (and we find that the unknown scalar σ^2 cancels out in our working), these estimates still have the same asymptotic distribution as the usual 3SLS estimates which do not directly use our knowledge of Σ_0 but depend instead on the preliminary 2SLS regressions. On the other hand, the FIML estimates in Part (a) which do depend on the knowledge of Σ_0 have an asymptotic distribution which is different from that of the FIML estimates of the coefficients obtained by treating Σ as entirely unknown. To see that there is an important difference in these two procedures we need only write down the reduced form of (6.17.1−2):

$$\begin{bmatrix} y_{1t} \\ y_{2t} \end{bmatrix} = \begin{bmatrix} \alpha\beta & \alpha\gamma \\ \beta & \gamma \end{bmatrix} \begin{bmatrix} x_{1t} \\ x_{2t} \end{bmatrix} + \begin{bmatrix} v_{1t} \\ v_{2t} \end{bmatrix} \tag{6.17.15}$$

where

$$\begin{bmatrix} v_{1t} \\ v_{2t} \end{bmatrix} = \begin{bmatrix} 1 & \alpha \\ 0 & 1 \end{bmatrix} \begin{bmatrix} u_{1t} \\ u_{2t} \end{bmatrix}$$

has covariance matrix given by

$$\Omega = \begin{bmatrix} 1 & \alpha \\ 0 & 1 \end{bmatrix} (\sigma^2 \Sigma_0) \begin{bmatrix} 1 & 0 \\ \alpha & 1 \end{bmatrix}$$

$$= \sigma^2 \begin{bmatrix} 1 + 2\alpha + 2\alpha^2 & 1 + 2\alpha \\ 1 + 2\alpha & 2 \end{bmatrix} \tag{6.17.16}$$

We see that the covariance matrix of the reduced form disturbances is also restricted (it depends only on α and σ^2) and its elements contain important information about the parameter α which must be used if we are to obtain asymptotically efficient estimates of α, β and γ. It will not, for instance, be sufficient to estimate (6.17.15) subject to the restrictions implied by the form of the coefficient matrix

$$\begin{bmatrix} \alpha\beta & \alpha\gamma \\ \beta & \gamma \end{bmatrix}$$

and employing only a consistent estimator of Ω. [Note that this means that Malinvaud's minimum distance estimator (Malinvaud, 1970b, pp. 675–678) is not asymptotically efficient here.] If we are to obtain asymptotically efficient estimates of α, β and γ then we must also consider the restrictions on Ω implied by (6.17.16). The simplest approach is to set up the likelihood function and maximise it jointly with respect to α, β, γ and σ^2 as we have done in Part (a).

Remark It is worth noting that model (6.17.1–2) bears a close resemblance to the errors in variables model discussed in Question (5.9) and in the work of Zellner (1970) and Goldberger (1972b). This is largely because (6.17.1) involves no exogenous variables and (6.17.2) is already in reduced form. But note that the stochastic properties of the errors in the two models are different. The covariance matrix of the errors is

$$\begin{bmatrix} \sigma_{11} & 0 \\ 0 & \sigma_{22} \end{bmatrix}$$

in Question (5.9) and

$$\sigma^2 \begin{bmatrix} 1 & 1 \\ 1 & 2 \end{bmatrix}$$

in this question. The same model occurs in a more general form in the later Question (6.18) where the covariance matrix is unrestricted. See also Wickens (1976).

Solution 6.18

Part (a) The remaining n_2 equations in the system may be written as

$$B_3 y_{1t} + B_4 y_{2t} + C_3 x_{1t} + C_4 x_{2t} = u_{2t} \qquad (t = 1, \ldots, T) \quad (6.18.2)$$

where the coefficient matrices B_3, B_4, C_3 and C_4 are unrestricted. The complete system of n equations is, therefore,

$$\begin{bmatrix} B_1 & B_2 \\ B_3 & B_4 \end{bmatrix} \begin{bmatrix} y_{1t} \\ y_{2t} \end{bmatrix} + \begin{bmatrix} C_1 & 0 \\ C_3 & C_4 \end{bmatrix} \begin{bmatrix} x_{1t} \\ x_{2t} \end{bmatrix} = \begin{bmatrix} u_{1t} \\ u_{2t} \end{bmatrix} \tag{6.18.3}$$

or

$$B y_t + C x_t = u_t. \tag{6.18.4}$$

We wish now to find a matrix H such that when (6.18.4) is pre-multiplied by H we obtain a new system of equations consisting of equation (6.18.1) and the unrestricted reduced form equations associated with y_{2t}. Let

$$H = \begin{bmatrix} I & 0 \\ B^{21} & B^{22} \end{bmatrix} \tag{6.18.5}$$

where B^{ij} is the ijth sub-matrix of B^{-1} for $i, j = 1, 2$ then

$$HB = \begin{bmatrix} B_1 & B_2 \\ 0 & I \end{bmatrix}, \quad HC = \begin{bmatrix} C_1 & 0 \\ \hline -P_2 \end{bmatrix} \quad \text{and} \quad HU_t = \begin{bmatrix} u_{1t} \\ v_{2t} \end{bmatrix},$$

where the reduced form of (6.18.4) is

$$y_t = Px_t + v_t = \begin{bmatrix} P_1 \\ P_2 \end{bmatrix} x_t + \begin{bmatrix} v_{1t} \\ v_{2t} \end{bmatrix} \tag{6.18.6}$$

with $P = -B^{-1}C$, and $v_t = B^{-1}u_t$. Thus the reduced form of y_{2t} is

$$y_{2t} = P_2 x_t + v_{2t}. \tag{6.18.7}$$

Using the above results, pre-multiplying (6.18.4) by H, defined in (6.18.5), gives the transformed system

$$\begin{bmatrix} B_1 & B_2 \\ 0 & I \end{bmatrix} y_t + \begin{bmatrix} C_1 & 0 \\ \hline -P_2 \end{bmatrix} x_t = \begin{bmatrix} u_{1t} \\ v_{2t} \end{bmatrix}. \tag{6.18.8}$$

As required, the first set of equations in (6.18.8) is the sub-system (6.18.1) and the second is the reduced form of y_{2t}, namely (6.18.7). Since (6.18.2) is unrestricted, P_2 is also unrestricted. The disturbance term of (6.18.8), namely $(u'_{1t}u'_{2t}) = u'_t H'$, is distributed as a $N(0, \Omega)$ variable where $E(Hu_t u'_t H') = H\Sigma H' = \Omega$, which is also unrestricted and non-singular. The top left-hand sub-matrix of Ω is Σ_{11}.

It can be shown that the values of B_1, B_2, C_1 and Σ_{11} which maximise the likelihood function associated with (6.18.8) are the same values that maximise the likelihood function associated with (6.18.4). The latter log likelihood is

$$L_1 = \text{const} + T \ln |B| - \tfrac{1}{2} T \ln |\Sigma| - \tfrac{1}{2} \text{tr} \sum_{t=1}^{T} u'_t \Sigma^{-1} u_t, \tag{6.18.9}$$

whilst the log likelihood of (6.18.8) is

$$L_2 = \text{const} + T \ln |HB| - \tfrac{1}{2} T \ln |H\Sigma H'| - \tfrac{1}{2} \text{tr} \left[\sum_{t=1}^{T} u'_t H'(H\Sigma H')^{-1} Hu_t \right]$$

$$= \text{const} + T \ln |H| \cdot |B| - \tfrac{1}{2} T \ln |H| \cdot |\Sigma| \cdot |H'| - \tfrac{1}{2} \text{tr} \left[\sum_{t=1}^{T} u'_t H'(H')^{-1} \Sigma^{-1} H^{-1} Hu_t \right]$$

$$= \text{const} + T \ln |B| - \tfrac{1}{2} T \ln |\Sigma| - \tfrac{1}{2} \text{tr} (u'_t \Sigma^{-1} u_t). \tag{6.18.10}$$

Thus (6.18.10) equals (6.18.9) and hence the values of B_1, B_2, C_2 and Σ_{11} which maximise (6.18.9) will also maximise (6.18.10). Consequently we can estimate B_1, B_2, C_1 and Σ_{11} by using FIML on the transformed model (6.18.8). The resulting estimator is known as the sub-system limited information maximum likelihood estimator or sub-system LIML.

Part (b) It was shown in Question (6.13) that the 3SLS estimator is a non-iterative asymptotically efficient estimator of the coefficients of a complete system of equations. In Question (6.14) the 3SLS estimator was derived for the coefficients of a subset of equations of a complete system in which the remaining equations were just-identified. These results can be used here.

The equations in (6.18.8) corresponding to the reduced form of y_{2t} are each just-identified because each equation excludes $n - 1$ coefficients associated with the other endogenous variables and the reduced form coefficient matrix P_2 and Ω are unrestricted. Hence the 3SLS estimators of B_1, B_2 and C_1 obtained from (6.18.8) are asymptotically efficient and are identical to the corresponding sub-system 3SLS estimator given by equation (6.14.14). Moreover, it follows from the asymptotic efficiency of 3SLS that the sub-system 3SLS estimator is as efficient asymptotically as the sub-system LIML estimator. Thus our required non-iterative instrumental variable estimator is the sub-system 3SLS estimator.

Part (c) In the special case where the sub-system consists of a single structural equation, the sub-system LIML estimator is simply the well-known single equation LIML estimator. This result implies that to calculate single-equation LIML, first we form a complete system by augmenting the single structural equation with the reduced forms of the included endogenous variables and then use FIML on this complete system. The resulting estimator of the coefficients of the original structural equation is the single-equation LIML estimator. Whilst this may not be as computationally efficient as the conventional way of calculating single-equation LIML it may, nonetheless, be computationally convenient (for instance, if a FIML program is readily available). Finally, we may note that in this special case, the sub-system 3SLS estimator of the structural equation is just the usual 2SLS estimator of the equation.

Solution 6.19

Part (a) The reduced form equations corresponding to (6.19.1−2) are

$$C_t = \frac{\alpha}{1 - \beta} + \frac{\beta}{1 - \beta} I_t + \frac{1}{1 - \beta} u_t \tag{6.19.3}$$

$$Y_t = \frac{\alpha}{1-\beta} + \frac{1}{1-\beta}I_t + \frac{1}{1-\beta}u_t \tag{6.19.4}$$

and we write (6.19.4) as

$$Y_t = \pi_0 + \pi_1 I_t + v_t \tag{6.19.5}$$

where

$$\pi_0 = \frac{\alpha}{1-\beta}, \quad \pi_1 = \frac{1}{1-\beta} \quad \text{and} \quad v_t = \frac{u_t}{1-\beta}. \tag{6.19.6}$$

Now $v_1, \ldots, v_T$ are independent, normally distributed variables each with zero mean and variance $\sigma^2/(1-\beta)^2$. The ordinary least squares estimators of π_0 and π_1 are then, under the given assumptions, the maximum likelihood estimators (see for instance, Theil, 1971, p. 126). We have

$$\pi_0^* = \bar{y} - \pi_1^* \bar{I}$$

and

$$\pi_1^* = \Sigma(y_t - \bar{y})(I_t - \bar{I})/\Sigma(I_t - \bar{I})^2$$

The maximum likelihood estimators of the structural parameters α and β are obtained from (6.19.6) by setting $\pi_0 = \pi_0^*$, $\pi_1 = \pi_1^*$ and solving for α and β. We have

$$\hat{\beta} = 1 - \frac{1}{\pi_1^*} \quad \text{and} \quad \hat{\alpha} = \frac{\pi_0^*}{\pi_1^*} \tag{6.19.7}$$

and these estimators correspond to what we call the indirect least squares estimators [notice that we can solve (6.19.6) uniquely for α and β, given values of π_0 and π_1].

Since $v_1, \ldots, v_T$ are normally distributed it follows that π_0^* and π_1^* are also normally distributed with means π_0 and π_1 and covariance matrix (compare Malinvaud, 1970b, p. 87 and p. 97; Theil, 1971, p. 129)

$$\frac{\sigma^2}{(1-\beta)^2} \begin{bmatrix} \dfrac{\Sigma_{t=1}^T I_t^2}{T\Sigma_{t=1}^T (I_t - \bar{I})^2} & -\dfrac{\bar{I}}{\Sigma_{t=1}^T (I_t - \bar{I})^2} \\[3ex] -\dfrac{\bar{I}}{\Sigma_{t=1}^T (I_t - \bar{I})^2} & \dfrac{1}{\Sigma_{t=1}^T (I_t - \bar{I})^2} \end{bmatrix}$$

$$= \frac{\sigma^2}{(1-\beta)^2} \begin{bmatrix} \bar{I}^2 + \dfrac{1}{T} & -\bar{I} \\[3ex] -\bar{I} & 1 \end{bmatrix}$$

since $\Sigma_{t=1}^{T}(I_t - \bar{I})^2 = 1$ by assumption.

The probability density of π_1^* is given by

$$g(\pi_1^*) = \frac{1}{\sqrt{2\pi}}\left(\frac{1-\beta}{\sigma}\right)\exp\left[-\frac{(1-\beta)^2}{2\sigma^2}(\pi_1^* - \pi_1)^2\right]$$

so that, from $g(\pi_1^*)$ and the first transformation of (6.19.7) we obtain the following probability density of $\hat{\beta}$

$$f(\hat{\beta}) = \begin{cases} 0 & \hat{\beta} = 1 \\ \frac{1-\beta}{\sqrt{2\pi}\,\sigma}\left(\frac{1}{1-\hat{\beta}}\right)^2\exp\left\{-\frac{(1-\beta)^2}{2\sigma^2}\left[\frac{1}{1-\hat{\beta}} - \frac{1}{1-\beta}\right]^2\right\} & \hat{\beta} \neq 1 \end{cases}$$

(6.19.8)

When $\hat{\beta} \neq 1$ the above expression for $f(\hat{\beta})$ follows from the representation $f(\hat{\beta}) = g(\pi_1^*)\,|\,d\pi_1^*/d\hat{\beta}\,|$. When $\hat{\beta} = 1$ we see that the function $\pi_1^* = 1/(1-\hat{\beta})$ is no longer differentiable. But π_1^* becomes infinitely large as $\hat{\beta}$ approaches 1 and $g(\pi_1^*)$ approaches zero as π_1^* becomes large; so we set $f(\hat{\beta}) = 0$ at $\hat{\beta} = 1$. We note that as $\hat{\beta}$ approaches 1 from below

$$\lim_{\hat{\beta}\to 1} f(\hat{\beta}) = \frac{1-\beta}{\sqrt{2\pi}\,\sigma}\lim_{x\to 0}\left\{\left(\frac{1}{x}\right)^2\exp\left[-\frac{(1-\beta)^2}{2\sigma^2}\left(\frac{1}{x} - \frac{1}{1-\beta}\right)^2\right]\right\}$$

$$= \frac{1-\beta}{\sqrt{2\pi}\,\sigma}\lim_{y\to\infty}\left\{y^2\exp\left[-\frac{(1-\beta)^2}{2\sigma^2}\left(y - \frac{1}{1-\beta}\right)^2\right]\right\}$$

$$= \frac{1-\beta}{\sqrt{2\pi}\,\sigma}\lim_{z\to\infty}\left[\left(z + \frac{1}{1-\beta}\right)^2\exp\left(-\frac{(1-\beta)^2}{2\sigma^2}z^2\right)\right]$$

$$= 0$$

since, for $a > 0$ and any $n > 0$, e^{-az^2} and $z^n e^{-az^2}$ both tend to zero as $z \to \infty$. It follows that $f(\hat{\beta})$ is continuous at the point $\hat{\beta} = 1$ as well as all other values of $\hat{\beta}$.

Part (b) The rth moment of $\hat{\beta}$ is defined by

$$E(\hat{\beta}^r) = \int_{-\infty}^{\infty} \hat{\beta}^r f(\hat{\beta})\,d\hat{\beta}$$

(6.19.9)

if this integral converges. To show that this integral does not converge for any value of $r \geq 1$ we need only show that it does not converge for $r = 1$. For, when $r > 1$, we have in the interval $[1, \infty)$

$$\hat{\beta} f(\hat{\beta}) \leq \hat{\beta}^r f(\hat{\beta}) \qquad (1 \leq \hat{\beta} < \infty)$$

and this inequality is sufficient to ensure that the integral (6.19.9) diverges for $r > 1$ when it diverges for $r = 1$ (see for instance, Widder, 1961, Theorem 2 p. 326).

To show that the integral (6.19.9) diverges when $r = 1$ we can use the following theorem proved, for instance, in Widder (1961, p. 330):

Theorem (limit test for divergence of an improper integral)
If $h(x)$ is continuous for all x in $[a, \infty)$ and

$$\lim_{x \to \infty} xh(x) = A \neq 0 \qquad (\text{or} \pm \infty)$$

then the integral $\int_a^\infty h(x)dx$ diverges.

To apply this theorem in our present context we set

$$h(x) = xf(x)$$

$$= \frac{1-\beta}{\sqrt{2\pi}\,\sigma} \frac{x}{(1-x)^2} \exp\left[-\frac{(1-\beta)^2}{2\sigma^2}\left(\frac{1}{1-x} - \frac{1}{1-\beta}\right)^2\right]$$

and then

$$\lim_{x \to \infty} xh(x) = \frac{1-\beta}{\sqrt{2\pi}\,\sigma} \lim_{x \to \infty} \left\{\left(\frac{x}{1-x}\right)^2 \exp\left[-\frac{(1-\beta)^2}{2\sigma^2}\left(\frac{1}{1-x}\right.\right.\right.$$

$$\left.\left.\left.- \frac{1}{1-\beta}\right)^2\right]\right\}$$

$$= \frac{1-\beta}{\sqrt{2\pi}\,\sigma} \exp\left(-\frac{1}{2\sigma^2}\right)$$

$$\neq 0.$$

It follows from the theorem that the integral $\int_a^\infty \hat{\beta}f(\hat{\beta})d\hat{\beta}$ does not converge for any value of a and, as a result, no integral moments of $\hat{\beta}$ exist.

Part (c) The ordinary least squares estimator of β is given by

$$b = \frac{\sum_{t=1}^T (C_t - \bar{C})(Y_t - \bar{Y})}{\sum_{t=1}^T (Y_t - \bar{Y})^2}$$

Its distribution is much more difficult to derive than that of $\hat{\beta}$. The probability density of b (for even $T \geqslant 4$) was first derived by Bergstrom (1962) and is a complicated function of b. But this density, like (6.19.8), can be readily graphed and used to compute the relative degrees of concentration about the true values of the two different estimators. The reader is referred to Bergstrom's study for a comparison of the two estimators along these lines. We note here only the main conclusion that emerged from Bergstrom's work:

> that the use of the maximum likelihood estimator gives the greater probability of obtaining a very accurate estimate but the greater probability, also, of making a large error.

and

> that, for samples of 10 or more observations, generated by the basic stochastic, Keynesian model (with realistic values of the parameters) the maximum likelihood estimator of the marginal propensity to consume is the 'better' general purpose estimator of this parameter. Moreover, it is doubtful whether there is any size of sample for which we could confidently conclude that the least squares estimator is the 'better' general purpose estimator.

We notice that this conclusion has been reached in spite of the fact that $\hat{\beta}$ has no finite integral order moments. Indeed, the fact that $\hat{\beta}$ has no integral order moments is associated with the tail behaviour of the probability density of $\hat{\beta}$. In particular, $\hat{\beta}$ has a thick left-hand tail and this explains why the use of $\hat{\beta}$ leads to a greater probability of making a large error than the use of the least squares estimator (whose probability density has thinner tails).

Remark For a further discussion of the exact finite sample theory aspects of the estimation of the model (6.19.1) the reader is referred to the recent survey paper by Basmann (1974). In this paper, Basmann details the exact marginal density functions of $\hat{\alpha}$ [in (6.19.5) above] and

$$\hat{\sigma}^2 \;=\; T^{-1} \sum_{t=1}^{T} (Y_t - \pi_0^* - \pi_1^* I_t)^2 \, (1 - \hat{\beta})^2$$

[the maximum likelihood estimator of the variance of the disturbance u_t in the model (6.19.1) — denoted by $\hat{\omega}^2$ in Basmann's notation]. Both of these distributions share with that of $\hat{\beta}$ the property that they do not possess finite moments of any integer order (c.f. Basmann, 1974, pp. 221–222).

Solution 6.20

We write the first equation (6.20.1), complete with T sample observations, in the form

$$y_1 \;=\; y_2 b + x_1 c + u_1 \tag{6.20.3}$$

where

$$y_1' \;=\; (y_{11} \ldots y_{1T})$$
$$y_2' \;=\; (y_{21} \ldots y_{2T})$$

$$x_1' = (x_{11} \ldots x_{1T})$$

$$b = b_{12}, \quad c = c_{12}$$

and we define

$$X' = \begin{bmatrix} x_{11} & \cdots & x_{1T} \\ x_{21} & \cdots & x_{2T} \\ x_{31} & \cdots & x_{3T} \\ x_{41} & \cdots & x_{4T} \end{bmatrix}$$

The two-stage least squares estimator of (b', c') in (6.20.3) is just

$$\begin{bmatrix} \hat{b} \\ \hat{c} \end{bmatrix} = \begin{bmatrix} y_2'X(X'X)^{-1}X'y_2 & y_2'x_1 \\ x_1'y_2 & x_1'x_1 \end{bmatrix}^{-1} \begin{bmatrix} y_2'X(X'X)^{-1}X'y_1 \\ x_1'y_1 \end{bmatrix}$$

and the Nagar expansion for the bias of this estimator up to order T^{-1} is given by (see Nagar, 1959, p. 569)

$$E\left\{ \begin{bmatrix} \hat{b} \\ \hat{c} \end{bmatrix} - \begin{bmatrix} b \\ c \end{bmatrix} \right\} = (L-1)Qq + \mathrm{O}(T^{-2}) \qquad (6.20.4)$$

where L is the degree of over-identification, given here by

$$L = \text{total number of restrictions}$$
$$- \text{(number of equations less one)}$$
$$= 3 - (2-1)$$
$$= 2$$

and the matrix Q and vector q in (6.20.4) are given by

$$Q = \begin{bmatrix} \bar{y}_2'\bar{y}_2 & \bar{y}_2'x_1 \\ x_1'\bar{y}_2 & x_1'x_1 \end{bmatrix}^{-1}$$

and

$$q = \frac{1}{T}\begin{bmatrix} E(\bar{v}_2'u_1) \\ 0 \end{bmatrix}$$

where $\bar{y}_2$ and $\bar{v}_2$ are the systematic component and disturbance component respectively of the reduced form of y_2, viz:

$$y_2' = p_2x' + \bar{v}_2' = \bar{y}_2' + \bar{v}_2'.$$

We have for the whole model

$$
\begin{bmatrix} 1 & -b_{12} \\ 0 & 1 \end{bmatrix} \begin{bmatrix} y_{1t} \\ y_{2t} \end{bmatrix} = \begin{bmatrix} c_{11} & 0 & 0 & 0 \\ c_{21} & c_{22} & c_{23} & c_{24} \end{bmatrix} \begin{bmatrix} x_{1t} \\ x_{2t} \\ x_{3t} \\ x_{4t} \end{bmatrix} + \begin{bmatrix} u_{1t} \\ u_{2t} \end{bmatrix}
$$

so that the reduced form is simply

$$
\begin{bmatrix} y_{1t} \\ y_{2t} \end{bmatrix} = \begin{bmatrix} c_{11} + b_{12}c_{21} & b_{12}c_{22} & b_{12}c_{23} & b_{12}c_{24} \\ c_{21} & c_{22} & c_{23} & c_{24} \end{bmatrix} \begin{bmatrix} x_{1t} \\ x_{2t} \\ x_{3t} \\ x_{4t} \end{bmatrix}
$$

$$
+ \begin{bmatrix} u_{1t} + b_{12}u_{2t} \\ u_{2t} \end{bmatrix}
$$

so that $\bar{y}_2' = [c_{21} \quad c_{22} \quad c_{23} \quad c_{24}] X'$ and $\bar{v}_2' = [u_{21}, \ldots, u_{2T}]$. It follows that

$$
\bar{y}_2'\bar{y}_2 = [c_{21} \quad c_{22} \quad c_{23} \quad c_{24}] X'X \begin{bmatrix} c_{21} \\ c_{22} \\ c_{23} \\ c_{24} \end{bmatrix}
$$

$$
= T(c_{21}^2 + c_{22}^2 + c_{23}^2 + c_{24}^2)
$$

since, by assumption, $X'X/T = I$; and

$$
\bar{y}_2'x_1 = [c_{21} \quad c_{22} \quad c_{23} \quad c_{24}] X'x_1
$$

$$
= [c_{21} \quad c_{22} \quad c_{23} \quad c_{24}] \begin{bmatrix} T \\ 0 \\ 0 \\ 0 \end{bmatrix}
$$

$$
= c_{21} T
$$

Finally

$$
\bar{v}_2'u_1 = [u_{21} \ldots u_{2T}] \begin{bmatrix} u_{11} \\ \vdots \\ u_{1T} \end{bmatrix} = \sum_{t=1}^{t} u_{2t}u_{1t}
$$

so that

$$E(\bar{v}_2' u_1) = TE(u_{2t} u_{1t}) = T\sigma^2$$

from the stated covariance matrix.

Hence, we obtain the following expression for Q and q in this case:

$$Q = \begin{bmatrix} T(c_{21}^2 + c_{22}^2 + c_{23}^2 + c_{24}^2) & T c_{21} \\ T c_{21} & T \end{bmatrix}^{-1}$$

and

$$q = \frac{1}{T} \begin{bmatrix} T\sigma^2 \\ 0 \end{bmatrix} = \begin{bmatrix} \sigma^2 \\ 0 \end{bmatrix}$$

It now follows from (6.20.4) and the above expressions that the bias of $(\hat{b}_{12}, \hat{c}_{12})$ up to $O(T^{-1})$ is given by

$$E \begin{bmatrix} \hat{b}_{12} \\ \hat{c}_{12} \end{bmatrix} - \begin{bmatrix} b_{12} \\ c_{12} \end{bmatrix} = \frac{2}{T} \begin{bmatrix} c_{21}^2 + c_{22}^2 + c_{23}^2 + c_{24}^2 & c_{21}^2 \\ c_{21} & 1 \end{bmatrix}^{-1} \begin{bmatrix} \sigma^2 \\ 0 \end{bmatrix}$$

$$= \frac{2}{T} \left(\frac{1}{c_{22}^2 + c_{23}^2 + c_{24}^2} \right) \begin{bmatrix} \sigma^2 \\ -c_{21}\sigma^2 \end{bmatrix}$$

That is

$$E(\hat{b}_{12} - b_{12}) = \frac{2\sigma^2}{T(c_{22}^2 + c_{23}^2 + c_{24}^2)} + O(T^{-2})$$

and

$$E(\hat{c}_{12} - c_{12}) = \frac{-2\sigma^2 c_{21}}{T(c_{22}^2 + c_{23}^2 + c_{24}^2)} + O(T^{-2}).$$

Remark Expressions for the Nagar expression of the bias of the two-stage least squares estimator are taken up to $O(T^{-2})$ by Mikhail (1972). The validity of the Nagar expansion for the bias must necessarily depend on the existence of first-order moments of the estimator itself (otherwise we are approximating by a finite expression a moment which is not finite) — the same is true of the Nagar expansions for higher order moments of the estimator. The question of the validity of these expansions has recently been explored in some depth by Hatanaka (1973) and Sargan (1974). The article by Sargan shows that the criteria for the validity of these expansions depend on the existence and orders of magnitude (as $T \to \infty$) of the moments of the estimators. The reader is referred to these interesting articles for further details.

Solution 6.21

The representations of the distribution functions of $\sqrt{T}(b_{2SLS} - b)$ and $\sqrt{T}(b_{LIML} - b)$ given by (6.21.4) and (6.21.5) are known as Edgeworth expansions. These expansions express the distribution function of interest in a series of terms involving the distribution function of a standard normal variate $[I(x)$ in our notation$]$ and its successive derivatives $[I'(x) = i(x), I^{(2)}(x) = i'(x)$ and so on$]$. They are particularly useful when the exact distribution function of the statistic or estimator in which we are interested is unknown or so complicated that it is difficult to interpret. These expansions also have the useful property that they are proper asymptotic series in the mathematical sense: that is, if we truncate the expansion after a finite number of terms then the remainder (or error, after truncation) has the same order of magnitude (in terms of some key parameter like the sample size T) as the first omitted term in the expansion. Thus, we can write (6.21.4) in terms which involve successively higher powers of $1/\sqrt{T}$:

$$P\left[\sqrt{T}(b_{2SLS} - b) \leqslant x\right] = I\left(\frac{x}{\lambda}\right)$$

$$+ \frac{\lambda}{\sqrt{T}}\left[\left(\frac{x}{\lambda}\right)^2 - (m-2)\right]i\left(\frac{x}{\lambda}\right)$$

$$+ \frac{\lambda^2}{2T}\left[-(m-2)(m-3)\left(\frac{x}{\lambda}\right) + (2m-3)\left(\frac{x}{\lambda}\right)^3 - \left(\frac{x}{\lambda}\right)^5\right]i\left(\frac{x}{\lambda}\right)$$

$$+ O(T^{-3/2}) \tag{6.21.6}$$

We see that as $T \to \infty$ we are left with only the first term on the right side of (6.21.6). This first term gives us, in fact, the limiting distribution of $\sqrt{T}(b_{2SLS} - b)$ as $T \to \infty$. We recall that this limiting distribution is, indeed, normal (see Theil, 1971, p. 497) and we know that the variance of this limiting distribution will be fhe first diagonal element of

$$\sigma^2\left[\plim_{T \to \infty}\left(\frac{Z_1'X}{T}\right)\left(\frac{X'X}{T}\right)^{-1}\left(\frac{X'Z_1}{T}\right)\right]^{-1} \tag{6.21.7}$$

where

$$\frac{Z_1'X}{T} = \begin{bmatrix} T^{-1}\Sigma_{t=1}^{T} y_{2t}x_{1t} & \cdots & T^{-1}\Sigma_{t=1}^{T} y_{2t}x_{mt} \\ T^{-1}\Sigma_{t=1}^{T} x_{1t}^2 & \cdots & T^{-1}\Sigma_{t=1}^{T} x_{1t}x_{mt} \end{bmatrix}$$

and

$$\frac{X'X}{T} = \left[\left(T^{-1}\sum_{t=1}^{T} x_{it}x_{jt}\right)_{ij}\right].$$

But, by assumption $X'X/T = I_m$ for all values of T, so that

$$\lim_{T \to \infty} \frac{X'X}{T} = I$$

and since

$$T^{-1} \sum_{t=1}^{T} y_{2t} x_{it} = \sum_{j=1}^{m} c_{2j}\left(T^{-1} \sum_{t=1}^{T} x_{jt} x_{it}\right)$$
$$+ T^{-1} \sum_{t=1}^{T} u_{2t} x_{it}$$

we find that

$$\operatorname*{plim}_{T \to \infty} \frac{1}{T} \sum_{t=1}^{T} y_{2t} x_{it} = c_{2i}$$

Hence

$$\operatorname*{plim}_{T \to \infty} \left(\frac{Z_1' X}{T}\right) = \begin{bmatrix} c_{21} & c_{22} & \cdots & c_{2m} \\ 1 & 0 & \cdots & 0 \end{bmatrix}$$

and (6.21.7) becomes

$$\sigma^2 \left\{ \begin{bmatrix} c_{21} & c_{22} & \cdots & c_{2m} \\ 1 & 0 & \cdots & 0 \end{bmatrix} \begin{bmatrix} 1 & \cdots & 0 \\ \cdot & \cdots & \cdot \\ 0 & \cdots & 1 \end{bmatrix} \begin{bmatrix} c_{21} & 1 \\ \cdot & \cdot \\ \cdot & \cdot \\ c_{2m} & 0 \end{bmatrix} \right\}^{-1}$$

$$= \sigma^2 \begin{bmatrix} \sum_{j=1}^{m} c_{2j}^2 & c_{21} \\ c_{21} & 1 \end{bmatrix}^{-1}$$

$$= \frac{\sigma^2}{\sum_{j=1}^{m} c_{2j}^2} \begin{bmatrix} 1 & -c_{21} \\ -c_{21} & \sum_{j=2}^{m} c_{2j}^2 \end{bmatrix}$$

So the first diagonal element of (6.21.7) is just

$$\sigma^2 / \sum_{j=2}^{m} c_{2j}^2 = \lambda^2$$

and this is the variance of the limiting distribution of $\sqrt{T}(b_{2\text{SLS}} - b)$. We note that the first term of (6.21.6) is

$$I\left(\frac{x}{\lambda}\right) = \int_{-\infty}^{x/\lambda} i(y)\,dy = \int_{-\infty}^{x} \frac{1}{\lambda} i\left(\frac{t}{\lambda}\right) dt = \int_{-\infty}^{x} \frac{1}{\sqrt{2\pi}\,\lambda} \exp\left(-\frac{t^2}{2\lambda^2}\right) dt$$

as we would expect for the form of a normal distribution with variance given by λ^2.

Turning to the second term on the right side of (6.21.6) we see that this has a coefficient of $\lambda/\sqrt{2T}$ which is of $O(T^{-1/2})$. The remaining factors in this term are a polynomial in x/λ and the normal density $i(x/\lambda)$. This second term gives us a correction on the large sample normal distribution $I(x/\lambda)$. We can argue that the error on an approximation to the true probability $P[\sqrt{T}(b_{2SLS} - b) \leqslant x]$ that is based on these first two terms tends to zero faster than the error on the large sample normal approximation. Similar considerations apply to the third term on the right side of (6.21.26) which we note is of $O(T^{-1})$. The fact that the error after the first three terms is of $O(T^{-3/2})$ (i.e. a higher power of $1/\sqrt{T}$) ensures the validity of this expansion as a proper asymptotic series in the sense we have described above. To establish this validity we need a formal mathematical theorem and the reader may profitably refer to the articles by Anderson (1974), Mariano (1973) and Sargan (1975) for rigorous demonstrations of the validity of such expansions in this context.

To answer the question as set on the concentration of the two estimators we take a positive number X and compute for each estimator

$$P(\sqrt{T} \, |b_{2SLS} - b| \leqslant X)$$

and

$$P(\sqrt{T} \, |b_{LIML} - b| \leqslant X)$$

up to $O(T^{-1})$ from the given expansions. We have from (6.21.4)

$$P(\sqrt{T} \, |b_{2SLS} - b| \leqslant X)$$

$$= P[-X \leqslant \sqrt{T}(b_{2SLS} - b) \leqslant X]$$

$$= P[\sqrt{T}(b_{2SLS} - b) \leqslant X] - P[\sqrt{T}(b_{2SLS} - b) \leqslant -X]$$

$$= I\left(\frac{X}{\lambda}\right) + i\left(\frac{X}{\lambda}\right)\left\{\frac{\lambda}{\sqrt{T}}\left[\left(\frac{X}{\lambda}\right)^2 - (m-2)\right]\right.$$

$$+ \frac{\lambda^2}{2T}\left[-(m-2)(m-3)\left(\frac{X}{\lambda}\right) + (2m-3)\left(\frac{X}{\lambda}\right)^3\right.$$

$$\left.\left. - \left(\frac{X}{\lambda}\right)^5\right]\right\}$$

$$- I\left(-\frac{X}{\lambda}\right) - i\left(-\frac{X}{\lambda}\right)\left\{\frac{\lambda}{\sqrt{T}}\left[\left(-\frac{X}{\lambda}\right)^2 - (m-2)\right]\right.$$

$$- \frac{\lambda^2}{2T}\left[-(m-2)(m-3)\left(-\frac{X}{\lambda}\right) + (2m-3)\left(-\frac{X}{\lambda}\right)^3\right.$$

$$- \left(-\frac{X}{\lambda}\right)^5 \right] + O(T^{-3/2})$$

$$= I\left(\frac{X}{\lambda}\right) - I\left(-\frac{X}{\lambda}\right)$$

$$+ \frac{\lambda}{\sqrt{T}} \left[\left(\frac{X}{\lambda}\right)^2 - (m-2)\right] i\left(\frac{X}{\lambda}\right)$$

$$- \frac{\lambda}{\sqrt{T}} \left[\left(\frac{X}{\lambda}\right)^2 - (m-2)\right] i\left(-\frac{X}{\lambda}\right)$$

$$+ \frac{\lambda^2}{2T} \left[-(m-2)(m-3)\left(\frac{X}{\lambda}\right) + (2m-3)\left(\frac{X}{\lambda}\right)^3 - \left(\frac{X}{\lambda}\right)^5\right] i\left(\frac{X}{\lambda}\right)$$

$$+ \frac{\lambda^2}{2T} \left[-(m-2)(m-3)\left(\frac{X}{\lambda}\right) + (2m-3)\left(\frac{X}{\lambda}\right)^3 - \left(\frac{X}{\lambda}\right)^5\right] i\left(-\frac{X}{\lambda}\right)$$

$$+ O(T^{-3/2})$$

$$= I\left(\frac{X}{\lambda}\right) - I\left(-\frac{X}{\lambda}\right)$$

$$+ \frac{\lambda^2}{T} \left[-(m-2)(m-3)\left(\frac{X}{\lambda}\right) + (2m-3)\left(\frac{X}{\lambda}\right)^3 - \left(\frac{X}{\lambda}\right)^5\right] i\left(\frac{X}{\lambda}\right)$$

$$+ O(T^{-3/2}) \tag{6.21.8}$$

where we use the fact that $i(z) = i(-z)$ from the symmetry of the normal distribution.

In a similar way we find that for the limited information maximum likelihood estimator we have

$$P(\sqrt{T} \,|b_{\text{LIML}} - b\,| \leqslant X)$$

$$= I\left(\frac{X}{\lambda}\right) - I\left(-\frac{X}{\lambda}\right)$$

$$+ \frac{\lambda^2}{T} \left[-(m-2)\left(\frac{X}{\lambda}\right) + \left(\frac{X}{\lambda}\right)^3 - \left(\frac{X}{\lambda}\right)^5\right] i\left(\frac{X}{\lambda}\right) + O(T^{-3/2})$$

$$\tag{6.21.9}$$

(The reader is left to check this expression for himself). Then, from (6.21.8) and (6.21.9) we obtain

$$P(\sqrt{T} \,|\, b_{2SLS} - b\,| \leqslant X) - P(\sqrt{T} \,|\, b_{LIML} - b\,| \leqslant X)$$

$$= \frac{\lambda^2}{T}\Bigg[- (m-2)(m-3)\left(\frac{X}{\lambda}\right) + (m-2)\left(\frac{X}{\lambda}\right)$$

$$+ (2m-3)\left(\frac{X}{\lambda}\right)^3 - \left(\frac{X}{\lambda}\right)^3 \Bigg] i\left(\frac{X}{\lambda}\right)$$

$$+ O(T^{-3/2})$$

$$= \frac{\lambda^2}{T}\Bigg\{ - (m-2)[(m-3)-1]\left(\frac{X}{\lambda}\right)$$

$$+ 2(m-2)\left(\frac{X}{\lambda}\right)^3 \Bigg\} i\left(\frac{X}{\lambda}\right) + O(T^{-3/2})$$

and neglecting the remainder of $O(T^{-3/2})$ we have

$$\frac{\lambda^2}{T}(m-2)\left(\frac{X}{\lambda}\right)\Bigg[- (m-4) + 2\left(\frac{X}{\lambda}\right)^2 \Bigg] i\left(\frac{X}{\lambda}\right) \qquad (6.21.10)$$

which is positive when $2 < m \leqslant 4$ for all values of X.

We notice that $m \geqslant 2$ is required for the identification of the first equation, (6.20.1). When $m = 2$ the equation is just-identified and in this case we know that the two estimators are equivalent (see, for instance, Goldberger, 1964, p. 334 and p. 344). It is easy to verify that when $m = 2$ the expansions for the two estimators given by (6.21.4) and (6.21.5) are the same up to $O(T^{-1})$ and this is consistent with the fact that their concentration about the true value is also the same, as seen from (6.21.10). When $m > 2$, equation (6.21.1) is over-identified and we can regard the size of $m - 2$ as an indicator of the degree of over-identification. The form of (6.21.10) then suggests to us that the two-stage least squares estimator has a greater concentration about the true value than the limited information maximum likelihood estimator when the degree of over-identification is small.

On the other hand, when $m - 2$ is large, it is clear from the factor in square brackets in (6.21.10) that *for some values of* X the limited information estimator will be the more concentrated. This will be so when X is not large. But, when X is also very large it is clear that the expression

$$-(m-4) + 2\left(\frac{X}{\lambda}\right)^2$$

will become positive and the advantage will turn to two-stage least squares. This information can be interpreted in the light of our knowledge concerning the existence of moments of the two estimators. For when X is very large, we are considering the bulk of the distribution and excluding only the tails. The probability that an estimator will lie in such a region will then be greater for the estimator whose density has thinner tails. In the present case, we know that the distribution of the two-stage least squares estimator has integral moments up to the degree of over-identification ($= m - 2$, here) — see, for instance, Hatanaka (1974); whereas the distribution of the limited information estimator has no finite integral moments (see Mariano and Sawa, 1972) and it will, therefore, certainly have thicker tails than that of the two-stage least squares estimator when $m - 2$ is large. It follows that although (6.21.10) holds, strictly speaking, only up to an error of $O(T^{-3/2})$ this expression contains a good deal of information which agrees with our knowledge derived from the form of the exact distributions.

The reader is referred to Anderson (1974) for a more detailed comparison of the two estimators based on their Edgeworth expansions. And, as a further exercise, the reader may wish to verify that the expansions (6.21.4) and (6.21.5) correspond to those given in the article by Anderson (1974) under our stated assumptions [the corresponding expansions in Anderson's article are (5.2) on p. 571 and (4.27) on p. 570].

Solution 6.22

The model (6.22.1–2) is a simultaneous equations model that is non-linear in the variables. These models have recently become a subject of great interest to econometricians and the reader is referred particularly to the papers by Amemiya (1974, 1977) and the special issue of the *Annals of Economic and Social Measurement* in 1974 (number 4) for details of the emerging body of theory. In the present case we notice that only the first equation contains a non-linearity and the second equation is already in reduced form.

Part (a) The ordinary least squares estimator of α in (6.22.1) has the form

$$\hat{\alpha} = \left(\sum_{t=1}^{T} y_{2t}^4\right)^{-1} \left(\sum_{t=1}^{T} y_{2t}^2 y_{1t}\right)$$

$$= \alpha + \left(\sum_{t=1}^{T} y_{2t}^4 \right)^{-1} \left(\sum_{t=1}^{T} y_{2t}^2 u_{1t} \right)$$

$$= \alpha + \left[\sum_{t=1}^{T} (\beta^4 + 4\beta^3 u_{2t} + 6\beta^2 u_{2t}^2 + 4\beta u_{2t}^3 + u_{2t}^4) \right]^{-1}$$

$$\left[\sum_{t=1}^{T} (\beta^2 + 2\beta u_{2t} + u_{2t}^2) u_{1t} \right] \tag{6.22.3}$$

To find the probability limit of $\hat{\alpha}$ as $T \to \infty$ we notice first that, from the stated assumptions about the u_{it} $(i = 1, 2)$ we have (from Khintchine's Theorem — see Cramér, 1946, p. 346):

$$\plim_{T \to \infty} T^{-1} \sum_{t=1}^{T} u_{it} = E(u_{it}) = 0 \qquad (i = 1, 2) \tag{6.22.4}$$

$$\plim_{T \to \infty} T^{-1} \sum_{t=1}^{T} u_{2t}u_{1t} = E(u_{2t}u_{1t}) = \sigma^2 \tag{6.22.5}$$

$$\plim_{T \to \infty} T^{-1} \sum_{t=1}^{T} u_{2t}^2 = E(u_{2t}^2) = 2\sigma^2 \tag{6.22.6}$$

$$\plim_{T \to \infty} T^{-1} \sum_{t=1}^{T} u_{2t}^2 u_{1t} = E(u_{2t}^2 u_{1t}) = 0 \tag{6.22.7}$$

$$\plim_{T \to \infty} T^{-1} \sum_{t=1}^{T} u_{2t}^3 = E(u_{2t}^3) = 0 \tag{6.22.8}$$

$$\plim_{T \to \infty} T^{-1} \sum_{t=1}^{T} u_{2t}^4 = E(u_{2t}^4) = 3(2\sigma^2)^2 = 12\sigma^4 \tag{6.22.9}$$

The above expectations can most simply be calculated from the joint characteristic function of (u_{1t}, u_{2t}) which has the form

$$E[\exp (iu_1 t + iu_2 s)] = \exp[-\tfrac{1}{2}(\sigma^2 t^2 + 2\sigma^2 ts + 2\sigma^2 s^2)]$$

(see, for instance, Cramér, 1946, p. 287, or Kendall and Stuart, 1969, p. 350) where $i^2 = -1$ and which we can expand as

$$\left. \begin{array}{l} 1 - \tfrac{1}{2}(\sigma^2 t^2 + 2\sigma^2 ts + 2\sigma^2 s^2) \\ + \tfrac{1}{2}[\tfrac{1}{2}(\sigma^2 t^2 + 2\sigma^2 ts + 2\sigma^2 s^2)]^2 \\ + o(t^4 + s^4) \end{array} \right\} \tag{6.22.10}$$

where the term $o(t^4 + s^4)$ indicates that higher order terms in the expansion go to zero faster than $t^4 + s^4$ as $t \to 0$ and $s \to 0$. We rewrite (6.22.10) as

$$f(t,s) = 1 + \frac{i^2}{2!} (\sigma^2 t^2 + 2\sigma^2 ts + 2\sigma^2 s^2)$$

$$+ \frac{i^4}{4!} [3(\sigma^2 t^2 + 2\sigma^2 ts + 2\sigma^2 s^2)^2] \qquad (6.22.11)$$

$$+ o(t^4 + s^4)$$

We know that moments of total order m are given by

$$E(u_1^j u_2^k) = \frac{1}{i^m} \left[\frac{\partial^m f(t,s)}{\partial t^j \partial s^k} \right]_{t=s=0} \qquad (j+k=m) \qquad (6.22.12)$$

(see, for instance, Lukacs and Laha, 1964, p. 25, or Dhrymes, 1970, pp. 13–14); and we can then deduce from (6.22.11) and (6.22.12) the second, third and fourth moments needed in (6.22.9) above.

Now, using the probability limits shown in (6.22.9) we obtain from (6.22.3)

$$\operatorname*{plim}_{T \to \infty} \hat{\alpha} = \alpha + [\beta^4 + 6\beta^2(2\sigma^2)^2 + 12\sigma^4]^{-1}(2\beta\sigma^2)$$

$$= \alpha + \frac{2\beta\sigma^2}{\beta^4 + 12\beta^2\sigma^2 + 12\sigma^4}.$$

Part (b) One method of obtaining a consistent estimator of α is to use the method of non-linear two-stage least squares, whose properties were explored by Amemiya (1974).

We write equation (6.22.1) as

$$y_1 = f(\alpha) + u_1$$

where

$$y_1 = \begin{bmatrix} y_{11} \\ \vdots \\ y_{1T} \end{bmatrix}, \quad f(\alpha) = \begin{bmatrix} \alpha y_{21}^2 \\ \vdots \\ \alpha y_{2T}^2 \end{bmatrix} \quad \text{and} \quad u_1 = \begin{bmatrix} u_{11} \\ \vdots \\ u_{1T} \end{bmatrix}$$

and then select a number of instrumental variables (possibly the exogenous variables in the model or simple polynomials in these variables) whose matrix of observations we denote by X. According to the method of non-linear two-stage least squares we now minimise with respect to α the expression

$$[y_1 - f(\alpha)]' X(X'X)^{-1} X'[y_1 - f(\alpha)]. \qquad (6.22.13)$$

In the present example the only exogenous variable is the constant in equation (6.22.2), so we can set

$$X' = (1, 1, \ldots, 1)$$

and then (6.22.13) becomes

$$\frac{1}{T} \left(\sum_{t=1}^{T} y_{1t} - \alpha \sum_{t=1}^{T} y_{2t}^2 \right)^2$$

It follows that the non-linear two-stage least squares estimator of α is just

$$\alpha^* = \left(\sum_{t=1}^{T} y_{1t} \right) \left(\sum_{t=1}^{T} y_{2t}^2 \right) \bigg/ \left(\sum_{t=1}^{T} y_{2t}^2 \right)^2 = \sum_{t=1}^{T} y_{1t} \bigg/ \sum_{t=1}^{T} y_{2t}^2$$

To verify that α^* is consistent we note that

$$\sum_{t=1}^{T} y_{1t} = \alpha \sum_{t=1}^{T} y_{2t}^2 + \sum_{t=1}^{T} u_{1t}$$

so that

$$\alpha^* = \alpha + \left(\sum_{t=1}^{T} u_{1t} \right) \bigg/ \left(\sum_{t=1}^{T} y_{2t}^2 \right)$$

$$= \alpha + \left(T^{-1} \sum_{t=1}^{T} u_{1t} \right) \bigg/ \left(T^{-1} \sum_{t=1}^{T} y_{2t}^2 \right).$$

But

$$\operatorname*{plim}_{T \to \infty} T^{-1} \sum_{t=1}^{T} u_{1t} = E(u_{1t}) = 0$$

and

$$\operatorname*{plim}_{T \to \infty} T^{-1} \sum_{t=1}^{T} y_{2t}^2 = \beta^2 + 2\sigma^2$$

which is greater than zero. Hence, α^* is consistent.

Part (c) From the theorem in Amemiya (1974, p. 106) we know that if α^* is the non-linear two-stage least squares estimator of α then $\sqrt{T}(\alpha^* - \alpha)$ has a limiting normal distribution as $T \to \infty$ with zero mean and variance given by

$$\sigma^2 \left[\operatorname*{plim}_{T \to \infty} \frac{1}{T} \frac{\partial f'}{\partial \alpha} X(X'X)^{-1} X' \frac{\partial f}{\partial \alpha} \right]^{-1} \tag{6.22.14}$$

where the derivative $\partial f/\partial \alpha$ is evaluated at the true value of α. In the present case, we have

$$\partial f'/\partial \alpha = (y_{21}^2, \ldots, y_{2T}^2)$$

and

$$X' = (1, 1, \ldots, 1)$$

so that (6.22.14) becomes

$$\sigma^2 \left[\operatorname*{plim}_{T \to \infty} \frac{1}{T^2} \left(\sum_{t=1}^{T} y_{2t}^2 \right)^2 \right]^{-1}$$

$$= \sigma^2 \left[\operatorname*{plim}_{T \to \infty} \left(\frac{1}{T} \sum_{t=1}^{T} y_{2t}^2 \right)^2 \right]^{-1}$$

$$= \sigma^2 \left[\left(\operatorname*{plim}_{T \to \infty} \frac{1}{T} \sum_{t=1}^{T} y_{2t}^2 \right)^2 \right]^{-1}$$

$$= \frac{\sigma^2}{\beta^2 + 2\sigma^2} \, .$$

Solution 6.23

Consider the model

$$\dot{K}_t = \beta_0 + \beta_1 I_{t-1}^{US} + \beta_2 I_t^{GB} + \beta_3 M_{t-1}^{US} + u_t \tag{6.23.5}$$

where u_t is a random disturbance term. Equations (6.23.1) and (6.23.2) are special cases of (6.23.5). The 'pull' hypothesis asserts that $\beta_1 > 0$ and the 'push' hypothesis that $\beta_2 < 0$. The sign of β_3 is not predicted in the question.

A naive interpretation of the numerical results is the following. Equation (6.23.1) supports the 'pull' hypothesis as a t test of $H_0 : \beta_1 = 0$ against $H_1 : \beta_1 > 0$ leads to the rejection of H_0 in favour of H_1. Equations (6.23.2) and (6.23.3), on the other hand, reject the 'pull' hypothesis in favour of the 'push' hypothesis since, whereas in neither equation is the estimate of β_1 significantly different from zero, the estimate of β_2 is significantly negative. But equation (6.23.4) restores the original conclusion, favouring the 'pull' hypothesis over the 'push' hypothesis because the estimate of β_1 is significantly positive whereas the estimate of β_2 is not significantly different from zero.

To see how these contradictory results could have occurred let us suppose that (6.23.5) is the correct model but possibly with certain coefficients equal to zero. Consider first the OLS estimates. If $\beta_3 \neq 0$ then equation (6.23.3) is correctly specified and if, in addition, the regressor variables are uncorrelated with the disturbance term, the OLS estimates of (6.23.3) are unbiased. If either β_1 or $\beta_2 = 0$ then these estimates will still be unbiased but will be inefficient (see Question 4.5). Equations (6.23.1) and (6.23.2) are misspecified if $\beta_3 \neq 0$, implying that the OLS estimates of these equations are biased (see Question 4.3). Relative to their standard errors, we notice that the estimates of β_1 and β_2 are similar in equations (6.23.2) and (6.23.3) suggesting that M_{t-1}^{US} is approximately uncorrelated with I_{t-1}^{US} and I_t^{GB} and the bias is unimportant. This explains the results of equation (6.23.2). Comparing equations (6.23.1) and (6.23.2) it is clear that the bias in the estimate of β_1 due to omitting I_t^{GB} in (6.13.1) is considerable. Moreover, since in (6.23.2) the estimate of β_2 has a higher t statistic than the estimate of β_1, it is not surprising that the sign of the estimate of β_1 changes (see Question 2.25). Using the following expression for the bias in the estimate of β_1

$$\text{bias} = \beta_2 \frac{\hat{\text{cov}}(I_{t-1}^{US}, I_t^{GB})}{\hat{\text{var}}(I_{t-1}^{US})},$$

where the terms 'cov' and 'var' denote sample moments, and assuming that $\beta_2 < 0$, it is apparent that, since the estimate of β_1 in (6.23.1) is biased upwards, $\hat{\text{cov}}(I_{t-1}^{US}, I_t^{GB}) < 0$. We also note that because we have omitted variables with coefficients having t statistics greater than unity, $\bar{R}^2$ for (6.23.1) is less than that for (6.23.2), which is in turn less than that for (6.23.3) (see Question 2.4).

The differences between equations (6.23.3) and (6.23.4) may be explained by the fact that (6.23.3) suffers from simultaneous equation bias and (6.23.4) does not. In (6.23.4) I_t^{GB} has been treated as a jointly dependent variable correlated with the disturbance term and hence has been replaced by its predicted value obtained from a regression of I_t^{GB} on $I_{t-1}^{US}, M_{t-1}^{US}$ plus additional variables which are correlated with I_t^{GB} but not with u_t. Let $x_{1t} = I_{t-1}^{US}, x_{2t} = I_t^{GB}, x_{3t} = M_{t-1}^{US}$ and b_i be the OLS estimates of β_i $(i = 1, 2, 3)$ in equation (6.23.3), then the large sample biases of the coefficients in equation (6.23.3) are given by

$$\text{plim} \begin{bmatrix} b_1 - \beta_1 \\ b_2 - \beta_2 \\ b_3 - \beta_3 \end{bmatrix} = \begin{bmatrix} M_{11} & M_{12} & M_{13} \\ M_{12} & M_{22} & M_{23} \\ M_{13} & M_{23} & M_{33} \end{bmatrix}^{-1} \begin{bmatrix} M_{1u} \\ M_{2u} \\ M_{3u} \end{bmatrix},$$

where $M_{ij} = \text{cov}(x_i x_j)$ and $M_{iu} = \text{cov}(x_i u)$ for $i = 1, 2, 3$. From our earlier results $M_{13} \approx 0$ and $M_{1u} = M_{3u} = 0$, thus

$$\begin{bmatrix} b_1 - \beta_1 \\ b_2 - \beta_2 \\ b_3 - \beta_3 \end{bmatrix} = \begin{bmatrix} M_{11} & M_{12} & 0 \\ M_{12} & M_{22} & 0 \\ 0 & 0 & M_{33} \end{bmatrix}^{-1} \begin{bmatrix} 0 \\ M_{2u} \\ 0 \end{bmatrix}$$

$$= \begin{bmatrix} -M_{12}M_{2u}/D \\ M_{11}M_{2u}/D \\ 0 \end{bmatrix}$$

where $D = M_{11}M_{22} - M_{12}^2 > 0$.

It follows that plim $(b_3 - \beta_3) = 0$ and hence we would expect little difference in the estimates of β_3 in equations (6.23.3) and (6.23.4) if the equations were estimated with a large sample of data. This is confirmed by the results obtained. Since $M_{12} < 0$, the signs of plim $(b_1 - \beta_1)$ and plim $(b_2 - \beta_2)$ are expected to be the same and to be the same as the sign of M_{2u}. We notice that in (6.23.3) the estimates of β_1 and β_2 are both much less than in (6.23.4), thereby confirming our prediction and in indicating that $M_{2u} < 0$.

We now summarise our conclusions. If (6.23.5) is correctly specified and if $\dot{K}_t$ and I_t^{GB} are jointly dependent, implying that I_t^{GB} is correlated with the disturbance term u_t, then the hypotheses should be evaluated using (6.23.4) as the estimated coefficients of this equation are consistent. Large sample tests on the coefficients of this equation lead us to prefer the 'pull' hypothesis to the 'push' hypothesis. Compared with equation (6.23.4), we explain the results of equation (6.23.3) as being due to simultaneous equation bias, the results of equations (6.23.2) as also being due to simultaneous equation bias and not to omitted variable bias and, finally, the results of equation (6.23.1) as being due to both simultaneous equation bias and omitted variable bias which, since the estimates of β_1 in (6.23.1) and (6.23.4) are very close, by chance, nearly cancel each other out.

Solution 6.24

Part (a) Totally differentiating (6.24.1) we obtain

$$dL_i = (\partial L_i/\partial W_m)dW_m + (\partial L_i/\partial W_f)dW_f + (\partial L_i/\partial Y)dY \qquad (i = m, f)$$
$$(6.24.4)$$

The Slutsky decomposition of the uncompensated wage effect $(\partial L_i/\partial W_i)$ as a substitution effect (s_{ij}) and an income effect is given by equation (6.24.3). Substituting (6.24.3) into (6.24.4) we get

$$dL_i = s_{im}dW_m + s_{if}dW_f + b_i(L_m dW_m + L_f dW_f + dY) \qquad (i = m, f)$$
$$(6.24.5)$$

where $b_i = \partial L_i/\partial Y$. Next we approximate the derivatives in (6.24.5) as deviations about the mean (see Barten, 1967, 1968) and, finally, we measure the last term of (6.24.5) by ΔF, the change in family income. An expression for the error in this latter approximation is obtained from

$$\Delta F = \Delta(L_m W_m + L_f W_f + Y)$$
$$= L_m \Delta W_m + L_f \Delta W_f + \Delta Y + (W_m \Delta L_m + W_f \Delta L_f), \quad (6.24.6)$$

and is the term in parentheses in (6.24.6). This error will be incorporated in the disturbance term, making ΔF an endogenous variable and, possibly, introducing biases into the estimates of the coefficients. As a result of this substitution we obtain (6.24.2).

Part (b) (i) The assumption that the own substitution effect s_{ii} is positive implies that an income-compensated increase in a husband's or wife's wage rate results in an increase in that person's supply of labour. Using a one-sided large sample test, the hypothesis $H_0 : s_{ii} = 0$ is rejected in favour of $H_1 : s_{ii} > 0$ for both husbands and wives at the 5% level of significance. The t ratios are 2.56 and 3.56 respectively.

(ii) The hypothesis $H_0 : s_{mf} = s_{fm}$ follows from the assumption of utility maximisation and provides a test of the theory. The restriction $s_{mf} = s_{fm}$ is a linear restriction on the vector of coefficients of the complete system of equations. Writing the complete system in the vector notation of question (6.13), we have:

$$y = Z\delta + u. \quad (6.24.7)$$

The linear restriction may now be written as

$$R\delta = r. \quad (6.24.8)$$

This restriction may be tested using unrestricted estimates of δ by the Wald test statistic. If $\hat{\delta}$ is a consistent estimate of δ and V is the asymptotic covariance matrix of $\hat{\delta}$ then the Wald criterion

$$(R\hat{\delta} - r)' (R V R')^{-1} (R\hat{\delta} - r) \quad (6.24.9)$$

has a limiting χ^2 distribution with k degrees of freedom where it is assumed that there are k independent linear restrictions in (6.24.8). It can be shown that the Wald test is asymptotically equivalent to a Lagrange multiplier test and a likelihood ratio test: Byron (1970), Dhrymes et al. (1972). See also Question 2.5. The latter test has the disadvantage that δ must be estimated twice, once subject to the restrictions (6.24.8) and again unrestrictedly.

In the present case, δ is estimated consistently by 3SLS. Partitioning δ' into (δ'_1, δ'_2) where $\delta'_1 = (s_{mf}, s_{mf})$ and V into $\begin{pmatrix} V_{11} & V_{12} \\ V_{21} & V_{22} \end{pmatrix}$, we can write the restriction $s_{mf} = s_{fm}$ as

$$(1, -1, 0) \begin{pmatrix} s_{mf} \\ s_{fm} \\ \delta_2 \end{pmatrix} = 0 \quad (6.24.10)$$

and (6.24.9) as

$$
(\hat{s}_{mf}, \hat{s}_{fm}, \hat{\delta}_2') \begin{pmatrix} 1 \\ -1 \\ 0 \end{pmatrix} \left[(1,-1,0) \begin{pmatrix} V_{11} & V_{12} \\ V_{21} & V_{22} \end{pmatrix} \begin{pmatrix} 1 \\ -1 \\ 0 \end{pmatrix} \right]^{-1} (1,-1,0) \begin{pmatrix} \hat{s}_{mf} \\ \hat{s}_{fm} \\ \hat{\delta}_2 \end{pmatrix}
$$

$$
= (\hat{s}_{mf} - \hat{s}_{fm})^2 \left\{ (1,-1) \ V_{11} \begin{bmatrix} 1 \\ -1 \end{bmatrix} \right\}^{-1}
$$

$$
= (\hat{s}_{mf} - \hat{s}_{fm})^2 / [\overline{\mathrm{var}}(\hat{s}_{mf}) + \overline{\mathrm{var}}(\hat{s}_{fm}) - 2\,\overline{\mathrm{cov}}(\hat{s}_{mf}\hat{s}_{fm})]
$$

$$
= (\hat{s}_{mf} - \hat{s}_{fm})^2 / \overline{\mathrm{var}}(\hat{s}_{mf} - \hat{s}_{fm}) \tag{6.24.11}
$$

where we estimate V_{11} by (bar denotes an estimate)

$$
\begin{bmatrix} \overline{\mathrm{var}}(\hat{s}_{mf}) & \overline{\mathrm{cov}}(\hat{s}_{mf}\hat{s}_{fm}) \\ \overline{\mathrm{cov}}(\hat{s}_{fm}\hat{s}_{mf}) & \overline{\mathrm{var}}(\hat{s}_{fm}) \end{bmatrix}
$$

But (6.24.11) is just the square of the variate $(\hat{s}_{mf} - \hat{s}_{fm})/[\overline{\mathrm{var}}(\hat{s}_{mf} - \hat{s}_{fm})]^{1/2}$ which has a limiting $N(0, 1)$ distribution on H_0. Hence for a single linear restriction the Wald test amounts to using the limiting distribution of a consistent estimate of the restriction. In this case, we require the limiting distribution of $\sqrt{K}(\hat{s}_{mf} - \hat{s}_{fm} - \hat{s}_{mf} + \hat{s}_{fm})$ under the null hypothesis $s_{mf} = s_{fm}$.

From table 6.24.1, $\hat{s}_{mf} - \hat{s}_{fm} = 0.220$ and from table 6.24.2 $[\overline{\mathrm{var}}(\hat{s}_{mf} - \hat{s}_{fm})]^{1/2} = [(2 \times 0.00454) - (2 \times 0.00217)]^{1/2} = 0.0688$. Therefore, the normal test statistic is 3.20. On this evidence we would reject the symmetry assumption.

(iii) The assumption $\partial L_i / \partial Y < 0$ implies that work is an inferior good and leisure is a normal good. Estimates of $\partial L_i / \partial Y$ are provided by the estimates of b_i. Each has the expected negative sign and t statistics for the hypothesis $H_0 : b_i = 0$ against $H_1 : b_i < 0$ of -1.67 and -3.36 for husbands and wives, respectively. Hence for husbands or wives H_0 is rejected at the 5% level in favour of H_1.

(iv) If $\partial L_i / \partial W_i < 0$ then the supply curves of husbands and wives are backward bending. In order to estimate $\partial L_i / \partial W_i$ we must use estimates of equation (6.14.4). Thus

$$
\partial \hat{L}_i / \partial W_i = \hat{s}_{ii} + \bar{L}_i \hat{b}_i \tag{6.24.12}
$$

where we replace L_i by the sample mean $\bar{L}_i$. Now (6.24.12) is just a linear combination of the complete coefficient vector $\hat{\delta}$ with $\bar{L}_i$ treated as a constant. We may, therefore, use once more the methods of Part (ii). Rather than repeat the analysis for this case we state the main results. Thus

$$
\partial L_m / \partial W_m = 0.110 - 0.979 \times 0.112 = 0.000
$$

and

$$\partial L_f / \partial W_f = 0.972 - 0.341 \times 0.594 = 0.769$$

The asymptotic standard error of $\partial L_i / \partial W_i$ is estimated by

$$[\overline{\text{var}}(\hat{s}_{ii}) + \bar{L}_i^2 \, \overline{\text{var}}(\hat{b}_i) + 2\bar{L}_i \, \overline{\text{cov}}(\hat{s}_{ii}\hat{b}_i)]^{1/2}$$

Thus

$$[\overline{\text{var}}(\partial L_m / \partial W_m)]^{1/2} = [0.00184 + (0.979)^2 \, 0.00451$$
$$+ 2(0.979)(-0.00265)]^{1/2} = 0.031$$

and

$$[\overline{\text{var}}(\partial L_f / \partial W_f)]^{1/2} = [0.0746 + (0.341)^2 \, 0.0313$$
$$+ 2(0.341)(-0.0428)]^{1/2} = 0.221$$

The normal test statistic for $H_0 : \partial L_i / \partial W_i = 0$ is 0.00 for husbands and 3.48 for wives. Clearly, therefore, on this evidence, we cannot reject the null hypothesis for husbands but we can for wives, albeit in favour of $\partial L_f / \partial W_f > 0$ and not $\partial L_f / \partial W_f < 0$. The assumption of backward bending supply curves is not supported by this evidence. (As mentioned in the question, the estimated covariance matrix used here is for the restricted model and hence is not strictly applicable to the unrestricted estimates. Consequently, many of the inferences drawn in this exercise are different from those in the original paper by Ashenfelter and Heckman.)

CHAPTER 7

Dynamic models

0. INTRODUCTION

Most econometric models that are applied to time series data in econom
are constructed in such a way that time lags play an important role in th
relationships between the variables. Models that fit this general descript
are often called dynamic and several different types of specification are
regular use. Many of these come within the framework of statistical
models that are well known in mathematical statistics, although the
detailed specification of the econometric equations often raises new an
intriguing problems of statistical inference. In this chapter we will be
looking at a selection of dynamic models starting with the simple first
order autoregression and single-equation models with autoregressive
errors. We also consider the problems of identification and statistical
estimation in simultaneous equation systems with errors that are serially
correlated and we examine both single equation and systems methods c
estimation in this type of model. Other types of model on which we ha
questions are distributed lag models, models of stochastic differential
equations and disequilibrium models involving different regression
'regimes'. In addition, a number of questions in the chapter relate to th
problem of forecasting and optimal prediction in dynamic models and,
as in previous chapters, we have included a selection of applied questio

1. QUESTIONS

Question 7.1

The observable random variables $y_t (t = 1, 2, \ldots, T)$ are known to sati
the relation

$$y_t = \alpha y_{t-1} + u_t \tag{7.1}$$

where α is an unknown parameter whose absolute value $|\alpha| < 1$, and the initial value y_0 is taken to be fixed and non-random. The u_t ($t = 1, 2, \ldots, T$) are random disturbances each of which has the same distribution with mean zero and variance σ^2 ; while u_t and u_s are independent for $t \neq s$.

(a) Discuss the properties of the least squares estimator of the parameter α in (7.1.1). Distinguish between large sample and small sample properties in your answer. Is the least squares estimator unbiased for any sample size?

(b) Comment briefly on the properties of the least squares estimator of α when $|\alpha| > 1$.

Question 7.2

In the model

$$y_t = \alpha y_{t-1} + \beta + u_t \tag{7.2.1}$$

$$u_t = \rho u_{t-1} + \epsilon_t \qquad (|\alpha| < 1, |\lambda| < 1; \quad t = 1, 2, \ldots) \tag{7.2.2}$$

the disturbances $\{\epsilon_t: t = 1, 2, \ldots \}$ are serially independent and identically distributed as $N(0, 1)$ for all t; the initial values y_0 and y_{-1} are given and non-random.

(a) By writing (7.2.1–2) as a second order difference equation in y_t, show that the likelihood function, L, satisfies

$$-\ln L = \tfrac{1}{2}T \ln (2\pi) + \tfrac{1}{2} \sum_{t=1}^{T} [y_t - (\alpha + \rho) y_{t-1}$$

$$+ \alpha\rho \, y_{t-2} - \beta(1 - \rho)]^2$$

(b) Show that (7.2.1–2) can be written as the first order difference equation system

$$x_t = Ax_{t-1} + b + v_t \tag{7.2.3}$$

where

$$x_t' = (y_t, y_{t-1}), \quad v_t' = (\epsilon_t, 0)$$

$$A = \begin{bmatrix} \alpha + \rho & -\alpha\rho \\ 1 & 0 \end{bmatrix} \quad \text{and} \quad b = \begin{bmatrix} \beta(1 - \rho) \\ 0 \end{bmatrix}$$

Hence, show that

$$\lim_{t \to \infty} E(x_t) = (I - A)^{-1} b$$

and if

$$V = \lim_{t \to \infty} E(x_t x_t')$$

then V satisfies the system

$$V = AVA' + bb' + A(I - A)^{-1} bb'$$ (7.2.4)
$$+ bb' (I - A')^{-1} A' + \Omega$$

where

$$\Omega = \begin{bmatrix} 1 & 0 \\ 0 & 0 \end{bmatrix}$$

(c) Indicate how you would solve (7.2.4) for the unknown elements of V.
(d) Discuss the identifiability of the parameters α, β and ρ in the model (7.2.1–2).

Question 7.3

For the linear model

$$y_t = \alpha y_{t-1} + \beta x_t + u_t \qquad (|\alpha| < 1; \quad t = 0, \dots, T)$$ (7.3.1)

obtain expressions for the asymptotic biases of the ordinary least squares estimators of α and β and evaluate the signs of the biases
(a) when

$$u_t = \rho u_{t-1} + e_t \qquad (|\rho| < 1)$$ (7.3.2)

(b) when

$$u_t = e_t + \lambda e_{t-1} \qquad (|\lambda| < 1).$$ (7.3.3)

x_t is a non-stochastic variable with $\lim T^{-1} \Sigma_{t=1}^{T} x_t^2 = m_{xx}$ which is finite, non-zero and $\lim T^{-1} \Sigma_{t=1}^{T} x_t x_{t-s}$ exists and is uniformly bounded for all s. The e_t are independent random variables with mean zero and constant variance σ^2.

Question 7.4

Consider the linear model

$$y_t = \alpha y_{t-1} + \beta x_t + u_t \qquad (|\alpha| < 1; \quad t = 1, \dots, T)$$ (7.4.1)

where x_t is an exogenous variable with $\lim_{T \to \infty} T^{-1} \Sigma_{t=1}^{T} x_t^2 = m_{xx}$ which is finite and non-zero

$$u_t = \rho u_{t-1} + e_t, \qquad (|\rho| < 1)$$ (7.4.2)

and the e_t are independent $N(0, \sigma^2)$ variables.
(a) Compare the maximum likelihood estimators of α, β, ρ and σ^2 when:
   (i) u_0 is assumed to be zero; and (ii) u_0 is assumed to be an unknown constant requiring estimation.

(b) Obtain the limiting distributions of these estimators of α, β, ρ and σ^2.

Question 7.5

Suppose the linear model

$$y_t = \alpha y_{t-1} + \beta x_t + u_t \qquad (|\alpha| < 1; \quad t = 1, \ldots, T) \qquad (7.5.1)$$

is estimated by ordinary least squares. From the least squares residuals, the Durbin–Watson statistic (d) and the regression coefficient of the residuals on themselves lagged one period (r) are calculated. It is hypothesised that

$$u_t = \rho u_{t-1} + e_t \qquad (|\rho| < 1) \qquad (7.5.2)$$

where the e_t are independent $N(0, \sigma^2)$ variables.
(a) Derive the limiting distributions associated with d and r on the null hypothesis of $\rho = 0$.
(b) Compare the limiting distribution associated with r with that of the maximum likelihood estimator of ρ on the null hypothesis.

Question 7.6

Consider the following model

$$y_{1t} + b_{12}^0 y_{2t} + b_{11}^1 y_{1, t-1} + c_{11} x_{1t} = u_{1t} \qquad (7.6.1)$$

$$y_{2t} + c_{21} x_{1t} = u_{2t} \qquad (7.6.2)$$

$$u_{1t} = r_{11} u_{1, t-1} + e_{1t} \qquad (7.6.3)$$

$$u_{2t} = r_{22} u_{2, t-1} + e_{2t} \qquad (7.6.4)$$

where y_{1t} and y_{2t} are endogenous variables, x_{1t} is an exogenous variable and u_{1t}, u_{2t}, e_{1t} and e_{2t} are random errors with

$$E \begin{bmatrix} e_{1t} \\ e_{2t} \end{bmatrix} = 0, \quad E \left[\begin{pmatrix} e_{1t} \\ e_{2t} \end{pmatrix} (e_{1t} e_{2t}) \right] = \Sigma,$$

which is unrestricted and non-singular.
Examine: (a) the local identifiability of the model; and (b) the global identifiability of the model.

Question 7.7

Consider the linear simultaneous equation system

$$B y_t + C x_t = u_t \qquad (t = 1, \ldots, T) \qquad (7.7.1)$$

where

$$u_t = R u_{t-1} + e_t \qquad (t = 1, \dots, T) \tag{7.7.2}$$

x_t is predetermined (any lagged endogenous variables are assumed to be fixed for $t = 0, -1, -2, \dots$), the e_t are serially independent and distributed as $N(0, \Sigma)$ for all t with Σ non-singular and the model is identified.

(a) Obtain the FIML estimators of B, C, R and Σ.

(b) Without attempting a rigorous discussion, derive the asymptotic distributions of the FIML estimators of B, C and R.

(c) Suggest an asymptotically efficient instrumental variable estimator for B, C and R.

Question 7.8

An alternative estimator to FIML for the model of Question 7.7 which is due to Hatanaka (1976) has the advantage of being non-iterative. It is given by

$$\begin{bmatrix} \hat{\delta} \\ \hat{r} \end{bmatrix} = \begin{bmatrix} 0 \\ r_0 \end{bmatrix} + [(\hat{\bar{Z}}^* : I \otimes \hat{U}_{-1})' (\hat{\Sigma}^{-1} \otimes I) (\hat{\bar{Z}}^* : I \otimes \hat{U}_{-1})]^{-1}$$

$$(\hat{\bar{Z}}^* : I \otimes \hat{U}_{-1})' (\hat{\Sigma}^{-1} \otimes I) \hat{y}^* \tag{7.8.1}$$

where $\hat{\bar{Z}}^*, \hat{U}_{-1}, \hat{\Sigma}$ and $\hat{y}^*$ are defined as in Question 7.7 with the difference that they are formed using initial consistent estimators d_0 and r_0 of δ and r, respectively.

(a) Prove that this estimator is equivalent to that obtained after one iteration of the Newton–Raphson algorithm.

(b) Show that this estimator is asymptotically efficient.

Question 7.9

Suppose that the first equation of the system of equations defined in Question 7.7 is

$$y_1 = Y \beta_1 + X_1 \gamma_1 + u_1 \tag{7.9.1}$$

where $(y_1 : Y_1)$ is a $T \times (m_1 + 1)$ matrix of observations of the endogenous variables, X_1 is a $T \times n_1$ matrix of observations of the predetermined variables, some of which are lagged endogenous variables, and u_1 is a $T \times 1$ vector of disturbances generated by the first order autoregressive process

$$u_1 = \rho_{11} u_{1,-1} + e_1 \qquad (|\rho_{11}| < 1). \tag{7.9.2}$$

with e_1 distributed as a $N(0, \sigma^2 I)$ variable.
(a) Compare the single equation estimators of β_1, γ_1 and ρ_{11} proposed by Sargan (1964), Fair (1970) and Hatanaka (1976).
(b) Explain how Hatanaka's estimator can be obtained by the successive use of least squares.

Question 7.10

Consider the finite distributed lag model

$$y_t = \sum_{s=0}^{n} \beta_s x_{t-s} + u_t \qquad (t = 1, \ldots, T) \qquad (7.10.1)$$

where the coefficients β_s are assumed to lie on the pth order polynomial

$$\beta_s = \alpha_0 + \alpha_1 s + \ldots + \alpha_p s^p \qquad (s = 0, \ldots, n) \qquad (7.10.2)$$

x_t is a non-random variable and the disturbances u_t are distributed as independent $N(0, \sigma^2)$ variables for all t.
(a) Explain how the coefficients β_s can be estimated using (i) ordinary least squares; and (ii) restricted least squares.
(b) Devise three tests of the hypothesis that the order to the approximating polynomial (7.10.2) is $p\,(<n)$ against the alternative hypothesis that the order is n. That is, test $H_0: \alpha_{p+1} = \ldots = \alpha_n = 0$ against $H_1: \alpha_{p+1}, \ldots, \alpha_n \neq 0$. Use estimates of β_s and α_s on H_1 ($s = 0, \ldots, n$) to construct the tests.
Reference: Trivedi and Pagan (1976).

Question 7.11

(a) Show that the polynomial distributed lag model

$$y_t = \beta_0 x_t + \beta_1 x_{t-1} + \ldots + \beta_n x_{t-n} + u_t, \qquad (7.11.1)$$

$$\beta_s = \alpha_0 + \alpha_1 s \qquad (7.11.2)$$

can be rewritten as a rational distributed lag model.
(b) Comment on this result when $n \to \infty$.

Question 7.12

In the model

$$x_1(t) - x_1(t-1) = \lambda_1 \left[\alpha \left(\frac{x_2(t) + x_2(t-1)}{2} \right) \right.$$

$$\left. - \left(\frac{x_1(t) + x_1(t-1)}{2} \right) \right] + \eta_1(t) \qquad (7.12.1)$$

$$x_2(t) - x_2(t-1) = \lambda_2 \left[\beta \left(\frac{x_3(t) + x_3(t-1)}{2} \right) \right.$$

$$\left. - \left(\frac{x_2(t) + x_2(t-1)}{2} \right) \right] + \eta_2(t) \qquad (7.12.2)$$

$$x_3(t) - x_3(t-1) = \lambda_3 \left[\gamma \left(\frac{x_1(t) + x_1(t-1)}{2} \right) \right.$$

$$\left. + \delta \left(\frac{x_2(t) + x_2(t-1)}{2} \right) - \left(\frac{x_3(t) + x_3(t-1)}{2} \right) \right]$$

$$+ \eta_3(t) \qquad (7.12.3)$$

$\eta(t)' = [\eta_1(t), \eta_2(t), \eta_3(t)]$ is a disturbance vector which has the same multivariate normal distribution with zero mean and unknown covariance matrix Ω for each integral value of t and $E[\eta(s)\,\eta(t)'] = 0$ if s and t are different integers.

(a) Show how to transform the above model into the conventional simultaneous equations framework, adding any identities you think may be necessary.

(b) Discuss the identifiability of the parameters α, β, γ, λ_1, λ_2 and λ_3 in the above model.

(c) Show how the model (7.12.3) can be derived as a discrete approximation to a system of stochastic differential equations.

Question 7.13

In the single equation model

$$\frac{dy(t)}{dt} = \alpha y(t) + \zeta(t) \qquad (\alpha < 0) \qquad (7.13.1)$$

$y(t)$ is a random function observable at discrete points in time, α is an unknown parameter and $\zeta(t)$ is a disturbance which satisfies the conditions

$$E\left[\int_{t_1}^{t_2} \zeta(t)\, dt\right] = 0 \qquad\qquad (7.13.2)$$

$$E\left\{\left[\int_{t_1}^{t_2} \zeta(t)\, dt\right]^2\right\} = \sigma^2(t_2 - t_1) \qquad\qquad (7.13.3)$$

$$E\left\{\left[\int_{t_1}^{t_2} \zeta(t)\, dt \int_{t_3}^{t_4} \zeta(s)\, ds\right]\right\} = 0 \qquad\qquad (7.13.4)$$

where $t_1 < t_2 < t_3 < t_4$.
(a) Comment on the interpretation of the above model.
(b) Show how you would obtain a consistent estimator $\hat{\alpha}$ of α from T observations $y(1), y(2), \ldots, y(T)$.
(c) Find the variance of the limiting distribution of $\sqrt{T}(\hat{\alpha} - \alpha)$ when $\alpha = -1$.

(Adapted from University of Essex MA examinations, 1973.)

Question 7.14

Consider the following model of a market in disequilibrium

$$D_t = X_{1t}\beta_1 + P_{t-1}\beta_2 + u_{1t} \qquad\qquad (7.14.1)$$

$$S_t = X_{2t}\beta_3 + P_{t-1}\beta_4 + u_{2t} \qquad\qquad (7.14.2)$$

$$Q_t = \min\{D_t, S_t\} \qquad\qquad (7.14.3)$$

with $\Delta P_t \gtreqless 0$ when $D_t - S_t \gtreqless 0$. D_t, S_t and Q_t are the quantities demanded, supplied and observed, respectively; P_t is the price, X_{1t} and X_{2t} are vectors of predetermined variables and u_{1t} and u_{2t} are disturbance terms which have a joint normal distribution, mean zero and covariance matrix Σ.
(a) Interpret the model given by (7.14.1–3).
(b) Show how the model can be estimated by OLS.
(c) Prove that the OLS estimator is inconsistent.
(d) Describe an alternative consistent estimator.

References: Fair and Kelejian (1974) and Maddala and Nelson (1974).

Question 7.15

The reduced form of an econometric model is given by

$$y_t = Py_{t-1} + Qx_t + v_t \qquad\qquad (7.15.1)$$

where y_t and y_{t-1} are n-vectors of endogenous and lagged endogenous variables respectively, x_t is an m-vector of non-random exogenous variables and v_t is a vector of serially independent disturbances with zero mean vector and non-singular covariance matrix Ω.

Consistent estimators $\hat{P}$ and $\hat{Q}$ are available for the parameter matrices P and Q in (7.15.1) and it is known that

$$T^{1/2} \text{ vec} \begin{bmatrix} \hat{P} - P \\ \hat{Q} - Q \end{bmatrix}$$

has a limiting normal distribution with zero mean vector and covariance matrix Ψ. Multi-period forecasts (with lead time $h \geqslant 1$) are constructed using $\hat{P}$ and $\hat{Q}$ according to the formulae

$$\hat{y}_{N+1} = \hat{P}y_N + \hat{Q}x_N \qquad (h = 1)$$

$$\hat{y}_{N+h} = \hat{P}\hat{y}_{N+h-1} + \hat{Q}x_{N+h}$$

$$= \hat{P}^h y_N + \sum_{j=0}^{h-1} \hat{P}^j \hat{Q} x_{N+h-j} \qquad (h > 1) \qquad (7.15.2)$$

and these forecasts are conditional on $y_N, x_N, x_{N+1} \cdots x_{N+h}$.

(a) Show that $\hat{y}_{N+h}$ can be written as

$$\hat{y}_{N+h} = W_h \hat{a}_h \qquad (7.15.3)$$

where

$$W_h = [I_n \otimes y_N' \vdots I_n \otimes x_{N+1}' \vdots \cdots \vdots I_n \otimes x_{N+h}'] \qquad (7.15.4)$$

$$\hat{a}_h = \text{vec}(\hat{A}_h) \qquad (7.15.5)$$

and

$$\hat{A}_h = \begin{bmatrix} \hat{P}^h \\ \hat{P}^{h-1}\hat{Q} \\ \vdots \\ \hat{Q} \end{bmatrix}$$

(b) Find the limiting distribution (as $T \to \infty$) of $T^{1/2}(\hat{y}_{N+h} - \bar{y}_{N+h})$, where $\bar{y}_{N+h} = W_h a_h$, $a_h = \text{vec}(A_h)$ and

$$A_h = \begin{bmatrix} P^h \\ P^{h-1}Q \\ \vdots \\ Q \end{bmatrix}$$

on the assumptions that

(i) statistically independent data are available for the estimation of P and Q by $\hat{P}$ and $\hat{Q}$; and that

(ii) the limiting distribution of $T^{1/2}(\hat{y}_{N+h} - \bar{y}_{N+h})$ is found, conditional on given values of $y_N, x_N, \ldots, x_{N+h}$.

(c) Obtain an expression for the asymptotic covariance matrix of $\hat{y}_{N+h} - y_{N+h}$, where y_{N+h} denotes the actual value of y in period $N + h$.

Question 7.16

In the model

$$
\begin{bmatrix} 1 & b_{12}^0 \\ b_{21}^0 & 1 \end{bmatrix} \begin{bmatrix} y_{1t} \\ y_{2t} \end{bmatrix} + \begin{bmatrix} b_{11}^1 & b_{21}^1 \\ 0 & 0 \end{bmatrix} \begin{bmatrix} y_{1t-1} \\ y_{2t-1} \end{bmatrix} + \begin{bmatrix} c_{11} \\ c_{21} \end{bmatrix} x_{1t} \qquad (7.16.1)
$$

$$
= \begin{bmatrix} a_{11}^0 & 0 \\ 0 & a_{22}^0 \end{bmatrix} \begin{bmatrix} u_{1t} \\ u_{2t} \end{bmatrix} + \begin{bmatrix} a_{11}^1 & a_{12}^1 \\ 0 & a_{22}^1 \end{bmatrix} \begin{bmatrix} u_{1t-1} \\ u_{2t-1} \end{bmatrix}
$$

the y_{it} are endogenous variables, x_{1t} is an exogenous variable and the u_{it} are serially independent random disturbances identically distributed with zero mean and covariance matrix

$$
E \left\{ \begin{bmatrix} u_{1t} \\ u_{2t} \end{bmatrix} [u_{1t} \quad u_{2t}] \right\} = \begin{bmatrix} 1 & 0 \\ 0 & 1 \end{bmatrix}
$$

for all t.

(a) Discuss the meaning of the term "observationally equivalent" in the context of a model such as (7.16.1).

(b) Discuss the identifiability of the parameters in the above model.

(c) Consider, in particular, the identifiability of the following structures:

(I): $b_{12}^0 = -1, b_{21}^0 = 2, b_{11}^1 = -1, b_{21}^1 = -1, c_{11} = 1,$

$\qquad c_{21} = 1, a_{11}^0 = 2, a_{22}^0 = 2, a_{11}^1 = 1, a_{12}^1 = -1, a_{22}^1 = 1;$

(II): $b_{12}^0 = -1, b_{21}^0 = 2, b_{11}^1 = -1, b_{21}^1 = -1, c_{11} = 1,$

$\qquad c_{21} = 0, a_{11}^0 = 2, a_{22}^0 = 2, a_{11}^1 = 1, a_{12}^1 = -1, a_{22}^1 = 0.$

Question 7.17

In the model

$$
\begin{bmatrix} 1 & b_{12}^0 \\ b_{21}^0 & 1 \end{bmatrix} \begin{bmatrix} y_{1t} \\ y_{2t} \end{bmatrix} + \begin{bmatrix} b_{11}^1 & 0 \\ 0 & b_{22}^1 \end{bmatrix} \begin{bmatrix} y_{1t-1} \\ y_{2t-1} \end{bmatrix} + \begin{bmatrix} c_{11} \\ c_{21} \end{bmatrix} x_{1t} = \begin{bmatrix} u_{1t} \\ u_{2t} \end{bmatrix}
$$

$$(7.17.1)$$

where

$$\begin{bmatrix} u_{1t} \\ u_{2t} \end{bmatrix} = \begin{bmatrix} r_{11} & r_{12} \\ r_{21} & r_{22} \end{bmatrix} \begin{bmatrix} u_{1t-1} \\ u_{2t-1} \end{bmatrix} + \begin{bmatrix} \epsilon_{1t} \\ \epsilon_{2t} \end{bmatrix} \qquad (7.17.2)$$

the y_{it} are endogenous variables, x_{1t} is an exogenous variable and the ϵ_{it} are serially independent random disturbances that are identically distributed with zero mean and non-singular covariance matrix for all t.

(a) Find the greatest common left divisor of the polynomial matrices

$$H(\zeta) = \begin{bmatrix} 1 + b_{11}^1 \zeta & b_{12}^0 \\ b_{21}^0 & 1 + b_{22}^1 \zeta \end{bmatrix} \quad \text{and} \quad J(\zeta) = \begin{bmatrix} c_{11} \\ c_{21} \end{bmatrix}$$

when

$$b_{12}^0 = \tfrac{1}{2}, b_{21}^0 = -\tfrac{1}{4}, b_{11}^1 = -\tfrac{1}{2}, b_{22}^1 = -\tfrac{1}{4}, c_{11} = 4 \quad \text{and} \quad c_{21} = 2.$$

(b) Hence, or otherwise, show that the following two structures of the model are observationally equivalent:

(I): $b_{12}^0 = \tfrac{1}{2}, b_{21}^0 = -\tfrac{1}{4}, b_{11}^1 = -\tfrac{1}{2}, b_{22}^1 = -\tfrac{1}{4}, c_{11} = 4,$

$\qquad c_{21} = 2, r_{11} = \tfrac{1}{3}, r_{12} = 0, r_{21} = \tfrac{1}{9}$ and $r_{22} = 0;$

(II): $b_{12}^0 = \tfrac{1}{2}, b_{21}^0 = -1, b_{11}^1 = -\tfrac{1}{2}, b_{22}^1 = 0, c_{11} = 4,$

$\qquad c_{21} = 0, r_{11} = \tfrac{1}{3}, r_{12} = 0, r_{21} = -\tfrac{2}{27}$ and $r_{22} = \tfrac{1}{3}.$

Question 7.18

(a) Given a series of observations generated by the autoregressive moving average (ARMA) model

$$x_t + \alpha_1 x_{t-1} + \ldots + \alpha_p x_{t-p} = u_t + \beta_1 u_{t-1} + \ldots + \beta_q u_{t-q} \quad (7.18.1)$$

where all the roots of $1 + \alpha_1 z + \ldots + \alpha_p z^p$ and $1 + \beta_1 z + \ldots + \beta_q z^q$ have modulus greater than unity, state a recursive relation for the calculation of the optimal linear predictor $\hat{x}_t(k)$ of x_{t+k} based on the observations $x_t, x_{t-1}, \ldots$.

(b) Find the ARMA model for which the exponentially weighted moving average forecast

$$\hat{x}_t(1) = \alpha(x_t + \beta x_{t-1} + \beta^2 x_{t-2} + \ldots) \qquad (\beta^2 < 1) \qquad (7.18.2)$$

gives an optimal linear predictor of x_{t+1}.

(c) In the model

$$q_t^d = \alpha p_t \qquad (7.18.3)$$

$$q_t^s = \beta p_t^e + u_t \qquad (7.18.4)$$

$$q_t^d = q_t^s \qquad (7.18.5)$$

q_t^d represents the quantity demanded of a certain product in period t and q_t^s the quantity supplied; the price p_t is determined in each period so that the market clears and p_t^e represents the optimal linear predictor of p_t based on the past observations $(p_{t-1}, p_{t-2}, \ldots)$ and, therefore, corresponds to a form of "rational expectations". The disturbance u_t satisfies the process

$$u_t = \rho u_{t-1} + \epsilon_t \qquad (0 < \rho < 1) \qquad (7.18.6)$$

where the $\epsilon_t (t = \ldots -1, 0, 1, \ldots)$ are serially independent random variables identically distributed as normal with zero mean and variance σ^2 for all t.

(i) Find a recursive relation which determines p_t^e from the past observations $p_{t-1}, p_{t-2}, \ldots$

(ii) Hence, find the ARMA model which generates the process $\{p_t\}$.

(Adapted, in part, from University of London MSc examinations, 1975 and University of Auckland M Com examinations, 1973).

Question 7.19

(a) Using the CES production function

$$Q_t = A \left[\delta L_t^{-\theta} + (1 - \delta) K_t^{-\theta} \right]^{-1/\theta} \qquad (7.19.1)$$

where Q is output, L is manhours, and K is capital, show that the level of output per manhour that maximises the short-run profit function

$$\pi_t = p_t Q_t - w_t L_t - F_t \qquad (7.19.2)$$

subject to a given level of output, a given product price p_t and a given hourly wage rate w_t, takes the form

$$\ln(Q_t/L_t)^* = \alpha + \beta \ln (w_t/p_t), \qquad (7.19.3)$$

where the asterisk denotes a profit maximising and, hence, a desired value and F_t in (7.19.2) represents fixed costs.

(b) In order to estimate the parameters in (7.19.3), we set up a statistical model first by adding the error term u_t to (7.19.3), where u_t is generated by

$$u_t = \rho u_{t-1} + e_t, \qquad (0 \leq |\rho| < 1) \qquad (7.19.4)$$

and the e_t are independent $N(0, \sigma^2)$ variables and second by introducing a partial adjustment mechanism as follows:

$$\Delta \ln (Q_t/L_t) = \lambda [\ln (Q_t/L_t)^* - \ln (Q_{t-1}/L_{t-1})] \qquad (0 \leq \lambda \leq 1.)$$
$$(7.19.5)$$

From the following regressions for US manufacturing industries

$$\ln (\hat{Q}_t/L_t) = \text{const.} + \underset{(0.047)}{1.198} \ln w_t, \qquad (R^2 = 0.606) \qquad (7.19.6)$$

$$\ln (\hat{Q}_t/L_t) = \text{const.} + \underset{(0.037)}{0.233} \ln w_t + \underset{(0.024)}{0.827} \ln (Q_{t-1}/L_{t-1}),$$

$$(R^2 = 0.890) \qquad (7.19.7)$$

$$\ln (\hat{Q}_t/L_t) = \text{const.} + \underset{(0.089)}{1.056} \ln w_t + \underset{(0.022)}{0.855} \ln (Q_{t-1}/L_{t-1})$$

$$- \underset{(0.0)}{0.900} \ln w_{t-1}, \qquad (R^2 = 0.918.) \qquad (7.19.8)$$

assess which of the following hypotheses is to be preferred

$H_0: \lambda = \rho = 0, \sigma = 1,$

$H_1: \lambda \neq 0, \rho = 0, \sigma = 1,$

$H_2: \lambda = 0, \rho \neq 0, \sigma = 1,$

where $\sigma = 1/(1 + \theta)$ is the elasticity of substitution of L for K.

Question 7.20

It has been hypothesised that changes in the price level (Δp_t) are determined mainly as a distributed lag response to the level of excess demand in the product market (e_t):

$$\Delta p_t = \gamma(1 - \xi) (e_t + \xi e_{t-1} + \xi^2 e_{t-2} + \ldots) \qquad (\gamma > 0, 0 < \xi < 1) \tag{7.20.1}$$

In order to test this theory it was decided to use the excess demand in the labour market (d_t) as a proxy variable for e_t, where d_t is a distributed lag function of e_t:

$$d_t = (1 - \mu) (e_{t-1} + \mu e_{t-2} + \mu^2 e_{t-3} + \ldots) \qquad (0 < \mu < 1) \tag{7.20.2}$$

The following least squares regression was obtained from UK post-war annual data:

$$\Delta \hat{p}_t = \underset{(1.06)}{3.914 d_{t+1}} - \underset{(1.14)}{3.200 d_t} + \underset{(0.096)}{0.8136 \Delta p_{t-1}}$$

$$(R^2 = 0.692, DW = 1.81) \tag{7.20.3}$$

The figures in parentheses are standard errors.

(a) From equations (7.20.1–3) obtain estimates of the parameters γ, ξ and μ.

(b) Discuss the suitability of the ordinary least squares estimator in this case.

(c) Assuming that the estimates of the parameters γ, ξ and μ are all significantly different from zero, discuss the policy implications of these results.

(Adapted from University of Essex BA examinations 1976.)

Question 7.21

The demand for money function is assumed to be

$$m_t = \beta_0 + \beta_1 y_t + \beta_2 r_t + \beta_3 \pi_t + \beta_4 m_{t-1} + u_t \qquad (7.21.1)$$

where m_t = the real money stock, y_t = real income, r_t = the real rate of interest, π_t = the expected rate of inflation and the u_t are serially independent random disturbances distributed as $N(0, \sigma^2)$ for each t, π_t is not directly observable but m_t, y_t and r_t are observable. Two competing hypotheses are made about the expectations generating process:

$$\pi_t = p_t + \theta_1(p_t - p_{t-1}) \qquad (7.21.2)$$

and

$$\pi_t = \pi_{t-1} + \theta_2(p_t - p_{t-1}), \qquad (7.21.3)$$

where p_t is the observed inflation rate. A general form that encompasses both (7.21.2) and (7.21.3) is

$$\pi_t = p_t + \alpha_1(p_t - p_{t-1}) + \alpha_2(p_t - \pi_{t-1}). \qquad (7.21.4)$$

(a) Indicate how to obtain efficient estimates of α_i and β_j ($i = 1, 2$; $j = 0, \ldots, 4$).
(b) Given the following estimated equation

$$m_t = \begin{array}{cccc} 192.6 + & 0.114 y_t & -47.1 r_t & -27.1 \\ (2.03) & (2.84) & (2.63) & (2.16) \end{array}$$

$$[p_t + \begin{array}{cc} 0.363 (p_t - p_{t-1}) + & 0.730 (p_t - \pi_{t-1})] \\ (1.17) & (1.15) \end{array}$$

$$+ \begin{array}{c} 0.859 \, m_{t-1} + \hat{u}_t, \\ (14.98) \end{array} \qquad (7.21.5)$$

where the figures in parentheses are t statistics, discuss which of the two expectations generating processes is the more compatible with the data.
(c) Omitting the term $p_t - \pi_{t-1}$ from (7.21.5) and assuming that the remaining coefficients are significantly different from zero, calculate (i) the long run multiplier of m with respect to p, and (ii) the mean lag associated with p.

2. SUPPLEMENTARY QUESTIONS

Question 7.22

In the first order autoregression

$$y_\theta = \alpha y_{\theta-1} + u_\theta \qquad (|\alpha| < 1)$$

the u_θ's are identically and independently distributed as $N(0, \sigma^2)$. The index θ records time which is measured in a *unit of 6 months* and y_θ represents an economic flow variable. It is assumed that T *annual observations* are available on the flow variable y.

(a) Show that successive *annual* observations on y are related by the equation

$$y_t = \alpha^2 y_{t-1} + w_t \tag{7.22.1}$$

where w_t is a moving average error.

(b) Let $\hat{\alpha}^2$ be the estimator of α^2 obtained by applying ordinary least squares to (7.22.1) and using the observations $\{y_t : t = 1, \ldots, T\}$. Derive the limit in probability of $\hat{\alpha}^2$ as $T \to \infty$ and explain why $\hat{\alpha}^2$ is inconsistent.

(c) Suggest an alternative procedure which will provide a consistent estimator of α^2 using the T annual observations. Justify the use of your procedure.

(d) Show that the moving average error w_t in (7.22.1) can be represented as

$$w_t = \epsilon_t + \lambda \epsilon_{t-1}$$

where the ϵ_t are serially independent random variables with zero mean and variance given by σ^2/λ and

$$\lambda = 3 - \sqrt{8}$$

(Adapted from University of Birmingham MSocSc examinations 1977.)

Question 7.23

(a) Discuss the effect of autocorrelation in the errors of the regression model

$$y_t = \beta x_t + u_t \qquad (t = 1, \ldots, T)$$

on the estimate of the variance of the least-squares estimate b of β. You may assume that $x_1, \ldots, x_T$ are fixed.

(b) Let R be the ratio of the usual estimate of the variance of b to the true variance of b. Find the asymptotic value of the ratio

$$\frac{\max R}{\min R}$$

when v_t is generated by the moving-average model

$$v_t = \epsilon_t + \alpha\epsilon_{t-1}$$

and where the max and min of R are obtained by varying $x_1, \ldots, x_T$.
(c) For the case in which $u_1, \ldots, u_m$ have variance matrix V and the vector $(x_1, \ldots, x_T)'$ is an eigenvector of V, obtain an expression for R in terms of the eigenvalues of V.

(Adapted from University of London MSc(Econ) examinations 1977.)

Question 7.24

In the model

$$y_t = \beta y_{t-1} + u_t \qquad (t = 1, \ldots, T)$$

the errors u_t obey the model

$$u_t = \alpha u_{t-1} + e_t \qquad (t = 1, \ldots, T)$$

where $0 < \alpha < \beta < 1$ and the e_t are independent $N(0, 1)$. Show that the limiting correlation as $T \to \infty$ between the maximum likelihood estimators of α and β is

$$-\frac{[(1-\alpha^2)(1-\beta^2)]^{1/2}}{1-\alpha\beta}.$$

Contrast this with the corresponding result when y_t is regressed upon an exogenous variable x_t instead of upon the lagged dependent variable y_{t-1}.

(Adapted from University of London, MSc(Econ) examinations 1976.)

Question 7.25

In the linear model

$$y_t = \alpha y_{t-1} + \beta x_t + u_t \qquad (|\alpha| < 1; \quad t = 1, \ldots, T)$$

x_t is a non-random exogenous variable for which $\lim_{T \to \infty} T^{-1} \sum_{t=1}^{T} x_t^2 = m_{xx}$ is finite and non-zero, and u_t is a random disturbance satisfying

$$u_t = e_t + \lambda e_{t-1} \qquad (|\lambda| < 1)$$

where the e_t are serially independent and distributed as $N(0, \sigma^2)$ for each t.
(a) Compare the maximum likelihood estimators of α, β, λ and σ^2 when
   (i) e_0 is assumed to be zero,
   (ii) e_0 is assumed to be an unknown constant requiring estimation.
(b) Obtain the limiting distributions of these estimators.

Question 7.26

The linear model

$$y_t = \alpha y_{t-1} + \beta x_t + u_t \qquad (|\alpha| < 1; \quad t = 1, \ldots, T) \qquad (7.26.1)$$

is estimated by ordinary least squares. It is known that

$$u_t = e_t + \lambda e_{t-1} \qquad (|\lambda| < 1)$$

where the e_t are serially independent $N(0, \sigma^2)$ variables.
(a) Find the asymptotic distribution of the Durbin–Watson statistic
calculated from the residuals of the least squares regression on (7.26.1).
(b) Hence derive a test statistic appropriate for the null hypothesis H_0:
$\lambda = 0$ against $H_1 : \lambda \neq 0$.

Question 7.27

Consider the following model for $t = 1, \ldots, T$

$$y_t = \alpha y_{t-1} + \beta x_t + u_t \qquad (|\beta| < 1)$$
$$x_t = \lambda x_{t-1} + z_t \qquad (|\lambda| < 1)$$
$$u_t = \rho u_{t-1} + e_t \qquad (|\rho| < 1)$$

where x_t is a variable which is not observable, z_t is an observable
non-random variable and the e_t are serially independent $N(0, \sigma^2)$ variables.
Discuss the problem of estimating the model in each of the following
cases:

(a) $\beta = 0$

(b) $\lambda = 0$

(c) $\rho = 0$

(d) $\lambda = \rho$

(e) none of the restrictions (a)–(d) is made.

(University of Essex BA examinations 1977.)

Question 7.28

The coefficients $\beta_i (i = 0, \ldots, s)$ of the distributed lag model

$$y_t = \sum_{i=0}^{s} \beta_i x_{t-i} + u_t \qquad (7.28.1)$$

are known to lie on a polynomial in i of degree n. The $u_t (t = 1, \ldots, T)$
are identically and independently normally distributed random variables

with expected value zero and finite variance. T observations are available on y_t and on the non-random quantities $x_t, x_{t-1}, \ldots, x_{t-s}$.

(a) Derive the Almon estimator of $\beta' = (\beta_0, \ldots, \beta_s)$ and find its covariance matrix.

(b) Since in (7.28.1) x_{t+1} and x_{t-s-1} do not appear, the so-called "end-point" constraints $\beta_{-1} = \beta_{s+1} = 0$ are often imposed on the Almon estimators. It has been suggested that this is bad practice. Explain why.

(c) Explain carefully why a test of the hypothesis $H_0: \beta_1 = \beta_2 = \beta_3 = \ldots = \beta_s = 0$ cannot in general be carried out satisfactorily using the Almon estimators, $\hat{\beta}_1, \ldots, \hat{\beta}_s$ and their estimated covariance matrix.

(Adapted from University of Birmingham MSocSc examinations 1977.)

Question 7.29

Consider the distributed lag model

$$y_t = \beta_0 x_t + \beta_1 x_{t-1} + \ldots + \beta_n x_{t-n} + u_t \qquad (t = 1, \ldots, T) \tag{7.29.1}$$

where the x_t are non-random variables and the u_t are distributed as independent $N(0, \sigma^2)$ variables. Let $\beta' = (\beta_0, \ldots, \beta_n)$ and b be the ordinary least squares estimator of β obtained from (7.29.1). It is assumed that the lag coefficients lie on a polynomial of order k ($k < n$) so that

$$\beta = A\alpha \tag{7.29.2}$$

where A is an $(n + 1) \times (k + 1)$ matrix with typical element $A_{rs} = r^s$ ($r = 0, \ldots, n$ and $s = 0, \ldots, k$) and $\alpha' = (\alpha_0, \alpha_1, \ldots, \alpha_k)$.

(a) Find $\hat{\alpha}$, the generalised least squares estimator of α obtained from the model

$$b = A\alpha + w \tag{7.29.3}$$

where $w = b - \beta$.

(b) Prove that $\hat{b} = A\hat{\alpha}$ is equal to the conventional Almon estimator of β.

(c) Show that $\hat{b}$ is at least as efficient as b.

(University of York, Graduate Qualifying Examinations 1977.)

Question 7.30

In the stochastic differential equation system

$$Dy(t) = Ay(t) + \zeta(t)$$

A is an $n \times n$ matrix of parameters whose eigenvalues all have negative real parts, $y(t)$ is a vector of random functions observable at integral points in time t and $D = d/dt$ is an operator denoting stochastic differentiation with respect to t. The vector of disturbances $\zeta(t)$ is assumed to satisfy the following conditions

$$E\left[\int_{t_1}^{t_2} \zeta(t)\,dt\right] = 0,$$

$$E\left[\int_{t_1}^{t_2} \zeta(t)\,dt \int_{t_1}^{t_2} \zeta(s)'\,ds\right] = \Sigma(t_2 - t_1),$$

$$E\left[\int_{t_1}^{t_2} \zeta(t)\,dt \int_{t_3}^{t_4} \zeta(s)'\,ds\right] = 0$$

where E is the expectation operator, $t_1 < t_2 < t_3 < t_4$ and Σ is an $n \times n$ positive definite matrix.

(a) Verify that the discrete observations $(\ldots y(1), y(2), \ldots)$ satisfy the difference equation system

$$y(t) = By(t-1) + \zeta(t)$$

where

$$B = \exp(A)$$

$$= I + A + \frac{A^2}{2!} + \frac{A^3}{3!} + \ldots$$

and

$$\zeta(t) = \int_0^1 \exp(sA)\,\zeta(t-s)\,ds.$$

(b) Show that

$$E[\zeta(t)\,\zeta(t)'] = \Omega = \int_0^1 \exp(sA)\,\Sigma\,\exp(sA')\,ds$$

and deduce that Ω satisfies the equation

$$\exp(A)\,\Sigma\,\exp(A') - \Sigma = A\Omega + \Omega A'$$

and hence that

$$\mathrm{vec}(\Omega) = [A \otimes I + I \otimes A]^{-1}\,[\exp(hA) \otimes \exp(hA) - I \otimes I]\,\mathrm{vec}(\Sigma).$$

(References: Bergstrom 1967, pp. 113–114, and Phillips 1973).

Question 7.31

In the differential equation system

$$Dy_1(t) = -\alpha y_1(t) + \zeta_1(t) \tag{7.31.1}$$

$$Dy_2(t) = \theta[\beta y_1(t) - y_2(t)] + \zeta_2(t) \tag{7.31.2}$$

the $y_i(t)$ are random functions observable at discrete points in time (t), α, β, and θ are unknown positive constants and $\zeta(t)$ is a vector of disturbances which satisfy the conditions

$$E\left[\int_{t_1}^{t_2} \zeta(t)dt\right] = 0,$$

$$E\left[\int_{t_1}^{t_2} \zeta(t)dt \int_{t_1}^{t_2} \zeta(s)'ds\right] = \Sigma(t_2 - t_1),$$

$$E\left[\int_{t_1}^{t_2} \zeta(t)dt \int_{t_3}^{t_4} \zeta(s)'ds\right] = 0$$

where $t_1 < t_2 < t_3 < t_4$ and

$$\Sigma = \begin{bmatrix} \sigma^2 & \sigma^2 \\ \sigma^2 & 2\sigma^2 \end{bmatrix}.$$

(a) Show that discrete observations on $y(t)' = [y_1(t), y_2(t)]$ satisfy the difference equation system

$$y(t) = By(t-1) + \zeta(t) \qquad (t = \ldots -1, 0, 1, \ldots) \tag{7.31.3}$$

where

$$B = \begin{bmatrix} e^{-\alpha} & 0 \\ \dfrac{\theta\beta}{\alpha-\theta}(e^{-\theta} - e^{-\alpha}) & e^{-\theta} \end{bmatrix}$$

and $\{\zeta(t): t = 1, 0, 1, \ldots\}$ is a sequence of serially independent random vectors.

(b) Verify that the parameters α, β, and θ are identifiable in the 'reduced form' (7.31.3)

(c) Show that the discrete approximation to (7.31.1–2) has reduced form given by

$$y(t) = B_1 y(t-1) + u(t)$$

where the coefficient matrix B_1 is

$$B_1 = \frac{1}{(1 - \tfrac{1}{2}\alpha)(1 - \tfrac{1}{2}\theta)} \begin{bmatrix} (1 - \tfrac{1}{2}\theta)(1 + \tfrac{1}{2}\alpha) & 0 \\ (\tfrac{1}{2}\theta\beta - 1)(1 + \tfrac{1}{2}\alpha) & (1 - \tfrac{1}{2}\alpha)(1 - \tfrac{1}{2}\theta) \\ + (1 - \tfrac{1}{2}\alpha)(1 + \tfrac{1}{2}\theta\beta) & \end{bmatrix}$$

and $u(t)$ is assumed to be a serially independent random disturbance vector with zero mean and non-singular covariance matrix.

(d) If we now estimate α by indirect least squares using the form of B_1 above, show that the limit in probability of this estimate of α is $2(1 - e^{-\alpha})/(1 + e^{-\alpha})$.

Question 7.32

An econometric model is defined by the following equations

$$DC(t) = \alpha[(1 - s)\, Y(t) - C(t)] + \zeta_1(t)$$
$$DK(t) = \gamma[v\, Y(t) - K(t)] + \zeta_2(t)$$
$$DY(t) = \lambda[C(t) + DK(t) - Y(t)] + \zeta_3(t)$$

where

$$Y(t) = \text{output,}$$
$$C(t) = \text{consumption,}$$
$$K(t) = \text{stock of capital,}$$
$$D = d/dt = \text{an operator denoting stochastic differentiation with respect to } t,$$
$$\zeta_i(t) = \text{a random disturbance function}$$

and $C(t)$, $K(t)$ and $Y(t)$ are random functions of the continuous time variable t. Discuss the problem of estimating α, γ, λ, s and v from a series of observations of these variables at discrete intervals of time.

(Reference: Phillips, 1972)

(Adapted from University of Essex MA examinations 1972.)

Question 7.33

Consider the following model of a market in disequilibrium

$$D_t = X_{1t}\beta_1 + P_t\beta_2 + u_{1t}$$
$$S_t = X_{2t}\beta_3 + P_t\beta_4 + u_{2t}$$
$$\Delta P_t = \alpha(D_t - S_t)$$
$$Q_t = \min\{D_t, S_t\}$$

where D_t, S_t and Q_t represent quantities demanded, supplied and observed, respectively, P_t is price, X_{1t} and X_{2t} are vectors of predetermined variables and u_{1t} and u_{2t} are disturbance terms which have a joint normal distribution with mean zero and covariance matrix Σ.

(a) Interpret the model.
(b) Show how OLS and instrumental variable estimates of the model may be obtained and examine their consistency.
(c) Obtained the likelihood function of the model in a form suitable for maximisation.

Question 7.34

Two alternative models of a certain market are proposed:

Model 1

$$q_t^D = \alpha_0 - \alpha_1 p_t + \alpha_2 y_t + u_{1t}$$
$$q_t^S = \beta_0 + \beta_1 p_{t-1} + \beta_2 t + u_{2t}$$
$$q_t^D = q_t^S = q_t$$

Model 2

$$q_t^D = \alpha_0 - \alpha_1 p_t + \alpha_2 y_t + u_{1t}$$
$$q_t^S = \beta_0 + \beta_1 t + u_{2t}$$
$$\Delta p_t = \theta (q_t^D - q_t^S)$$

where q_t^D is quantity demanded, q_t^S is quantity supplied, q_t is quantity exchanged, p_t is price, y_t is income (which is taken to be exogenous), u_{1t} and u_{2t} are serially independent disturbances with zero means, variances σ_{11} and σ_{22}, respectively, and covariance σ_{12}; and q_t, p_t and y_t are observable variables. The coefficients, σ_{11}, σ_{22}, and σ_{12} are unknown.
(a) Compare the two models.
(b) Discuss the identification and estimation of the models.
(c) Consider the problem of selecting one of these models on the basis of the available data.

Question 7.35

Consider the single equation

$$y_t = b y_{t-1} + c y_{t-2} + d y_{t-3} + e x_t + f x_{t-1} + g x_{t-2} + h x_{t-3} \quad (7.35.1)$$

where y_t represents an endogenous variable and x_t an exogenous variable. The parameters b, c, d, e, f, g and h may be taken as estimates and the residual in (7.35.1) is suppressed.
(a) Obtain the final form of (7.35.1)
(b) Find the interim multipliers $\partial y_t / \partial x_{t-1}$ and $\partial y_t / \partial x_{t-2}$. How do these results differ from those obtained by the method of Theil and Boot (1963)?

(Reference: Brissimis, 1976.)

Question 7.36

(a) Discuss the representation of the series generated by the model

$$x_t + \alpha_1 x_{t-1} + \ldots + \alpha_k x_{t-k} = \epsilon_t + \beta_1 \epsilon_{t-1} + \ldots + \beta_h \epsilon_{t-h}$$

where ϵ_t is white noise, as
   (i) a stationary infinite moving average; and
   (ii) a stationary infinite autoregression.
(b) For the model

$$x_t + \alpha x_{t-1} = \epsilon_t + \beta \epsilon_{t-1}$$

show that

$$V(x_t) = \frac{1 - 2\alpha\beta + \beta^2}{1 - \alpha^2} V(\epsilon_t)$$

$$\rho_1 = \frac{(\beta - \alpha)(1 - \alpha\beta)}{1 - 2\alpha\beta + \beta^2}$$

$$\rho_r = \alpha\rho_{r-1} \qquad (r = 2, 3, \ldots).$$

where $V(x_t)$ and $V(\epsilon_t)$ are the variances of x_t and ϵ_t and $\rho_r = E(x_t x_{t-r})/E(x_t^2)$.
(c) How would you infer the values of α, β from a knowledge of ρ_r for $r = 1, 2, \ldots$?

(Adapted from University of London, MSc (Econ.) examinations 1977.)

Question 7.37

The market for a certain storable good is described by the following system:

$$\Delta X_t = \alpha\Delta P_t + \beta\Delta Y_t + U_{1t} \qquad (\alpha < 0, \quad \beta > 0)$$

$$\Delta Q_t = \gamma\Delta P_t^e \qquad\qquad\ + U_{2t} \qquad (\gamma > 0)$$

$$\Delta P_t = \theta(X_t - Q_t) \quad + U_{3t} \qquad (\theta > 0)$$

$$\Delta I_t = Q_t - X_t$$

$$\Delta P_t^e = \lambda\Delta P_{t-1}^e + (1 - \lambda)\Delta P_{t-1} \qquad (1 \geqslant \lambda \geqslant 0)$$

where $X_t, Q_t, P_t, P_t^e, I_t$ and Y_t are purchases, output, actual and expected price, end-period inventory level and exogenously determined income, respectively; and Δ denotes a first difference (e.g. $\Delta I_t = I_t - I_{t-1}$ is inventory change).
(a) Derive the final equation for ΔI_t when $\lambda = 0$. In the special case, when ΔY_t is constant, derive the steady state value for ΔI and determine the conditions under which the system has a *stable* steady state path.

(b) Derive the more general final equation for ΔI_t (i.e. when $\lambda \neq 0$).
(c) You have data only on inventory change and income so that only this final equation for ΔI_t can be estimated. Which of the original structural parameters are identifiable from this? Carefully explain how you would estimate these.

(University of London, MSc (Econ) examinations 1977.)

Question 7.38

In the following model

$$y_{1t} + b_{12}y_{2t} + c_{11}x_{1t} = u_{1t} \tag{7.38.1}$$

$$y_{2t} + c_{21}x_{1t} = u_{2t} \tag{7.38.2}$$

$$u_{1t} = r_{11}u_{1, t-1} + r_{12}u_{2, t-1} + e_{1t} \tag{7.38.3}$$

$$u_{2t} = e_{2t} \tag{7.38.4}$$

the y_{it} are endogenous variables, x_{1t} is an exogenous variable and the u_{it} are random disturbances. The e_{it} are random variables which are serially independent and distributed with

$$E\begin{bmatrix} e_{1t} \\ e_{2t} \end{bmatrix} = 0 \quad \text{and} \quad E\left[\begin{pmatrix} e_{1t} \\ e_{2t} \end{pmatrix} (e_{1t}, e_{2t}) \right] = \Sigma, \text{ for all } t, \text{ where}$$

Σ is unrestricted and non-singular.
Examine the local and global identifiability of the model given by equations (7.38.1–4).

Question 7.39

An investiment function used in an income distribution model of Australia was

$$I_t = 106 + 0.381 \text{RGC}_t - 0.355 \text{RGC}_{t-1} + 0.259 \text{RGC}_{t-2} + 0.626 I_{t-1} - 0.596 U_t^{\text{SA}}$$

where RGC_t is gross operating surplus of companies and U_t^{SA} is number registered for employment with the Commonwealth Employment Service.
(a) Express the equation in lag operator form.
(b) Write the model in the form

$$I_t = \frac{A(L)}{C(L)} \text{RGC}_t + \frac{D(L)}{C(L)} U_t^{\text{SA}} \text{ where}$$

$A(L)$, $C(L)$, $D(L)$ are polynomials in the lag operator, L.

(c) Compute the lag weights associated with the response of investment to gross operating surplus and registered unemployed up to 5 lags.
(d) Compute the response of investment to a transient unit increase in gross operating surplus and registered unemployed 3 periods ahead.
(e) Compute the total impact on investment of a unit change in each of gross operating surplus and registered unemployed.

(Adapted from The Australian National University, Master of Economics examinations 1976.)

Question 7.40

Consider the estimated regression equation for $t = 1, \ldots , 100$

$$y_t = 10.2 + 0.82\, x_t + \hat{u}_t \qquad (R^2 = 0.92)$$
$$ (2.3)\ (0.10)$$

where the figures in parentheses are standard errors, x_t is a non-random variable and $\hat{u}_t$ is a residual. From the residuals the following estimates of the autocorrelation function (AF) and the partial autocorrelation function (PAF) were obtained:

lag	1	2	3	4	5	6	7	8
AF:	0.10	0.55	0.26	0.11	0.07	0.01	−0.03	0.04
PAF:	0.10	0.49	0.01	−0.02	0.00	0.03	−0.01	0.02

Using the results above:
   (i) derive an estimate of the Durbin–Watson statistic and hence test the hypothesis that the disturbances u_t are generated by an AR(0) against the alternative hypothesis of an AR(1).
   (ii) assess whether or not the disturbances are generated by an AR(p) process with $p > 1$ or an ARMA (p, q) process with $p, q > 0$.

(Adapted from University of Essex BA examinations 1977.)

Question 7.41

A researcher has data on y_t = log of consumption of spirits per head, x_{t1} = log of real income per head, and x_{t2} = log of an appropriate relative price index for the period 1870–1932. These data are used to estimate some consumption of spirits equations and the results of equations (1) and (2) below are obtained by OLS estimation. Equation (1) is also estimated by autoregressive least squares, assuming that its error is generated by a first order autoregressive process with parameter ρ and these results are given in equation (3).
   Discuss the results presented in equations (1)–(3), paying particular

attention to their implications for the presence and treatment of serial correlation in the errors of the consumption function.

(1) $y_t = \underset{(0.15)}{4.50} - \underset{(0.10)}{0.12} \; x_{t1} - \underset{(0.05)}{1.20} \; x_{t2} + \hat{u}_t$

$\qquad (T = 63, R^2 = 0.96, \text{var}(\hat{u}) = 0.003, d = 0.24)$

(2) $y_t = \underset{(0.30)}{0.30} + \underset{(0.18)}{0.90} \; y_{t-1} + \underset{(0.14)}{0.70} \; x_{t1} - \underset{(0.15)}{0.65} \; x_{t-1,\,1}$

$\qquad \underset{(0.09)}{-0.90} \; x_{t2} + \underset{(0.09)}{0.81} \; x_{t-1,\,2} + \hat{w}_t$

$\qquad (T = 62, R^2 = 0.99, \text{var}(\hat{w}) = 0.0005, d = 2.2, h = -1.1)$

(3) $y_t = \underset{(1.0)}{3.0} + \underset{(0.13)}{0.78} \; x_{t1} - \underset{(0.07)}{0.84} \; x_{t2} + \tilde{u}_t, \; \tilde{\rho} = \underset{(0.13)}{0.91} \qquad (T = 62)$

where figures in parentheses are estimated asymptotic standard errors

$\qquad \hat{u}, \hat{w}, \tilde{u} =$ estimated residuals

$\qquad R^2 =$ squared multiple correlation coefficient

$\qquad d =$ Durbin-Watson statistic

$\qquad T =$ number of observations available for estimation

$\qquad h =$ Durbin's test statistic for dynamic equations

$\qquad \tilde{\rho} =$ autoregressive least squares estimate of ρ.

(University of York Graduate Qualifying examinations 1977.)

Question 7.42

The following consumption function is based on the permanent income hypothesis

$$c_t = ky_t^P + u_t$$

$$y_t^P = (1 - \lambda) \sum_{r=0}^{\infty} \lambda^r y_{t-r} \qquad (0 < \lambda < 1)$$

where $c_t =$ real consumption expenditures, $y_t^P =$ permanent real income and $y_t =$ measured real income. Four alternative assumptions are made about the error term u_t:

(i) $u_t = \lambda u_{t-1} + e_t$

(ii) $u_t = e_t$

(iii) $u_t = \rho u_{t-1} + e_t$

(iv) $u_t = \lambda u_{t-1} + \sum_{r=0}^{\infty} \gamma^r e_{t-r}$ $(|\gamma| < 1)$

where the e_t are independent $N(0, \sigma^2)$ variables.

(a) For each assumption (i)–(iv) indicate how maximum likelihood estimates can be obtained.

(b) From the following maximum likelihood estimates evaluate which of the assumptions is the most appropriate:

	λ	k	ρ	γ
(i)	0.670	0.91	—	—
	(0.108)	(0.031)		
(ii)	0.45	0.94	—	—
	(0.029)	(0.16)		
(iii)	0.66	0.94	0.69	—
	(0.085)	(0.46)	(0.079)	
(iv)	0.772	0.96	—	−0.13
	(0.091)	(0.014)		(0.14)

(The figures in parentheses are standard errors.)

(Reference: Zellner and Geisel, 1970.)

Question 7.43

It is maintained that investment I_t is explained by the model

(1) $I_t = \beta_0 + \beta_1 (S_t^* - S_{t-1}^*) + X_t \beta + u_t$

where S_t^*, expected sales, is unobservable but is explained by

(2) $S_t^* = Z_t \gamma + e_t$

Actual sales S_t is related to S_t^* through

(3) $S_t = S_t^* + w_t$.

X_t and Z_t are vectors of predetermined variables, and u_t, e_t and w_t are serially and mutually independent random variables with zero means and constant variances.

Two methods of estimating equation (1) are proposed

(a) replace expected sales by actual sales and use OLS;

(b) replace expected sales by the predicted values of sales obtained from the regression of S_t on Z_t.

Examine the consistency of these methods of estimation when S_{t-1} appears in X_t and Z_t and when it does not.

(Reference: E.M. Birch and C.D. Siebert, 1976)

(University of Essex, BA 1977.)

3. SOLUTIONS

Solution 7.1

The model (7.1.1) is a particularly simple example of a stochastic difference equation. The statistical properties of least squares estimators in such models have been developed by several authors. The first systematic discussion is that by Mann and Wald (1943) who developed a large sample theory for quasi-maximum likelihood estimators. In the case of (7.1.1) where the initial value y_0 is taken to be fixed and non-random it is readily shown that the quasi-maximum likelihood estimator is the same as the least squares estimator (c.f. Johnston, 1972, p. 305). Multiple equation generalisations of the model (7.1.1) were also considered by Mann and Wald in their seminal paper and a recent extensive discussion of the large sample theory of regression in such models is given by Anderson (1971, Chapter 5). In addition, Anderson deals with models which are similar to (7.1.1) but which also include non-random exogenous variables (see also Schönfeld, 1971). This type of model is very general and of great importance in econometrics since many econometric models imply that the stochastic properties of the variables of interest are determined by such relations.

Part (a) Returning to (7.1.1) we see that the least squares estimator of α is given by

$$\hat{\alpha} = \sum_{t=1}^{T} y_t y_{t-1} \bigg/ \sum_{t=1}^{T} y_{t-1}^2$$

Under the assumptions made in the question we know that $\hat{\alpha}$ has the following large sample properties:

(i) $\text{plim}_{T \to \infty} \hat{\alpha} = \alpha$;

(ii) $\sqrt{T}(\hat{\alpha} - \alpha)$ has a limiting normal distribution with zero mean and variance $1 - \alpha^2$.

A proof of (i) under the same conditions on the model is given by Anderson (1971, Theorem 5.5.3, p. 196). A proof of (ii), also under the same conditions on the model, is given by Anderson (1959, Theorem 4.3, p. 686). We emphasise the conditions on the model because these results seem to be the most general available when the u_t are independently and identically distributed. Similar results hold when the u_t are independently but not necessarily identically distributed provided

$$E(|u_t|^r) < M \qquad (t = 1, 2, \ldots)$$

for some constants M and r with $r > 2$ (c.f. Anderson, 1971, Chapter 5).
Thus, we can replace the identically distributed condition on the u_t by the
condition that there exist moments of a higher order than the second
which are uniformly bounded.

The small sample properties of the estimate $\hat{\alpha}$ are not as well charted.
In an important early paper, Hurwicz (1950) showed that $\hat{\alpha}$ is, in general,
biased. We note, however, that when $T = 1$ we have

$$\hat{\alpha} = \frac{y_1 y_0}{y_0^2} = \frac{y_1}{y_0} = \alpha + \frac{u_1}{y_0}$$

and, since y_0 is non-random,

$$E(\hat{\alpha}) = \alpha.$$

Thus, the least squares estimator is unbiased when $T = 1$.

For some larger values of $T (T = 3, 4)$ Hurwicz obtained an exact
expression for $E(\hat{\alpha})$, taking the disturbances u_t to be normally distributed.
He considered the fixed initial value case (setting $y_0 = 0$) and the case
where the process (7.1.1) is on-going for all t and has no initial value. In
every case, Hurwicz found that $E(\hat{\alpha})$ was substantially smaller than α in
absolute value. For some values of α the downward bias can amount to as
much as 25% of the true parameter value.

More general formulae for $E(\hat{\alpha})$ which hold for any T have not been
found in closed form but representations of $E(\hat{\alpha})$ in terms of infinite series
are available. Hurwicz (1950) and Shenton and Johnson (1965) both give
a series for $E(\hat{\alpha})$ in terms of ascending powers of α^2. A finite number of
terms of this series is then a useful approximation when α is small.
Shenton and Johnson also give a series expansion of $E(\hat{\alpha})$ in terms of
ascending powers of $1/T$. Omitting terms of $0(T^{-2})$ in this latter series we
have the approximation for the bias given by

$$E(\hat{\alpha} - \alpha) \approx -\frac{2\alpha}{T}.$$

Similar expansions for higher order moments of $\hat{\alpha}$ are also given by
Shenton and Johnson.

Knowledge of the moments of $\hat{\alpha}$ is useful to the extent that it provides
a guide to the distribution of $\hat{\alpha}$. But, it would seem desirable to develop a
distribution theory for $\hat{\alpha}$ directly. To do so we must specify explicitly the
distribution of the disturbances so that the joint distribution of the
observations $y_1, \ldots, y_T$ is uniquely determined. This points to an
immediate disadvantage: that an exact distribution theory is exact only if
the distribution of the disturbances is specified correctly. We might
remark in passing that a similar comment holds good for the moment
formulae mentioned above.

Without modifications to the model (7.1.1), an exact theory causes
extraordinary difficulties. So much so that as yet the distribution of $\hat{\alpha}$

(when the u_t are normally distributed) has not been found. However, if (7.1.1) is modified so that $y_0 \equiv y_T$ and the population becomes circular, then an exact theory is possible. An extensive discussion of the results that have been obtained in this so called 'circular' model is given by Anderson (1971, Chapter 6). These results are then relevant in the present context only to the extent that they provide useful approximations when the circular definition is relaxed.

An alternative approach is to continue to deal with the non-circular model (7.1.1) and to try to develop directly approximations to the distribution of $\hat{\alpha}$. This approach is used by Daniels (1956) and Phillips (1977). In the latter, the following expansion is obtained:

$$P\left[\frac{\sqrt{T}(\hat{\alpha} - \alpha)}{\sqrt{1 - \alpha^2}} \leqslant x\right] = I(x) + \frac{i(x)}{\sqrt{T}}\left(\frac{\alpha}{\sqrt{1 - \alpha^2}}\right) \quad (x^2 + 1) + O(T^{-1})$$

$$\text{(7.1.2)}$$

where

$$I(x) = \int_{-\infty}^{x} \frac{e^{-t^2/2}}{\sqrt{2\pi}}\, dt$$

and

$$i(x) = \frac{e^{-x^2/2}}{\sqrt{2\pi}}$$

are the standard normal distribution function and density respectively. The expansion (7.1.2) is called an Edgeworth expansion (c.f. Cramér, 1946, Chapter 17 and Solution 6.20) of the distribution function of $\sqrt{T}(\hat{\alpha} - \alpha)/\sqrt{1 - \alpha^2}$; and the first two terms on the right-hand side of (7.1.2) yield a simple approximation to the distribution of $\hat{\alpha}$. When α is small (less than 0.5) this approximation appears to be very good even for quite small values of T. The distribution of $\hat{\alpha}$ has a long left-hand tail and, as suggested by the moment formulae earlier, has a substantial downward bias.

Part (b) When $|\alpha| > 1$, the difference equation (7.1.1) is unstable. In this case it is known that

(i) $\text{plim}_{T \to \infty}\ \hat{\alpha} = \alpha$;

(ii) if $y_0 = 0$ and the u_t are normally distributed then

$$\frac{|\alpha|^T}{\alpha^2 - 1}(\hat{\alpha} - \alpha)$$

has a limiting Cauchy distribution as $T \to \infty$;

(iii) If the u_t are normally distributed then

$$\left(\sum_{t-1}^{T} y_{t-1}^2\right)^{1/2}(\hat{\alpha} - \alpha)$$

has a limiting normal distribution as $T \to \infty$. If the u_t are not normally distributed then no central limit theorem is applicable and the asymptotic distribution of $\hat{\alpha}$ depends on the distribution of the u_t.

These results have been derived by several authors: (i) was demonstrated in an early paper by Rubin (1950); (ii) was shown by White (1958) and (iii) by Anderson (1959). The last two results are of particular interest and suggest to us that statistical inference based on an asymptotic normal distribution theory has only limited justification in the present model when $|\alpha| > 1$.

Remark When dealing with a first-order stochastic difference equation the two cases of $|\alpha| < 1$ and $|\alpha| > 1$ can be readily distinguished. In higher order difference equations such as

$$y_t = \alpha_1 y_{t-1} + \ldots + \alpha_p y_{t-p} + u_t \qquad (7.1.3)$$

the stability of the model depends on the magnitude of the largest root of the equation

$$z^p + \alpha_1 z^{p-1} + \ldots + \alpha_p = 0. \qquad (7.1.4)$$

In this case several roots may have modulus greater than unity and a completely general theory would need to consider all the different possibilities. Such a theory has recently been developed by Stigum (1974 and 1976). Stigum (1976) shows that if there is at least one root of (7.1.4) with modulus less than unity and if all other roots have modulus different from unity then the vector of least squares estimates of the coefficients in (7.1.3) converges in distribution to a normally distributed vector; and this distribution is degenerate if there is at least one root of (7.1.4) with modulus greater than unity. Under the same assumption that the roots of (7.1.4) have modulus different from unity, Stigum (1976) shows that the least squares estimates of the coefficients in (7.1.4) converge with probability one to the true values (see Solution 5.1 for a discussion of convergence with probability one).

Solution 7.2

Part (c) From equation (7.2.1) we have

$$y_t = \alpha y_{t-1} + \beta + u_t$$

and

$$\rho y_{t-1} = \rho \alpha y_{t-2} + \rho \beta + \rho u_{t-1}$$

so that

$$y_t - \rho y_{t-1} = \alpha y_{t-1} - \alpha \rho y_{t-2} + \beta(1 - \rho) + u_t - \rho u_{t-1}$$

or, using (7.2.2),

$$y_t = (\alpha + \rho) y_{t-1} - \alpha\rho y_{t-2} + \beta(1 - \rho) + \epsilon_t. \tag{7.2.6}$$

Now the joint probability density of $\epsilon_1, \ldots, \epsilon_T$ is given by

$$\frac{1}{(2\pi)^{T/2}} \exp\left(-\tfrac{1}{2} \sum_{t=1}^{T} \epsilon_t^2\right)$$

To find the corresponding joint density of $y_1, \ldots, y_T$ conditional on the given initial values y_0 and y_{-1} we write (7.2.5) complete with T observations as the system

$$
\begin{bmatrix}
1 & 0 & 0 & 0 & \cdots & 0 & 0 & 0 \\
-(\alpha + \rho) & 1 & 0 & 0 & \cdots & 0 & 0 & 0 \\
\alpha\rho & -(\alpha + \rho) & 1 & 0 & \cdots & 0 & 0 & 0 \\
0 & \alpha\rho & -(\alpha + \rho) & 1 & \cdots & 0 & 0 & 0 \\
\vdots & \vdots & \vdots & \vdots & \vdots\vdots\vdots & \vdots & \vdots & \vdots \\
0 & 0 & 0 & 0 & \cdots & 1 & 0 & 0 \\
0 & 0 & 0 & 0 & \cdots & -(\alpha + \rho) & 1 & 0 \\
0 & 0 & 0 & 0 & \cdots & \alpha\rho & -(\alpha + \rho) & 1
\end{bmatrix}
\begin{bmatrix}
y_1 \\ y_2 \\ \vdots \\ y_T
\end{bmatrix}
$$

$$
+ \begin{bmatrix}
-(\alpha + \rho) y_0 + \alpha\rho y_{-1} \\
+\alpha\rho y_0 \\
0 \\
\vdots \\
0
\end{bmatrix}
= \begin{bmatrix}
\epsilon_1 \\ \epsilon_2 \\ \vdots \\ \epsilon_T
\end{bmatrix}
$$

or

$$By + c = \epsilon$$

where $y' = (y_1, \ldots, y_T)$, $\epsilon' = (\epsilon_1, \ldots, \epsilon_T)$ and the elements of the matrix B and vector c are constants. It follows directly that the Jacobian of the transformation from $\epsilon_1, \ldots, \epsilon_T$ to $y_1, \ldots, y_T$ is given by

$$\left|\frac{\partial\epsilon}{\partial y'}\right| = \det(B) = 1.$$

Hence, the joint probability density of $y_1, \ldots, y_T$ conditional on the given values y_0 and y_{-1} is just

$$\frac{1}{(2\pi)^{T/2}} \exp\left\{-\tfrac{1}{2} \sum_{t=1}^{T} [y_t - (\alpha + \rho) y_{t-1} + \alpha\rho y_{t-2} - \beta(1 - \rho)]^2\right\}$$

and the likelihood function L satisfies

$$\ln L = -\tfrac{1}{2}T \ln(2\pi) - \tfrac{1}{2} \sum_{t=1}^{T} [y_t - (\alpha + \rho) y_{t-1}$$

$$+ \alpha\rho y_{t-2} - \beta(1 - \rho)]^2$$

giving the required result.

Part (b) Writing (7.2.3) out in full we have the system

$$\begin{bmatrix} y_t \\ y_{t-1} \end{bmatrix} = \begin{bmatrix} \alpha + \rho & -\alpha\rho \\ 1 & 0 \end{bmatrix} \begin{bmatrix} y_{t-1} \\ y_{t-2} \end{bmatrix} + \begin{bmatrix} \beta(1 - \rho) \\ 0 \end{bmatrix} + \begin{bmatrix} \epsilon_t \\ 0 \end{bmatrix}.$$

It is clear that the second equation in this system is just the identity $y_{t-1} = y_{t-1}$ and the first equation is (7.2.6), the equation of the model.

From (7.2.3) we have

$$x_t = A x_{t-1} + b + v_t$$
$$x_{t-1} = A x_{t-2} + b + v_{t-1}$$
$$. \quad . \quad . \quad . \quad . \quad . \quad . \quad . \quad .$$
$$x_1 = A x_0 + b + v_1$$

so that

$$x_t = \sum_{s=0}^{t-1} A^s b + A^t x_0 + \sum_{s=0}^{t-1} A^s v_{t-s} \tag{7.2.7}$$

and

$$E(x_t) = \sum_{s=0}^{t-1} A^s b + A^t x_0$$

where we note that $x_0' = (y_0, y_{-1})$ is the vector of given, non-random, initial values. Hence

$$\lim_{t \to \infty} E(x_t) = \sum_{s=0}^{\infty} A^s b + \lim_{t \to \infty} \left(A^t x_0 \right) \tag{7.2.8}$$

$$= (I - A)^{-1} b \tag{7.2.9}$$

To see why (7.2.9) holds, we note that the matrix A has eigenvalues α and ρ, both of which have modulus less than unity (by assumption) and we have the following equations:

$$A \begin{bmatrix} 1 \\ 1/\alpha \end{bmatrix} = \alpha \begin{bmatrix} 1 \\ 1/\alpha \end{bmatrix} \quad \text{and} \quad A \begin{bmatrix} 1 \\ 1/\rho \end{bmatrix} = \rho \begin{bmatrix} 1 \\ 1/\rho \end{bmatrix}$$

so that,

$$\begin{bmatrix} 1 & 1 \\ 1/\alpha & 1/\rho \end{bmatrix}^{-1} A \begin{bmatrix} 1 & 1 \\ 1/\alpha & 1/\rho \end{bmatrix} = \begin{bmatrix} \alpha & 0 \\ 0 & \rho \end{bmatrix} \tag{7.2.10}$$

[This follows because the vectors $(1, 1/\alpha)$ and $(1, 1/\rho)$ are the eigenvectors of A corresponding to α and ρ so that the matrix operations on the left side of (7.2.10) diagonalise the matrix A — see, for instance, Dhrymes, 1970, pp. 572–573; but the reader can also readily verify (7.2.10) by direct multiplication of the matrices.]

From (7.2.10) we then have

$$A = \begin{bmatrix} 1 & 1 \\ 1/\alpha & 1/\rho \end{bmatrix} \begin{bmatrix} \alpha & 0 \\ 0 & \rho \end{bmatrix} \begin{bmatrix} 1 & 1 \\ 1/\alpha & 1/\rho \end{bmatrix}^{-1}$$

and so, taking powers of both sides, we obtain

$$A^t = \begin{bmatrix} 1 & 1 \\ 1/\alpha & 1/\rho \end{bmatrix} \begin{bmatrix} \alpha^t & 0 \\ 0 & \rho^t \end{bmatrix} \begin{bmatrix} 1 & 1 \\ 1/\alpha & 1/\rho \end{bmatrix}^{-1}. \tag{7.2.11}$$

It is clear that $\alpha^t \to 0$ and $\rho^t \to 0$ as $t \to \infty$ so the elements of the matrix on the right side of (7.2.11) tend to zero and thus $\lim_{t \to \infty} A^t = 0$. Hence, the second term on the right side of (7.2.8) is zero. Equation (7.2.9) follows because the series $\sum_{s=0}^{\infty} A^s$ sums to $(I - A)^{-1}$ (see, for instance, Halmos, 1958, p. 186); or the result can be established directly by using (7.2.11) and the sum of a geometric series.

Turning now to the second moment of x_t, we first write

$$x_t = d_t + \sum_{s=0}^{t-1} A^s v_{t-s}$$

where, from (7.2.7)

$$d_t = \sum_{s=0}^{t-1} A^s b + A^t x_0.$$

We note that, from the properties of ϵ_t and the definition of v_t,

$$E(v_t v_t') = \begin{bmatrix} 1 & 0 \\ 0 & 0 \end{bmatrix} = \Omega,$$

say, and

$$E(v_t v_t') = 0 \qquad (t \neq s)$$

Hence

$$E(x_t x_t') = d_t d_t' + \sum_{s=0}^{t-1} A^s \Omega A'^s$$

and

$$V = \lim_{t \to \infty} E(x_t x_t') = \lim_{t \to \infty} d_t d_t' + \sum_{s=0}^{\infty} A^s \Omega A'^s$$

$$= (I - A)^{-1} bb'(I - A')^{-1}$$

$$+ \sum_{s=0}^{\infty} A^s \Omega A'^s. \tag{7.2.12}$$

It follows that

$$AVA' = A(I - A)^{-1} bb'(I - A')^{-1} A'$$

$$+ \sum_{s=1}^{\infty} A^s \Omega A'^s \tag{7.2.13}$$

and, by subtraction of (7.2.13) from (7.2.12), we have

$$V - AVA = (I - A)^{-1} bb'(I - A')^{-1}$$
$$\qquad - A(I - A)^{-1} bb'(I - A')^{-1} A' + \Omega$$
$$= (I - A)^{-1} bb'(I - A')^{-1}$$
$$\qquad + (I - A)(I - A)^{-1} bb'(I - A')^{-1} A'$$
$$\qquad - (I - A)^{-1} bb'(I - A')^{-1} A' + \Omega$$
$$= (I - A)^{-1} bb'(I - A')^{-1}(I - A')$$
$$\qquad + bb'(I - A')^{-1} A' + \Omega$$
$$= (I - A)^{-1} bb' + bb'(I - A')^{-1} A' + \Omega$$
$$= (I - A)(I - A)^{-1} bb' + A(I - A)^{-1} bb'$$
$$\qquad + bb'(I - A')^{-1} A' + \Omega$$
$$= bb' + A(I - A)^{-1} bb' + bb'(I - A')^{-1} A' + \Omega$$

as required.

Remark The above expressions which define $\lim_{t \to \infty} E(x_t)$ and $\lim_{t \to \infty} E(x_t x_t')$ are exactly what we would obtain for the first and second moments if the model were stationary. More precisely, suppose x_t^* is defined by

$$x_t^* = Ax_{t-1}^* + b + v_t \qquad (t = \ldots, -1, 0, 1, \ldots) \qquad (7.2.13)$$

where A, b and v_t are as before, but now there are no initial conditions at $t = 0$. Instead, the initial conditions are taken to be in the infinite past and we have

$$x_t^* = \sum_{s=0}^{\infty} A^s b + \sum_{s=0}^{\infty} A^s v_{t-s}$$

$$= (I - A)^{-1} b + \sum_{s=0}^{\infty} A^s v_{t-s} \qquad (7.2.14)$$

then have, from (7.2.13),

$$E(x_t^*) = (I - A)^{-1} b \qquad (7.2.15)$$

and

$$E(x_t^* x_t^{*'}) = (I - A)^{-1} bb'(I - A')^{-1}$$

$$+ \sum_{s=0}^{\infty} A^s \Omega A'^s \qquad (7.2.16)$$

for all values of t. The fact that the expressions (7.2.15) and (7.2.16) hold only when $t \to \infty$ for the process x_t is the reason why the original model (7.2.3) with initial values at $t = 0$ is sometimes referred to as 'asymptotically stationary'.

Part (c) We can solve (7.2.4) for the elements of the matrix V by writing both sides of the equation as a vector. We use the stacking operator vec(M) which stacks the rows of a matrix M sequentially into a long column vector, and writing (7.2.4) first of all as

$$V = AVA' + X \qquad (7.2.17)$$

where

$$X = bb' + A(I - A)^{-1} bb' + bb'(I - A')^{-1} A' + \Omega$$

we obtain

$$\text{vec}(V) = \text{vec}(AVA') + \text{vec}(X)$$

$$= (A \otimes A) \text{vec}(V) + \text{vec}(X)$$

or

$$[I - (A \otimes A)] \text{vec } V = \text{vec } (X) \qquad (7.2.18)$$

and thus

$$\text{vec}(V) = [I - (A \otimes A)]^{-1} \text{vec } (X).$$

Finally, we note that V and X are symmetric matrices; so we need only use those rows and columns of (7.2.18) which correspond to distinct elements of V and X. In the present case, (7.2.7) comprises four equations and from the fact that

$$V = \lim_{t \to \infty} E(x_t x_t') = \lim_{t \to \infty} \begin{bmatrix} E(y_t^2) & E(y_t y_{t-1}) \\ E(y_{t-1} y_t) & E(y_{t-1}^2) \end{bmatrix}$$

it follows that there are *only two* distinct elements in V, namely

$$v_{11} = \lim_{t \to \infty} E(y_t^2)$$

and

$$v_{12} = \lim_{t \to \infty} E(y_t y_{t-1})$$

Remark From (7.2.17) we obtain the following alternative representation of V:

$$V = \sum_{s=0}^{\infty} A^s X A'^s. \tag{7.2.19}$$

To see this, we write

$$V - AVA' = X$$

and

$$AVA' - A^2 VA'^2 = AXA'$$

so that by addition of the last two equations we have

$$V - A^2 VA'^2 = X + AXA'$$

Continuing this process indefinitely we end up with the representation (7.2.19).

Part (d) As we have seen in Part (a), the model (7.2.1–2) reduces to the second order difference equation

$$y_t = a_0 + a_1 y_{t-1} + a_2 y_{t-2} + \epsilon_t$$

where

$$a_0 = \beta(1 - \rho), \quad a_1 = \alpha + \rho \quad \text{and} \quad a_2 = -\alpha\rho. \tag{7.2.20}$$

The coefficients a_0, a_1 and a_2 in this equation are identifiable and, under the stated assumptions, these coefficients can, indeed, be consistently estimated by least squares regression. However, it follows from the transformations in (7.2.20) that α and ρ cannot be separately identified. For we have

$$a_1 \alpha = \alpha^2 + \alpha\rho$$

so that

$$a_1\alpha = \alpha^2 - a_2$$

which has solutions

$$\alpha = \frac{a_1 \pm \sqrt{a_1^2 - 4a_2}}{2}$$

The corresponding solutions for ρ are

$$\rho = \frac{a_1 \mp \sqrt{a_1^2 - 4a_2}}{2}$$

It follows that we cannot separately distinguish the true values of α and ρ.

Solution 7.3

The OLS estimators of α and β are

$$\begin{bmatrix} a \\ b \end{bmatrix} = \begin{bmatrix} \sum_{t=1}^{T} y_{t-1}^2 & \sum_{t=1}^{T} y_{t-1}x_t \\ \sum_{t=1}^{T} y_{t-1}x_t & \sum_{t=1}^{T} x_t^2 \end{bmatrix}^{-1} \begin{bmatrix} \sum_{t=1}^{T} y_t y_{t-1} \\ \sum_{t=1}^{T} y_t x_t \end{bmatrix} \tag{7.3.4}$$

Substituting (7.3.1) into (7.3.4) we obtain

$$\begin{bmatrix} a - \alpha \\ b - \beta \end{bmatrix} = \begin{bmatrix} \sum_{t=1}^{T} y_{t-1}^2 & \sum_{t=1}^{T} y_{t-1}x_t \\ \sum_{t=1}^{T} y_{t-1}x_t & \sum_{t=1}^{T} x_t^2 \end{bmatrix}^{-1} \begin{bmatrix} \sum_{t=1}^{T} u_t y_{t-1} \\ \sum_{t=1}^{T} u_t x_t \end{bmatrix} \tag{7.3.5}$$

The asymptotic biases are, therefore,

$$\text{plim} \begin{bmatrix} a - \alpha \\ b - \beta \end{bmatrix} = \begin{bmatrix} \text{plim } T^{-1} \sum_{t=1}^{T} y_{t-1}^2 & \text{plim } T^{-1} \sum_{t=1}^{T} y_{t-1}x_t \\ \text{plim } T^{-1} \sum_{t=1}^{T} y_{t-1}x_t & \text{plim } T^{-1} \sum_{t=1}^{T} x_t^2 \end{bmatrix}^{-1}$$

$$\begin{bmatrix} \text{plim } T^{-1} \sum_{t=1}^{T} u_t y_{t-1} \\ \text{plim } T^{-1} \sum_{t=1}^{T} u_t x_t \end{bmatrix} \tag{7.3.6}$$

The evaluation of each of these probability limits depends on whether the error structure is (7.3.2) or (7.3.3).

Part (a) Introducing the lag operator $z_{t-r} = L^r z_t$ into (7.3.1) we find that

$$y_t = (\beta x_t + u_t)/(1 - \alpha L)$$

$$= \sum_{r=0}^{\infty} \alpha^r (\beta x_{t-r} + u_{t-r})$$

$$= \beta \bar{y}_t + v_t \tag{7.3.7}$$

where $\bar{y}_t = \sum_{r=0}^{\infty} \alpha^r x_{t-r}$ and $v_t = \sum_{r=0}^{\infty} \alpha^r u_{t-r}$. From question (2.15), if z_T is a function of T independent random variables such that $\lim_{T \to \infty} E(z_T)$ exists and $\lim_{T \to \infty} \text{var}(z_T) = 0$, then plim z_T exists and is equal to $\lim_{T \to \infty} E(z_T)$. Therefore, if plim $T^{-1} \sum_1^T y_{t-1}^2$ exists, it is equal to

$$\lim_{T \to \infty} E \left(\sum_{t=1}^{T} y_t^2 \right) = \lim_{T \to \infty} \left[E \left(T^{-1} \sum_{t=1}^{T} \beta^2 \bar{y}_t^2 \right) + E \left(T^{-1} \sum_{t=1}^{T} v_t^2 \right) \right.$$

$$\left. + 2E \left(T^{-1} \sum_{t=1}^{T} \beta \bar{y}_t v_t \right) \right]. \tag{7.3.8}$$

Since x_t is non-stochastic and $E(u_t) = 0$,

$$E(\bar{y}_t v_t) = \left(\beta \sum_{r=0}^{\infty} \alpha^r x_{t-r} \right) \left[\sum_{r=0}^{\infty} \alpha^r E(u_{t-r}) \right] = 0$$

so that the last term in (7.3.8) is zero. Given the assumptions on x_t, the first term on the right-hand side of (7.3.8) is

$$\lim_{T \to \infty} E \left(T^{-1} \sum_{t=1}^{T} \beta^2 \bar{y}_t^2 \right) = \beta^2 \lim_{T \to \infty} T^{-1} \sum_{t=1}^{T} \left(\beta \sum_{r=0}^{\infty} \alpha^r x_{t-r} \right)^2$$

$$= \beta^4 \left[\sum_{r=0}^{\infty} \alpha^{2r} \lim_{T \to \infty} \left(T^{-1} \sum_{t=1}^{T} x_{t-r}^2 \right) \right.$$

$$\left. + \sum_{r \neq s} \sum \alpha^r \alpha^s \lim_{T \to \infty} \left(T^{-1} \sum_{t=1}^{T} x_{t-r} x_{t-s} \right) \right]$$

$$= \beta^2 m_{\bar{y}\bar{y}}, \tag{7.3.9}$$

say, which is finite and non-zero.

In evaluating the second term on the right-hand side of (7.3.8) we note first that the moments of v_t do not depend on t. Hence

$$\lim_{T \to \infty} E \left(T^{-1} \sum_{t=1}^{T} v_t^2 \right) = E(v_t^2). \tag{7.3.10}$$

Second, from (7.3.2), $u_t = \sum_{s=0}^{\infty} \rho^s e_{t-s}$ and $E(e_t e_{t-s}) = 0$ for $s > 0$; so we have

$$E(u_t u_{t-1}) = \rho E(u_{t-1}^2) + E(e_t u_{t-1})$$

$$= \rho E(u_{t-1}^2) + E\left(\sum_{s=0}^{\infty} \rho^s e_t e_{t-s-1}\right)$$

$$= \rho E(u_{t-1}^2)$$

and

$$E(u_t u_{t-2}) = \rho E(u_{t-1} u_{t-2}) + E(e_t u_{t-2})$$

$$= \rho E(u_{t-1} u_{t-2}) + E\left(\sum_{s=0}^{\infty} \rho^s e_t e_{t-s-2}\right)$$

$$= \rho^2 E(u_{t-2}^2)$$

In general, we can show that for $s \geqslant 0$

$$E(u_t u_{t-s}) = \rho^s E(u_{t-s}^2). \tag{7.3.11}$$

Furthermore, for all t,

$$E(u_t^2) = E\left(\sum_{s=0}^{\infty} \rho^s e_{t-s}\right)^2$$

$$= \sum_{s=0}^{\infty} \rho^{2s} E(e_{t-s}^2) + \sum_r \sum_s \rho^r \rho^s E(e_{t-r} e_{t-s})$$

$$= \sum_{s=0}^{\infty} \rho^{2s} E(e_{t-s}^2) = \sigma^2/(1 - \rho^2). \tag{7.3.12}$$

Thus, from (7.3.11–12) we obtain

$$E(u_t u_{t-s}) = \rho^s \sigma^2/(1 - \rho^2) \tag{7.3.13}$$

Using (7.3.12–13) we can show that

$$E(v_t^2) = E\left(\sum_{r=0}^{\infty} \alpha^r u_{t-r}\right)^2 = E\left(\sum_r \sum_s \alpha^r \alpha^s u_{t-r} u_{t-s}\right)$$

$$= \sum_r \sum_s \alpha^r \alpha^s \rho^{|r-s|} \sigma^2/(1 - \rho^2)$$

$$= (1 + \alpha\rho + \alpha^2\rho^2 + \alpha^3\rho^3 + \ldots$$
$$+ \alpha\rho + \alpha^2 + \alpha^3\rho + \alpha^4\rho^2 + \ldots$$
$$+ \alpha^2\rho + \alpha^3\rho + \alpha^4 + \alpha^5\rho + \ldots$$
$$\cdots \cdots \cdots \cdots \cdots \cdots) \, \sigma^2/(1 - \rho^2)$$

$$= \left[\sum_{r=0}^{\infty} \alpha^{2r} + 2\alpha\rho \, (1 + \alpha\rho + \alpha^2\rho^2 + \ldots) \right.$$
$$\left. + 2\alpha^3\rho(1 + \alpha\rho + \alpha^2\rho^2 + \ldots) + \ldots \right] \sigma^2/(1 - \rho^2)$$

$$= \left\{ \sum_{r=0}^{\infty} \alpha^{2r} + 2 \left(\sum_{s=0}^{\infty} (\alpha\rho)^{s+1} \right) \left(\sum_{r=0}^{\infty} \alpha^{2r} \right) \right\} \sigma^2/(1-\rho^2)$$

$$= [1 + 2\alpha\rho/(1-\alpha\rho)] \ \sigma^2/[(1-\alpha^2)(1-\rho^2)]$$

$$= (1+\alpha\rho) \ \sigma^2/[(1-\alpha\rho)(1-\alpha^2)(1-\rho^2)]. \qquad (7.3.14)$$

Remark Notice that we can derive (7.3.14) in a different way as follows. We have $v_t = \sum_{r=0}^{\infty} \alpha^r u_{t-r} = \sum_r \sum_s \alpha^r \rho^s e_{t-r-s}$ so that

$$E(v_t^2) = \sum_r \sum_s \sum_p \sum_q \alpha^r \rho^s \alpha^p \rho^q \ E(e_{t-r-s} e_{t-p-q})$$

$$= \sigma^2 \sum_{\substack{r+s=p+q}} \alpha^r \rho^s \alpha^p \rho^q$$

$$= \sigma^2 \sum_r \sum_s \sum_{p=0}^{r+s} \alpha^r \rho^s \alpha^p \rho^{r+s-p}$$

$$= \sigma^2 \sum_{r=0}^{\infty} \sum_{s=0}^{\infty} \alpha^r \rho^s \rho^{r+s} \sum_{p=0}^{r+s} \left(\frac{\alpha}{\rho} \right)^p$$

$$= \sigma^2 \sum_{r=0}^{\infty} \sum_{s=0}^{\infty} \alpha^r \rho^s \rho^{r+s} \left[\frac{1-(\alpha/\rho)^{r+s+1}}{1-(\alpha/\rho)} \right]$$

$$= \sigma^2 \sum_{r=0}^{\infty} \sum_{s=0}^{\infty} \alpha^r \rho^s \left(\frac{\rho^{r+s+1} - \alpha^{r+s+1}}{\rho - \alpha} \right)$$

$$= \frac{\rho\sigma^2}{\rho - \alpha} \sum_{r=0}^{\infty} \sum_{s=0}^{\infty} (\alpha\rho)^r \rho^{2s} - \frac{\alpha\sigma^2}{\rho - \alpha} \sum_{r=0}^{\infty} \sum_{s=0}^{\infty} \alpha^{2r} (\alpha\rho)^s$$

$$= \frac{\rho\sigma^2}{\rho - \alpha} \left(\frac{1}{1-\alpha\rho} \right) \left(\frac{1}{1-\rho^2} \right) - \frac{\alpha\sigma^2}{\rho - \alpha} \left(\frac{1}{1-\alpha^2} \right) \left(\frac{1}{1-\alpha\rho} \right)$$

$$= \frac{\sigma^2}{\rho - \alpha} \left[\frac{\rho(1-\alpha^2) - \alpha(1-\rho^2)}{(1-\alpha^2)(1-\rho^2)(1-\alpha\rho)} \right]$$

$$= \frac{\sigma^2}{\rho - \alpha} \left[\frac{(\rho - \alpha)(1+\alpha\rho)}{(1-\alpha^2)(1-\rho^2)(1-\alpha\rho)} \right]$$

$$= \sigma^2 \left(\frac{1+\alpha\rho}{1-\alpha\rho} \right) \left[\frac{1}{(1-\alpha^2)(1-\rho^2)} \right].$$

which is the same as (7.3.14). (Note that v_t is generated by the second order autoregression $v_t = (\alpha + \rho) v_{t-1} + \alpha\rho v_{t-2} = e_t$ and for an alternative derivation of the variance of v_t in such a case see Bartlett, 1966, p. 157.)

Hence, from (7.3.8–9) and (7.3.14), we have

$$\underset{T \to \infty}{\text{plim}} \ T^{-1} \sum_{t=1}^{T} y_{t-1}^2 = \beta^2 m_{\bar{y}\bar{y}} + (1 + \alpha\rho) \sigma^2 / [(1 - \alpha\rho)(1 - \alpha^2)$$

$$(1 - \rho^2)] \tag{7.3.15}$$

If the further condition that $\lim_{T \to \infty} \text{var} \ (T^{-1} \Sigma_{t=1}^T y_{t-1}^2) = 0$ holds the existence of plim $T^{-1} \Sigma_{t=1}^T y_{t-1}^2$ is established. The proof of this result, and of the corresponding conditions for the remaining terms of (7.3.6), is omitted here.

Turning to another term of (7.3.6), by a similar argument to that above, we can show that

$$\underset{T \to \infty}{\text{plim}} \ T^{-1} \sum_{t=1}^{T} y_{t-1} x_t = \lim_{T \to \infty} E\left(T^{-1} \sum_{t=1}^{T} y_{t-1} x_t\right)$$

$$= \lim_{T \to \infty} T^{-1} \sum_{t=1}^{T} [\beta \bar{y}_{t-1} x_t + E(v_t) x_t]$$

$$= \beta \lim_{T \to \infty} T^{-1} \sum_{t=1}^{T} \bar{y}_{t-1} x_t$$

$$= \beta m_{x\bar{y}_{-1}}, \tag{7.3.16}$$

say, where $m_{x\bar{y}_{-1}} = \lim_{T \to \infty} T^{-1} \Sigma_{t=1}^T \bar{y}_{t-1} x_t$. We also have

$$\underset{T \to \infty}{\text{plim}} \ T^{-1} \sum_{t=1}^{T} u_t y_{t-1} = \lim_{T \to \infty} T^{-1} \sum_{t=1}^{T} [\beta E(u_t \bar{y}_{t-1}) + E(u_t v_{t-1})]$$

Since x_t is non-stochastic, so is $\bar{y}_t$; and with $E(u_t) = 0$, we obtain

$$\underset{T \to \infty}{\text{plim}} \ T^{-1} \sum_{t=1}^{T} u_t y_{t-1} = \lim_{T \to \infty} T^{-1} \sum_{t=1}^{T} E(u_t v_{t-1}). \tag{7.3.17}$$

From (7.3.12–13), it now follows that

$$E(u_t v_{t-1}) = E\left(\sum_{r=0}^{\infty} \alpha^r u_t u_{t-r-1}\right)$$

$$= \sum_{r=0}^{\infty} \alpha^r \rho^{r+1} \sigma^2 / (1 - \rho^2) = \rho\sigma^2 / [(1 - \rho^2)(1 - \alpha\rho)].$$

$$\tag{7.3.18}$$

Hence,

$$\underset{T \to \infty}{\text{plim}} \ T^{-1} \sum_{t=1}^{T} u_t y_{t-1} = \rho\sigma^2 / [(1 - \rho^2)(1 - \alpha\rho)] \tag{7.3.19}$$

As x_t is non-stochastic and $E(u_t) = 0$, it is clear that plim $T^{-1} \Sigma_{t=1}^T u_t x_t =$

$\lim_{T \to \infty} T^{-1} \Sigma_{t=1}^{T} E(u_t) x_t = 0$ [we need only verify that $\lim_{T \to \infty}$ var $(T^{-1} \Sigma_t u_t x_t) = 0$]. Substituting (7.3.15), (7.3.16) and (7.3.19) into (7.3.6) we obtain

$$\text{plim} \begin{bmatrix} a - \alpha \\ b - \beta \end{bmatrix} = \begin{bmatrix} \beta^2 m_{yy} + \dfrac{(1 + \alpha\rho)\,\sigma^2}{(1-\alpha\rho)(1-\alpha^2)(1-\rho^2)} & \bigm| & \beta m_{xy_{-1}} \\ \hline \beta m_{xy_{-1}} & \bigm| & m_{xx} \end{bmatrix}^{-1}$$

$$\begin{bmatrix} \dfrac{\rho\sigma^2}{(1-\alpha\rho)(1-\rho^2)} \\ \hline 0 \end{bmatrix}. \tag{7.3.20}$$

Or, after simplification,

$$\text{plim} \begin{bmatrix} a - \alpha \\ b - \beta \end{bmatrix} = \left(\beta^2 m_{yy} + \frac{(1+\alpha\rho)\,\sigma^2}{(1-\alpha\rho)(1-\alpha^2)(1-\rho^2)} \right.$$

$$\left. - \beta^2 m_{xy_{-1}}^2 / m_{xx} \right)^{-1} \frac{\rho\sigma^2}{(1-\alpha\rho)(1-\rho^2)} \begin{bmatrix} 1 \\ \hline -\beta \dfrac{m_{xy_{-1}}}{m_{xx}} \end{bmatrix}$$

$$= [m_{yy}(1 - r_{xy_{-1}}^2 R_{yy}^2)]^{-1} \frac{\rho\sigma^2}{(1-\alpha\rho)(1-\rho^2)} \begin{bmatrix} 1 \\ \hline -\beta b_{\bar{y}x_{-1}} \end{bmatrix} \tag{7.3.21}$$

where $m_{yy} = \text{plim } T^{-1} \Sigma_{t=1}^{T} y_t^2$, $r_{xy_{-1}}^2 = m_{xy_{-1}}^2 / m_{xx} m_{yy}$, $R_{yy}^2 = \beta^2 m_{yy} / m_{yy}$ and $b_{\bar{y}x_{-1}} = \beta m_{xy_{-1}} / m_{xx}$. Thus $r_{xy_{-1}}^2$ is the (limit in probability of the) squared sample correlation coefficient between x and $\bar{y}_{-1}$, R_{yy}^2 is the squared multiple correlation coefficient from a regression of y on $\bar{y}_{-1}$. Note that $R_{yy}^2 = r_{yy}^2$ and $b_{\bar{y}_{-1}x}$ is the regression coefficient from a regression of $\bar{y}_{-1}$ on x. Since $m_{yy} > 0$ and $1 \geqslant r_{xy_{-1}}^2, r_{yy}^2 \geqslant 0$, we find that

$$\text{plim } (a - \alpha) \gtrless 0 \quad \text{as} \quad \rho \gtrless 0$$

and

$$\text{plim } (b - \beta) \gtrless 0 \quad \text{as} \quad \rho\beta b_{\bar{y}_{-1}x} \gtrless 0.$$

Remark By inspection of (7.3.21) we can infer a relationship between the asymptotic bias of the OLS estimator of α in the case we have just considered and that when there are no exogenous variables in the equation to be estimated, i.e. (7.3.1). For when there are no exogenous variables we have

$$\plim_{T \to \infty} (a - \alpha) = m_{yy}^{-1} \frac{\rho \sigma^2}{(1 - \alpha \rho)(1 - \rho^2)} \tag{7.3.22}$$

where m_{yy} is now just

$$\frac{\sigma^2 (1 + \alpha \rho)/(1 - \alpha \rho)}{(1 - \alpha^2)(1 - \rho^2)}.$$

Thus

$$\plim_{T \to \infty} (a - \alpha) = \frac{\rho (1 - \alpha^2)}{1 + \alpha \rho}. \tag{7.3.23}$$

By comparing (7.3.22) and the first row of (7.3.21) it is clear that the presence of the exogenous variable must reduce the magnitude of the asymptotic bias of the OLS estimator of α. This was shown in a rather different way by Malinvaud (1970b, pp. 559—560).

Part (b) For u_t generated by the first order moving average process (7.3.3) we have

$$v_t = \sum_{r=0}^{\infty} \alpha (e_{t-r} + \lambda e_{t-r-1}).$$

Thus, $E(v_t^2) = (1 + \lambda^2) \sigma^2/(1 - \alpha^2)$, and hence

$$\plim T^{-1} \sum_{t=1}^{T} \bar{y}_{t-1}^2 = \beta^2 m_{\bar{y}\bar{y}} + (1 + \lambda^2) \sigma^2/(1 - \alpha^2). \tag{7.3.22}$$

Further,

$$E(u_t u_{t-r-1}) = E(e_t + \lambda e_{t-1})(e_{t-r-1} + \lambda e_{t-r-2})$$

$$= \begin{cases} \lambda \sigma^2 & \text{for } r = 0 \\ 0 & \text{for } r > 0. \end{cases}$$

Thus

$$\plim T^{-1} \sum_{t=1}^{T} u_t y_{t-1} = \lambda \sigma^2. \tag{7.3.23}$$

Apart from these changes, the remaining elements of (7.3.6) are unaltered. It follows that

$$\plim \begin{bmatrix} a - \alpha \\ b - \beta \end{bmatrix} = [m_{yy}(1 - r_{x\bar{y}_{-1}}^2 R_{y\bar{y}}^2)]^{-1} \lambda \sigma^2 \begin{bmatrix} 1 \\ \hline -\beta b_{\bar{y}_{-1}x} \end{bmatrix} \tag{7.3.24}$$

Consequently, $\plim (a - \alpha) \gtrless 0$ as $\lambda \gtrless 0$ and $\plim (b - \beta) \gtrless 0$ as $\lambda \beta b_{\bar{y}_{-1}x} \lessgtr 0$.

Solution 7.4

Part (a) First we rewrite the model in matrix form. Thus (7.4.1) can be written as

$$y = Z\delta + u, \tag{7.4.3}$$

where

$$y = \begin{bmatrix} y_1 \\ \vdots \\ y_T \end{bmatrix}, Z = \begin{bmatrix} y_0 & x_1 \\ \vdots & \vdots \\ y_{T-1} & x_T \end{bmatrix}, \delta = \begin{bmatrix} \alpha \\ \beta \end{bmatrix} \text{ and } u = \begin{bmatrix} u_1 \\ \vdots \\ u_T \end{bmatrix}$$

and equation (7.4.2) can be written as

$$Ru + R_0 u_0 = e, \tag{7.4.4}$$

where

$$R = \begin{bmatrix} 1 & 0 & 0 & \cdots & 0 \\ -\rho & 1 & 0 & \cdots & 0 \\ 0 & -\rho & 1 & \cdots & 0 \\ \cdot & \cdot & \cdot & \cdot & \cdot \\ 0 & & \cdot & -\rho & 1 \end{bmatrix}, R_0 = \begin{bmatrix} -\rho \\ 0 \\ \vdots \\ 0 \end{bmatrix} \text{ and } e = \begin{bmatrix} e_1 \\ \vdots \\ e_T \end{bmatrix}.$$

In case (i), u_0 is zero and hence (7.4.4) simplifies to

$$Ru = e. \tag{7.4.5}$$

We can combine (7.4.3) and (7.4.5) to eliminate u, obtaining

$$R(y - Z\delta) = e. \tag{7.4.6}$$

The log likelihood function of (7.4.6) is

$$L_1(\delta, \rho, \sigma^2; y, Z, u_0) = \text{const} - \tfrac{1}{2}T \ln(\sigma^2) - (2\sigma^2)^{-1} e'e \tag{7.4.7}$$

Concentrating L_1 with respect to δ and ρ, we first obtain $\hat{\sigma}^2 = e'e/T$ and then the concentrated likelihood function is

$$L_1^*(\delta, \rho; y, Z, \hat{\sigma}^2, u_0) = \text{const} - \tfrac{1}{2}T \ln(e'e). \tag{7.4.8}$$

Thus, maximising L_1^* is equivalent to minimising

$$e'e = (y - Z\delta)' R'R(y - Z\delta)$$

$$= \sum_{t=1}^{T} [(y_t - z_t'\delta) - \rho(y_{t-1} - z_{t-1}'\delta)]^2 \tag{7.4.9}$$

where $z_t' = (y_{t-1}, x_t)$ for $t = 1, \ldots, T$ and $y_0 - z_0'\delta = u_0 = 0$.

Consequently, if $u_0 = 0$, the estimation of (7.4.1) and (7.4.2) reduces to the use of non-linear least squares on (7.4.6).

In case (ii), u_0 is assumed to be an unknown constant. Combining (7.4.3) with (7.4.4) we get

$$R(y - Z\delta) + R_0 u_0 = e. \tag{7.4.10}$$

The log likelihood function is now

$$L_2(\delta, \rho, \sigma^2, u_0; y, Z) = \text{const} - \tfrac{1}{2}T \ln(\sigma^2) - (2\sigma^2)^{-1} e'e. \tag{7.4.11}$$

Once more we concentrate the likelihood function with respect to σ^2 to obtain

$$L_2^*(\delta, \rho, u_0; y, Z, \hat{\sigma}^2) = \text{const} - \tfrac{1}{2}T \ln(e'e). \tag{7.4.12}$$

Thus, maximising L_2^* is again equivalent to minimising $e'e$ but this time

$$e'e = (y - Z\delta)' R'R(y - Z\delta) + 2u_0 R_0' R(y - Z\delta) + u_0^2 R_0' R_0. \tag{7.4.13}$$

Consider, therefore, concentrating L_2^* with respect to δ and ρ. Now

$$\frac{\partial L_2^*}{\partial u_0} = \frac{-T}{2e'e} [2R_0'R(y - Z\delta) + 2\hat{u}_0 R_0' R_0] = 0, \tag{7.4.14}$$

so that

$$\hat{u}_0 = -(R_0'R_0)^{-1} R_0' R(y - Z\delta) \tag{7.4.15}$$
$$= \rho^{-1}(y_1 - z_1'\delta).$$

Substituting $\hat{u}_0$ into L_2^* we obtain the new concentrated likelihood function

$$L_2^{**}(\delta, \rho; y, Z, \hat{\sigma}^2, \hat{u}_0) = \text{const} - \tfrac{1}{2}T \ln(\bar{e}'\bar{e}), \tag{7.4.16}$$

where

$$\bar{e} = [I - R_0(R_0'R_0)^{-1}R_0'] R(y - Z\delta)$$

$$= \begin{bmatrix} 0 & | & 0 \\ -- & -| & -- \\ 0 & | & I_{T-1} \end{bmatrix} R(y - Z\delta). \tag{7.4.17}$$

Hence, maximising L_2^{**} is equivalent to minimising

$$\bar{e}'\bar{e} = (y - Z\delta)'R' \begin{bmatrix} 0 & | & 0 \\ -- & -| & -- \\ 0 & | & I_{T-1} \end{bmatrix} R(y - Z\delta)$$

$$= \sum_{t=2}^{T} [(y_t - z_t'\delta) - \rho(y_{t-1} - z_{t-1}'\delta)]^2. \tag{7.4.18}$$

This may be accomplished by the Cochrane–Orcutt iterative technique (see Question 4.11).

Comparing (7.4.9) with (7.4.18) we see that the two expressions differ only in the number of terms in the summation. When u_0 is unknown, the summation runs from $t = 2, \ldots, T$, whereas when u_0 is known to be zero, the summation runs from $t = 1, \ldots, T$. Clearly, the two estimators will be numerically different but asymptotically equivalent. Accordingly, in Part (b) we shall consider only the estimator for the case $u_0 = 0$. The generalisation of the above result to higher order autoregressive processes should be fairly obvious.

Part (b) Let $\theta' = (\alpha, \beta, \rho, \sigma^2)$. The limiting distribution of $\sqrt{T}(\hat\theta - \theta)$, where $\hat\theta$ is the maximum likelihood estimator of θ, is $N(0, V)$ where

$$V^{-1} = -\lim_{T \to \infty} E\left(\frac{1}{T}\frac{\partial^2 L_1}{\partial\theta\partial\theta'}\right)$$

$$= -\text{plim}\left(\frac{1}{T}\frac{\partial^2 L_1}{\partial\theta\partial\theta'}\right). \tag{7.4.19}$$

Now

$$\frac{\partial L_1}{\partial \delta} = \frac{1}{\sigma^2} Z'R'R(y - Z\delta).$$

$$\frac{\partial L_1}{\partial \rho} = -\frac{1}{\sigma^2}(y - Z\delta)'\frac{\partial R'}{\partial \rho}R(y - Z\delta),$$

$$\frac{\partial L_1}{\partial \sigma^2} = -\frac{T}{2\sigma^2} + \frac{1}{2\sigma^4}e'e,$$

and

$$\frac{\partial^2 L_1}{\partial\delta\partial\delta'} = -\frac{1}{\sigma^2}Z'R'Rz = -\frac{1}{\sigma^2}\left[\sum_{t=2}^{T}(z_t - \rho z_{t-1})(z_t - \rho z_{t-1})' + z_1 z_1'\right].$$

$$\frac{\partial^2 L_1}{\partial\rho^2} = -\frac{1}{\sigma^2}(y - Z\delta)'\frac{\partial R'}{\partial\rho}\frac{\partial R}{\partial\rho}(y - Z\delta)$$

$$= -\frac{1}{\sigma^2}\sum_{t=1}^{T-1}(y_t - z_t'\delta)^2 = -\frac{1}{\sigma^2}\sum_{t=1}^{T-1}u_t^2,$$

$$\frac{\partial^2 L_1}{\partial\sigma^4} = \frac{T}{2\sigma^4} - \frac{1}{\sigma^6}e'e,$$

$$\frac{\partial^2 L_1}{\partial\delta\partial\rho} = \frac{1}{\sigma^2}Z'\frac{\partial R'}{\partial\rho}R(y-Z\delta) + \frac{1}{\sigma^2}Z'R'\frac{\partial R}{\partial\rho}(y-Z\delta)$$

$$= -\frac{1}{\sigma^2}\sum_{t=2}^{T}z_{t-1}e_t - \frac{1}{\sigma^2}\sum_{t=2}^{T}(z_t - \rho z_{t-1})u_{t-1},$$

$$\frac{\partial^2 L_1}{\partial\delta\partial\sigma^2} = -\frac{1}{\sigma^4}Z'R'R(y-Z\delta) = -\frac{1}{\sigma^4}\sum_{t=2}^{T}(z_t - \rho z_{t-1})e_t - \frac{1}{\sigma^4}z_1 e_1,$$

$$\frac{\partial^2 L_1}{\partial\rho\partial\sigma^2} = -\frac{2}{\sigma^4}(y-Z\delta)'\frac{\partial R'}{\partial\rho}R(y-Z\delta) = -\frac{2}{\sigma^4}\sum_{t=2}^{T}u_{t-1}e_t$$

It can be shown, therefore, that

$$V^{-1} = \frac{1}{\sigma^2}\left[\begin{array}{cc|cc} \mathrm{plim}\ T^{-1}\sum_{t=2}^{T}(z_t - \rho z_{t-1})(z_t - \rho z_{t-1})' & & \dfrac{\sigma^2}{(1-\alpha\rho)} & 0 \\[2mm] \hline & & 0 & 0 \\[2mm] \dfrac{\sigma^2}{(1-\alpha\rho)} & 0 & \dfrac{\sigma^2}{1-\rho^2} & 0 \\[4mm] 0 & 0 & 0 & \dfrac{1}{2\sigma^4} \end{array}\right]$$

$$(7.4.20)$$

In obtaining V^{-1} we can argue as follows. First, since $T^{-1}z_1 z_1'$ is $O(T^{-1})$ in probability and plim $T^{-1}\ \partial^2 L_1/\partial\delta\partial\delta'$ is $O(1)$ in probability, we can ignore plim $T^{-1}z_1 z_1'$. Second, since

$$\mathrm{plim}\ T^{-1}\sum_{t=2}^{T}z_{t-1}e_t = 0,$$

we have

$$\mathrm{plim}\ T^{-1}\frac{\partial^2 L_1}{\partial\delta\partial\rho} = -\sigma^{-2}\,\mathrm{plim}\ T^{-1}\sum_{t=2}^{T}z_{t-1}e_t$$

$$-\sigma^{-2}\,\mathrm{plim}\ T^{-1}\sum_{t=2}^{T}(z_t - \rho z_{t-1})u_{t-1}$$

$$= -\sigma^{-2}\,\mathrm{plim}\ T^{-1}\sum_{t=2}^{T}z_t u_{t-1}$$

$$+\rho\sigma^{-2}\,\mathrm{plim}\ T^{-1}\sum_{t=2}^{T}z_{t-1}u_{t-1}$$

$$= -\sigma^{-2} \left[\begin{matrix} \text{plim } T^{-1} \sum_{t=2}^{T} y_{t-1}u_{t-1} \\ \text{plim } T^{-1} \sum_{t=2}^{T} x_t u_{t-1} \end{matrix} \right] + \rho\sigma^{-2} \left[\begin{matrix} \text{plim } T^{-1} \sum_{t=2}^{T} y_{t-2}u_{t-1} \\ \text{plim } T^{-1} \sum_{t=2}^{T} x_{t-1}u_{t-1} \end{matrix} \right]$$

$$= - \left[\begin{matrix} 1/[(1-\alpha\rho)(1-\rho^2)] \\ 0 \end{matrix} \right] + \rho^2 \left[\begin{matrix} 1/[(1-\alpha\rho)(1-\rho^2)] \\ 0 \end{matrix} \right]$$

$$= - \left[\begin{matrix} 1/(1-\alpha\rho) \\ 0 \end{matrix} \right]. \tag{7.4.21}$$

In arriving at the last line (7.4.21) we have used (7.3.7) of Question 7.3 and the fact that $E\ T^{-1}\ \Sigma_{t=2}^{T} x_t u_s = 0$ for all t and s, from which we obtain

$$\text{plim } T^{-1} \sum_{t=2}^{T} y_{t-1}u_{t-1} = \text{plim } T^{-1} \sum_{t=2}^{T} \beta\bar{y}_{t-1}u_{t-1}$$

$$+ \text{plim } T^{-1} \sum_{t=2}^{T} v_{t-1}u_{t-1}$$

$$= \text{plim } T^{-1} \sum_{t=2}^{T} \sum_{r=0}^{\infty} \alpha^r u_{t-r-1}u_{t-1}$$

$$= \lim_{T\to\infty} T^{-1} \sum_{t=2}^{T} \sum_{r=0}^{\infty} \alpha^r \rho^r \sigma^2/(1-\rho^2)$$

$$= \sigma^2/[(1-\alpha\rho)(1-\rho^2)];$$

similarly, we find that [c.f. (7.3.19) above]

$$\text{plim } T^{-1} \sum_{t=2}^{T} y_{t-2}u_{t-1} = \rho\sigma^2/[(1-\alpha\rho)(1-\rho^2)].$$

Remark 1 It is important to notice from the form of V^{-1} that we cannot obtain the limiting distribution of $\sqrt{T}(\hat{\delta}-\delta)$ solely from the moment matrix of the transformed explanatory variables. That is, the limiting distribution of $\sqrt{T}(\hat{\delta}-\delta)$ is *not* $N(0, V^*)$, where $V^* = \sigma^2[\text{plim } T^{-1} \Sigma_{t=2}^{T} (z_t - \rho z_{t-1})(z_t - \rho z_{t-1})']^{-1}$, because we must take into account that the limiting distribution of $\sqrt{T}(\hat{\delta}-\delta)$ is not distributed independently of the limiting distribution of $\sqrt{T}(\hat{\rho}-\rho)$. In fact, the limiting distribution of $\sqrt{T}(\hat{\delta}-\delta)$ is $N(0, V^{**})$ where

$$V^{**} = \sigma^2 \left\{ \text{plim } T^{-1} \sum_{t=2}^{T} (z_t - \rho z_{t-1}) (z_t - \rho z_{t-1})' \right.$$

$$\left. - \frac{\sigma^2 (1 - \rho^2)}{(1 - \alpha\rho)^2} \begin{bmatrix} 1 & 0 \\ 0 & 0 \end{bmatrix} \right\}^{-1}$$

Remark 2 If ρ is known , then the limiting distribution of $\sqrt{T}(\hat{\delta} - \delta)$ *is* $N(0, V^*)$. Moreover, since $V^{**-1} = V^{*-1} - H$, where

$$H = \frac{1 - \rho^2}{(1 - \alpha\rho)^2} \begin{bmatrix} 1 & 0 \\ 0 & 0 \end{bmatrix}$$

is positive semi-definite, it follows that $V^{**} - V^*$ is positive semi-definite (Goldberger, 1964, p. 38). Hence, the asymptotic covariance matrix of the maximum likelihood estimator of δ when ρ is *unknown* and requires estimation is at least as great (in the usual matrix sense) as the asymptotic covariance matrix of the maximum likelihood estimator of δ when ρ is *known*. Thus, knowledge of ρ, and hence the covariance matrix of the residual vector u in (7.4.3), is useful asymptotically in obtaining efficient estimates of the coefficients in a model containing lagged endogenous variables. This is to be contrasted with the case in which the equation to be estimated contains only fixed regressors; for instance, if the variable y_{t-1} in (7.4.1) were replaced by an exogenous regressor w_t whose properties were the same as those of x_t then we would readily find that

$$\text{plim } T^{-1} \frac{\partial^2 L_1}{\partial \delta \partial \rho} = 0$$

and V^{-1} in (7.4.20) would become block diagonal [i.e. $\sigma^2/(1 - \alpha\rho)$ in the off diagonal blocks would be replaced by zero) and in this case we would have $V^{**} = V^*$.

These issues were first raised in an interesting investigation by Maddala (1971b). They have an important bearing on the choice of an appropriate estimation procedure in models such as (7.4.1–2). As we have seen, there is a loss in asymptotic efficiency when ρ is not known. There is, in fact, a further loss in efficiency unless ρ is estimated by a procedure which is asymptotically equivalent to maximum likelihood. The reader is referred to Maddala's paper for further discussion of this and other related points.

Solution 7.5

Part (a) On the null hypothesis we can write (7.5.1) in matrix form as

$$y = Z\delta + e \qquad (7.5.3)$$

where

$$y = \begin{bmatrix} y_1 \\ \vdots \\ y_T \end{bmatrix}, Z = \begin{bmatrix} y_0 & x_1 \\ \vdots & \vdots \\ y_{T-1} & x_T \end{bmatrix} = [y_{-1}, x], \delta = \begin{bmatrix} \alpha \\ \beta \end{bmatrix} \text{ and } e = \begin{bmatrix} e_1 \\ \vdots \\ e_T \end{bmatrix}$$

Let $\hat{\delta}' = (\hat{\alpha}, \hat{\beta})$ denote the OLS estimator of δ; then the residuals from the regression of y on Z are

$$\hat{e} = y - Z\hat{\delta}$$
$$= e - Z(\hat{\delta} - \delta). \qquad (7.5.4)$$

Now

$$r = \hat{e}'\hat{e}_{-1}/\hat{e}'_{-1} \qquad (7.5.5)$$

where the subscript -1 denotes the result of lagging by one period. Hence, from (7.5.4–5) we have

$$r = [e - Z(\hat{\delta} - \delta)]' \, [e_{-1} - Z_{-1}(\hat{\delta} - \delta)]/[e_{-1} - Z_{-1}(\hat{\delta} - \delta)]'$$
$$[e_{-1} - Z_{-1}(\hat{\delta} - \delta)] \qquad (7.5.6)$$

and

$$T^{1/2}r = \frac{\begin{array}{c} T^{-1/2}e'e_{-1} - T^{-1}e'Z_{-1} \cdot T^{1/2}(\hat{\delta} - \delta) - T^{-1}e'_{-1}Z \cdot T^{1/2}(\hat{\delta} - \delta) \\ + T^{1/2}(\hat{\delta} - \delta)' \, T^{-1}Z'Z_{-1}(\hat{\delta} - \delta) \end{array}}{T^{-1}e'_{-1}e_{-1} - T^{-1}2e'_{-1}Z_{-1}(\hat{\delta} - \delta) + (\hat{\delta} - \delta)' T^{-1}Z'_{-1}Z_{-1}(\hat{\delta} - \delta)}$$

$$(7.5.7)$$

Using the results of Question 7.3, on the null hypothesis, $\hat{\delta}$ is a consistent estimator of δ and $T^{1/2}(\hat{\delta} - \delta)$ possesses a limiting distribution. Thus, $T^{1/2}(\hat{\delta} - \delta)$ is $O(1)$ in probability. Moreover, plim $T^{-1}e'Z_{-1} =$ plim $T^{-1}e'_{-1}Z_{-1} = 0$. It follows that the second and last terms in the numerator and the last two terms in the denominator of the right hand side of (7.5.7) are $O(T^{-1/2})$ in probability or smaller. The remaining terms are $O(1)$ in probability; and using the results in Question 2.16, asymptotically, we can ignore the terms which are $O(T^{-1/2})$ in probability or smaller. Thus $T^{1/2}r$ has the same limiting distribution as

$$[T^{-1/2}e'e_{-1} - \text{plim}\,(T^{-1}e'_{-1}Z)\,T^{1/2}(\hat{\delta} - \delta)]/\text{plim}\,(T^{-1/2}e'_{-1}e_{-1}).$$

$$(7.5.8)$$

But

$$\text{plim } T^{-1}e'_{-1}Z = (\text{plim } T^{-1}e'_{-1}y_{-1}, \text{plim } T^{-1}e'_{-1}x)$$

$$= \left[\sum_{r=0}^{\infty} \alpha^r E(e_{t-1}e_{t-r-1}), 0 \right] = (\sigma^2, 0)$$

and plim $T^{-1}e'_{-1}e_{-1} = \sigma^2$. Thus (7.5.8) becomes

$$\sigma^{-2} T^{-1/2} e'e_{-1} - T^{1/2}(\hat{\alpha} - \alpha) \tag{7.5.9}$$

We must now find the limiting distribution of (7.5.9). Considering the first term of (7.5.9), we can define $\xi_t = e_t e_{t-1}$ and then

$$\sigma^{-2} T^{-1/2} e'e_{-1} = \sigma^{-2} T^{-1/2} \sum_{t=1}^{T} \xi_t \tag{7.5.10}$$

and we note that $E(\xi_t) = 0$, $E(\xi_t^2) = \sigma^4$ and ξ_t and ξ_{t-r} are distributed independently if $r > 1$ (ξ_t is an example of an m-dependent sequence of random variables; by this we mean that ξ_{t-r}, ξ_t and ξ_{t+r} are statistically dependent if the difference between the indices is not too great — here $r \leqslant m = 1$; we refer the reader to Dhrymes, 1971, for a discussion of m-dependent sequences and to Schonfeld, 1971, and Anderson, 1971, for useful central limit theorems involving these sequences). The limiting distribution of (7.5.10) is obtained from the following theorem which is proved in Anderson (1971, p. 431):

Theorem *If*

(i) $y_1, y_2, \ldots$ is a sequence of random variables such that for every n and $t_1, \ldots, t_n$ ($0 < t_1 < \ldots < t_n$) $y_{t_1}, \ldots, y_{t_n}$ is distributed independently of $y_1, \ldots, y_{t_1 - m - 1}$ and $y_{t_n + m + 1}, \ldots$.

(ii) $E(y_t) = 0$ and $E \mid y_t \mid^{2+\delta} < M$ for all t, for some $\delta > 0$ and for some M.

(iii) $\{a_1, a_2 \ldots\}$ is a sequence of constants for which $\mid a_t \mid < L$ for all t and some L and the following limit exists

$$\lim_{T \to \infty} T^{-1} \sum_{t, s=1}^{T} a_t a_s E(y_t y_s). \tag{7.5.11}$$

Then $T^{-1/2} \Sigma_{t=1}^{T} a_t y_t$ has a limiting normal distribtion with zero mean and variance given by (7.5.11).

Applying this theorem to (7.5.10) we have $a_t = 1$ for all t and we require as an additional condition on the e_t (if the e_t are *not* normally distributed — in the question the e_t are assumed to be normally distributed but this is not necessary):

$$E(\mid \xi_t \mid^{2+\delta}) = E(\mid e_t \mid^{2+\delta}) E(\mid e_{t-1} \mid^{2+\delta})$$

$$= [E(\mid e_t \mid^{2+\delta})]^2 < M$$

for some M. We note that

$$E(\xi_t \xi_s) = \begin{cases} \sigma^4 & t = s \\ 0 & t \neq s \end{cases}$$

so that

$$\lim_{T \to \infty} T^{-1} \sum_{t, s=1}^{T} E(\xi_t \xi_s) = \sigma^4$$

It follows that (7.5.10) has a limiting $N(0, 1)$ distribution when $T \to \infty$.

We now turn to the second term of (7.5.9). Since $\rho = 0$ on the null hypothesis, the limiting distribution of $T^{1/2}(\hat{\delta} - \delta)$ is $N(0, \sigma^2 \bar{M}^{-1})$ where $\bar{M} = \text{plim} (T^{-1}Z'Z)$. (See Anderson, 1971, pp. 209–210, and the results in Remark 2 of Solution 7.4.). It follows that the limiting distribution of $T^{1/2}(\hat{\alpha} - \alpha)$ is $N(0, \sigma^2 \bar{m}^{11})$ where $\bar{m}^{ij}$ denotes the ijth element of $\bar{M}^{-1}$.

Hence, (7.5.9) is the sum of two terms, both of which have limiting normal distributions. Thus, (7.5.9) will also have a limiting normal distribution. The mean of this distribution will be zero and the variance will depend on the variances of the limiting distributions of the two components of (7.5.9) as well as their asymptotic covariance. To find the latter we proceed as follows:

$T^{1/2}(\hat{\delta} - \delta)$ has the same limiting distribution as $\bar{M}^{-1} Z'e/T^{1/2}$ and writing $y_t = \beta \bar{y}_t + v_t$ as in (7.3.7), or in vector form $y = \beta \bar{y} + v$, we see that $T^{1/2}(\hat{\alpha} - \alpha)$ has the same limiting distribution as

$$T^{-1/2} \bar{m}^{11} y_{-1}'e + T^{-1/2} \bar{m}^{12} x'e$$

$$= T^{-1/2} \bar{m}^{11} \beta \bar{y}_{-1}'e + T^{-1/2} \bar{m}^{11} v_{-1}'e + T^{-1/2} \bar{m}^{12} x'e \qquad (7.5.12)$$

Now

$$E\left[\left(T^{-1/2} \sum_{t=1}^{T} e_t e_{t-1}\right)\left(T^{-1/2} \sum_{s=1}^{\infty} \bar{y}_{s-1} e_s\right)\right]$$

$$= T^{-1} \sum_{t, s} \sum_{r=0} \alpha^r x_{s-r-1} E(e_t e_{t-1} e_s) = 0,$$

$$E\left[\left(T^{-1/2} \sum_{t=1}^{T} e_t e_{t-1}\right)(T^{-1/2} v_{-1}'e)\right]$$

$$= E\left[\left(T^{-1/2} \sum_{t=1}^{T} e_t e_{t-1}\right)\left(T^{-1/2} \sum_{s=1}^{T} \sum_{r=0}^{\infty} \alpha^r e_{s-r-1} e_s\right)\right]$$

$$= T^{-1} \sum_{t, s} \sum_{r=0}^{\infty} \alpha^r E(e_t e_{t-1} e_{s-r-1} e_s)$$

$$= T^{-1} \sum_{t=1}^{T} \sigma^4 = \sigma^4$$

(the only non-zero term occurs when $t = s$ and $r = o$). Thus

$$E\left[\left(T^{-1/2} \sum_{t=1}^{T} e_t e_{t-1}\right)\left(T^{-1/2} \sum_{s=1}^{T} x_s e_s\right)\right]$$

$$= T^{-1} \sum_{t,s} x_s E(e_t e_{t-1} e_s) = 0.$$

It follows that

$$\mathrm{cov}\,(\sigma^{-2}\,T^{-1/2}\,e'e_{-1},\ T^{-1/2}\bar{m}^{11}y'_{-1}e + T^{-1/2}\bar{m}^{12}x'e)$$

$$= \mathrm{cov}\,(\sigma^{-2}\,T^{-1/2}\,e'e_{-1},\ T^{-1/2}\bar{m}^{11}v'_{-1}e)$$

$$= \sigma^{-2}\bar{m}^{11}E\,[(T^{-1/2}\,e'e_{-1})\,(v'_{-1}e)]$$

$$= \sigma^2\bar{m}^{11},$$

and this is the asymptotic covariance between (7.5.10) and (7.5.12).

It now follows that the variance of the limiting distribution of (7.5.9) is

$$V_r = 1 + \sigma^2\bar{m}^{11} - 2\sigma^2\bar{m}^{11} = 1 - \sigma^2\bar{m}^{11}.$$

$$= 1 - V_\alpha$$

where V_α denotes the variance of the limiting distribution of $T^{1/2}\,(\hat{\alpha} - \alpha)$. Since $T^{1/2}\,r$ has the same limiting distribution as (7.5.9) we can now deduce that this distribution is $N(0, V_r)$ as $T \to \infty$.

It follows that the limiting distribution of

$$V_r^{-1/2}\,T^{1/2}r = T^{1/2}r/(1 - V_\alpha)^{1/2}$$

is $N(0, 1)$. V_α is unknown but can be estimated by $\hat{V}_\alpha$, the variance of the least squares estimator of $T^{1/2}\alpha$. In finite samples, $h = T^{1/2}r/(1 - \hat{V}_\alpha)^{1/2}$ will be approximately $N(0, 1)$. The h statistic was first proposed by Durbin (1970) as an alternative to the Durbin–Watson statistic when a lagged dependent variable appears amongst the regressors. Durbin's derivation was, however, somewhat different from this and relied on the assumption that the e_t are independent $N(0, \sigma^2)$. Our own derivation does not require the normality of the e_t, although normality *is* assumed in the question.

The asymptotic distribution of d, the Durbin–Watson statistic, is obtained as follows: d is defined as

$$d = \sum_{t=2}^{T} (\hat{u}_t - \hat{u}_{t-1})^2 \Big/ \sum_{t=1}^{T} \hat{u}_t^2,$$

where the $\hat{u}_t$ are the residuals from the regression of y on Z. d can also be written as (see Question 4.12)

$$d = 2(1 - \hat{u}'\hat{u}_{-1}/\hat{u}'_{-1}\hat{u}_{-1}) + \mathrm{O}(T^{-1}), \tag{7.5.13}$$

where $\hat{u}' = (\hat{u}_1, \dots, \hat{u}_T)$ and the last term of (7.5.13) is $\mathrm{O}(T^{-1})$ in probability. On the null hypothesis of $\rho = 0$, $\hat{u} = \hat{e}$ and

$$d = 2(1 - \hat{e}'\hat{e}_{-1}/\hat{e}'_{-1}\hat{e}_{-1}) + \mathrm{O}(T^{-1}).$$

Using (7.5.5),

$$d = 2(1 - r) + O(T^{-1})$$

and, hence, on H_0, plim $d = 2(1 - \text{plim } r) = 2$. The limiting distribution of $T^{1/2}(d - 2)$ is, therefore, equal to the limiting distribution of $2T^{1/2}r$, which is $N(0, 4V_r)$ or $N[0, 4(1 - V_\alpha)]$. An approximate finite sample test of H_0 based on the Durbin–Watson statistic is obtained by assuming that, in finite samples, d is approximately distributed as a $N[2, 4T^{-1}(1 - \hat{V}_\alpha)]$ variable, or, equivalently, that $T^{1/2}(d - 2)/2(1 - \hat{V}_\alpha)^{1/2}$ is distributed approximately as a $N(0, 1)$ variable.

Part (b) The limiting distribution of $T^{1/2}(\hat{\rho} - \rho)$, where $\hat{\rho}$ is the maximum likelihood estimator, is obtained from Solution 7.4. Thus, the limiting distribution of $T^{1/2}(\hat{\rho} - \rho)$ is $N(0, V_{33})$ where V_{ij} is the ijth element of V defined in equation (7.4.20). But

$$V_{33} = \left\{ \frac{1}{1 - \rho^2} - \sigma^2 \left[\frac{1}{(1 - \alpha\rho)}, 0 \right] D^{-1} \begin{bmatrix} \dfrac{1}{(1 - \alpha\rho)} \\ 0 \end{bmatrix} \right\}^{-1}$$

where $D = \text{plim } T^{-1} \sum_{t=2}^{T} (z_t - \rho z_{t-1})(z_t - \rho z_{t-1})'$ and $z'_t = (y_{t-1}, x_t)$. Hence

$$V_{33} = \left[\frac{1}{1 - \rho^2} - \frac{\sigma^2}{(1 - \alpha\rho)^2} D^{11} \right]^{-1}$$

where D^{ij} is the ijth element of D^{-1}. On the null hypothesis of $\rho = 0$, V_{33} can be written as $V_{33}^0 = (1 - \sigma^2 \bar{m}^{11})^{-1}$. Consequently, $T^{1/2}r$ and $T^{1/2}\hat{\rho}$ both have limiting normal distributions when $\rho = 0$ but the variances of these distributions are not the same.

Remark From the above results we can derive three asymptotically equivalent test statistics for $H_0: \rho = 0$ against $H_1: \rho \neq 0$. They are

$$h = T^{1/2}r/(1 - \hat{V}_\alpha)^{1/2}$$

$$g_1 = T^{1/2}\hat{\rho}/(V_{33}^0)^{1/2}$$

and

$$g_2 = T^{1/2}\hat{\rho}/(\hat{V}_{33})^{1/2}$$

where $\hat{V}_{33}$ is the estimate of V_{33} obtained by replacing α, ρ, and σ^2 by their maximum likelihood estimates. All three estimators are assumed to be approximately distributed as $N(0, 1)$ variates in finite samples.

It can be shown that h can be regarded as a Lagrange multiplier type statistic and g_2 as a Wald type statistic. To see the former, we maximise the likelihood function of the model (7.5.1–2) given by equation (7.4.7) subject to the restriction that $\rho = 0$. We set up the Lagrangean

$$L = \tfrac{1}{2}T \ln (\sigma^2) + \frac{1}{2\sigma^2}e'e + \lambda\rho$$

where λ is the Lagrange multiplier and the first order conditions are (in the notation of Solution 7.4)

$$\frac{\partial L}{\partial \delta} = -\frac{1}{\sigma^2}Z'R'R(y - Z\delta) = 0$$

$$\frac{\partial L}{\partial \sigma^2} = \frac{T}{\sigma^2} - \frac{1}{2\sigma^4}e'e = 0$$

$$\frac{\partial L}{\partial \rho} = \frac{1}{\sigma^2}(y - Z\delta)'\frac{\partial R'}{\partial \rho}R(y - Z\delta) + \lambda = 0$$

$$\frac{\partial L}{\partial \lambda} = \rho = 0$$

Solving these equations we obtain $\hat{\sigma}^2 = \hat{e}'\hat{e}/T$ and

$$\hat{\lambda} = (y_{-1} - Z_{-1}\hat{\delta})'(y - Z\hat{\delta})/\hat{\sigma}^2 = T\hat{e}'_{-1}\hat{e}/\hat{e}'\hat{e}.$$

Since $T^{1/2}r$ and $\hat{\lambda}/T^{1/2}$ are asymptotically equivalent, the h-statistic, whose limiting distribution is based on that of $T^{1/2}r$, can be regarded as a Lagrange multiplier type test.

Solution 7.6

Part (a) We write the equations (7.6.1–2) as

$$\begin{bmatrix} 1 & b^0_{12} \\ 0 & 1 \end{bmatrix}\begin{bmatrix} y_{1t} \\ y_{2t} \end{bmatrix} + \begin{bmatrix} b^1_{11} & 0 \\ 0 & 0 \end{bmatrix}\begin{bmatrix} y_{1, t-1} \\ y_{2, t-1} \end{bmatrix} + \begin{bmatrix} c_{11} \\ c_{21} \end{bmatrix}x_{1t} = \begin{bmatrix} u_{1t} \\ u_{2t} \end{bmatrix} \qquad (7.6.5)$$

which can be rewritten as

$$B_0 y_t + B_1 y_{t-1} + Cx_t = u_t, \qquad (7.6.6)$$

or as

$$Aw_t = u_t, \qquad (7.6.7)$$

where $y'_t = (y_{1t}, y_{2t})$, $x_t = x_{1t}$, $u'_t = (u_{1t}, u_{2t})$, $w'_t = (y'_t, y'_{t-1}, x'_t)$ and $A = [B_0 \vdots B_1 \vdots C]$. Equations (7.6.3–4) can be written as

$$u_t = Ru_{t-1} + e_t \qquad (7.6.8)$$

where $e'_t = (e_{1t}, e_{2t})$. Using (7.6.8) we can eliminate u_t from (7.6.7) to obtain

$$Aw_t - RAw_{t-1} = e_t. \tag{7.6.9}$$

The reduced form of (7.6.9) is

$$y_t = -B_0^{-1}B_1 y_{t-1} - B_0^{-1}Cx_t + B_0^{-1}RAw_{t-1} + B_0^{-1}e_t \tag{7.6.10}$$

$$= P_1 y_{t-1} + P_2 x_t + P_3 w_{t-1} + v_t, \tag{7.6.11}$$

where $P_1 = -B_0^{-1}B_1$, $P_2 = -B_0^{-1}C$, $P_3 = B_0^{-1}RA$ and $v_t = B_0^{-1}e_t$.

Using the $\overline{\text{vec}}$ operator described in Appendix A, we denote $b_0 \underset{R}{=} \overline{\text{vec}}(B_0)$, $b_1 \underset{R}{=} \overline{\text{vec}}(B_1)$, $c \underset{R}{=} \overline{\text{vec}}(C)$, $r \underset{R}{=} \overline{\text{vec}}(R)$, $\theta' = (b'_0, b'_1, c', r')$, $p_1 = \overline{\text{vec}}(P_1)$, $p_2 = \overline{\text{vec}}(P_2)$, $p_3 = \overline{\text{vec}}(P_3)$ and $p' = (p'_1, p'_2, p'_3)$. The symbol $\underset{R}{=}$ implies that the equality only holds for unrestricted elements.

We introduce $\theta^* \underset{R}{=} \theta$ which is a vector of the unrestricted elements of θ. θ^* will not be locally identified if

$$H^* = \frac{\partial p}{\partial \theta^{*'}} \tag{7.6.12}$$

has full column rank, (see Rothenberg, 1973, p. 66). Now

$$P_1 = -B_0^{-1}B_1 = -\begin{bmatrix} 1 & -b_{12}^0 \\ 0 & 1 \end{bmatrix}\begin{bmatrix} b_{11}^1 & 0 \\ 0 & 0 \end{bmatrix} = \begin{bmatrix} -b_{11}^1 & 0 \\ 0 & 0 \end{bmatrix}$$

$$= \begin{bmatrix} p_{11}^1 & p_{12}^1 \\ p_{21}^1 & p_{22}^1 \end{bmatrix}, \tag{7.6.13}$$

$$P_2 = -B_0^{-1}C = -\begin{bmatrix} 1 & -b_{12}^0 \\ 0 & 1 \end{bmatrix}\begin{bmatrix} c_{11} \\ c_{21} \end{bmatrix} = \begin{bmatrix} -c_{11} + b_{12}^0 c_{21} \\ -c_{21} \end{bmatrix} = \begin{bmatrix} p_{11}^2 \\ p_{21}^2 \end{bmatrix} \tag{7.6.14}$$

and

$$P_3 = B_0^{-1}RA$$

$$= \begin{bmatrix} 1 & -b_{12}^0 \\ 0 & 1 \end{bmatrix}\begin{bmatrix} r_{11} & 0 \\ 0 & r_{22} \end{bmatrix}\begin{bmatrix} 1 & b_{12}^0 & b_{11}^1 & 0 & c_{11} \\ 0 & 1 & 0 & 0 & c_{21} \end{bmatrix}$$

$$= \begin{bmatrix} r_{11} & b_{21}^0(r_{11}-r_{22}) & b_{11}^1 r_{11} & 0 & c_{11}r_{11} - b_{12}^0 c_{21} r_{22} \\ 0 & r_{22} & 0 & 0 & c_{21}r_{22} \end{bmatrix} \tag{7.6.15}$$

$$= \begin{bmatrix} p_{11}^3 & p_{12}^3 & p_{13}^3 & p_{14}^3 & p_{15}^3 \\ p_{21}^3 & p_{22}^3 & p_{23}^3 & p_{24}^3 & p_{25}^3 \end{bmatrix}. \qquad (7.6.16)$$

Now,

$$\theta*' = (b_{12}^0, b_{11}^1, c_{11}, c_{21}, r_{11}, r_{22})$$

and

$$p' = (p_{11}^1, p_{21}^1, p_{12}^1, p_{22}^1, p_{11}^2, p_{21}^2, p_{11}^3, p_{21}^3, p_{12}^3, p_{22}^3, p_{13}^3, p_{23}^3, p_{14}^3,$$
$$p_{24}^3, p_{15}^3, p_{25}^3).$$

In order to obtain H^*, we differentiate each element of p with respect to each element of θ^*. Where an element of p is zero the corresponding row of H^* is zero. To simplify our results we omit these rows of H^*. Denote the consequent matrix by $\bar{H}$, then

$$\bar{H} = \begin{bmatrix} 0 & -1 & 0 & 0 & 0 & 0 \\ c_{21} & 0 & -1 & b_{12}^0 & 0 & 0 \\ 0 & 0 & 0 & -1 & 0 & 0 \\ 0 & 0 & 0 & 0 & 1 & 0 \\ r_{11} - r_{22} & 0 & 0 & 0 & b_{12}^0 & -b_{12}^0 \\ 0 & 0 & 0 & 0 & 0 & 1 \\ 0 & r_{11} & 0 & 0 & b_{11}^1 & 0 \\ -c_{21}r_{22} & 0 & r_{11} & -b_{12}^0 r_{22} & c_{11} & -b_{12}^0 c_{21} \\ 0 & 0 & 0 & r_{22} & 0 & c_{21} \end{bmatrix}$$

Thus H^* has full column rank if $\bar{H}$ has full column rank, that is, if we can find a non-zero minor of $\bar{H}$ which is of order 6. There are $^9C_6$ minors of $\bar{H}$ of order 6. But consider, for example, the minor formed from the first 6 rows of $\bar{H}$. We find that this minor has the scalar value $r_{22} - r_{11}$ which is non-zero provided that $r_{11} \neq r_{22}$. If this condition holds, then the model is locally identified.

Part (b) Sufficient conditions for the global identification of dynamic linear models with autocorrelated errors have been obtained by Sargan (1972) and are reported in Hendry (1974). The reader is also referred to a very useful discussion of local identification and of Sargan's result on global identification in Hatanaka (1974). The sufficient conditions are that the usual rank and order conditions are satisfied and that the rank of the coefficient matrix of the current exogenous variables in the model equals m, the number of equations. Lagged exogenous variables which also appear in current form are not counted for this purpose. This result is obtained as follows:

Equation (7.6.10) can be rewritten as

$$y_t = -B_0^{-1} B_1 y_{t-1} - B_0^{-1} C x_t + B_0^{-1} R B_0 y_{t-1} + B_0^{-1} R B_1 y_{t-2}$$
$$+ B_0^{-1} R C x_{t-1} + B_0^{-1} e_t \tag{7.6.17}$$
$$= (-B_0^{-1} B_1 + B_0^{-1} R B_0) y_{t-1} + B_0^{-1} R B_1 y_{t-2} - B_0^{-1} C x_t$$
$$+ B_0^{-1} R C x_{t-1} + B_0^{-1} e_t \tag{7.6.18}$$
$$= \pi_1 y_{t-1} + \pi_2 y_{t-2} + \pi_3 x_t + \pi_4 x_{t-1} + v_t. \tag{7.6.19}$$

The structural coefficients of (7.6.6 and 8) are globally identified if there is no observationally equivalent equation to (7.6.19), that is, if there is no equation of the form (7.6.19) which satisfies the restrictions of (7.6.18).

From (7.6.11) and (7.6.18–19) we find that the coefficients $\pi_1, \ldots, \pi_4$ embody the following restrictions:

$$\pi_1 = P_1 + Q \tag{7.6.20}$$
$$\pi_2 = -Q P_1 \tag{7.6.21}$$
$$\pi_3 = P_2 \tag{7.6.22}$$

and

$$\pi_4 = -Q P_2 \tag{7.6.23}$$

where

$$Q = B_0^{-1} R B_0. \tag{7.6.24}$$

If we can identify P_1, P_2 and Q from (7.6.20–24) given $\pi_1, \ldots, \pi_4$, we can use the rank and order conditions to identify the structural coefficients of (7.6.6) from P_1 and P_2 and, given B_0, we can identify R from (7.6.24). Now P_2 is identified by (7.6.22) and, given Q, we can identify P_1 from (7.6.20). In order to identify Q, consider equations (7.6.22–23) which can be combined as

$$Q \pi_3 + \pi_4 = 0. \tag{7.6.25}$$

If π_3 has rank m then we can obtain Q by solving (7.6.25). But $\pi_3 = -B_0^{-1} C$. Since B_0 is non-singular, the rank of π_3 is m if C has rank m. It follows that sufficient conditions for the global identification of the model are that the rank and order conditions are satisfied and that the rank of C is m. A necessary condition for C to have rank m is that $n \geqslant m$, that is, there are at least as many current exogenous variables in the model after deleting duplicated exogenous variables due to lagging as there are equations.

If the rank of π_3 is less than m then we must seek the identification of Q from (7.6.20–21), which may be combined as

$$Q^2 - Q \pi_1 - \pi_2 = 0. \tag{7.6.26}$$

We then try to find a solution of (7.6.26) for Q which satisfies (7.6.25). If there is more than one solution for Q then we obtain more than one solution of P_1 and P_2. Nevertheless, there may still be only one solution of B_0, B_1, C and R.

In the present example $m = 2$ and $n = 1$. Hence the model fails to satisfy Sargan's sufficient condition. However, even if we had satisfied this condition, we would still not be able to identify B_0, B_1, C and R, because the usual rank and order conditions are not met. The reader may check this for himself.

To sum up, therefore, we have shown that the model fails to satisfy the usual rank and order conditions, it is not globally identified but it is, in fact, locally identified. We will discuss further aspects of the problem of identification in dynamic models with serially correlated errors in Solutions 7.16 and 7.17.

Solution 7.7

Part (a) Equations (7.7.1) and (7.7.2) can be written more compactly as

$$BY' + CX' = U' \qquad (7.7.3)$$

or

$$AW' = U' \qquad (7.7.4)$$

and

$$U' = RU'_{-1} + E' \qquad (7.7.5)$$

where $Y' = [y_1, \ldots, y_T]$, $X' = [x_1, \ldots, x_T]$, $U' = [u_1, \ldots, u_T]$, $W = [Y \vdots X]$, $E' = [e_1, \ldots, e_T]$, $A = [B \vdots C]$ and U_{-1} is constructed from U by lagging each element of U one period.

Combining (7.7.4) and (7.7.5) we get

$$AW' - RAW'_{-1} = E' \qquad (7.7.6)$$

or

$$\tilde{A}\tilde{W}' = E' \qquad (7.7.7)$$

where

$$\tilde{A} = [A \vdots -RA] \quad \text{and} \quad \tilde{W} = [W \vdots W_{-1}].$$

The log likelihood function of (7.7.7) is

$$\ln(L) = \text{const} + T \ln |B| + \tfrac{1}{2} T \ln |\Sigma^{-1}| - \tfrac{1}{2} \text{tr}(\tilde{A}\tilde{W}'\tilde{W}\tilde{A}'\Sigma^{-1}). \quad (7.7.8)$$

Assuming that Σ and R are unrestricted and that A is subject to zero-one identifying restrictions, we can maximise $\ln(L)$ with respect to the unrestricted elements of A, R and Σ. Thus, writing $\Sigma = (\sigma_{ij})$, our first order conditions are:

$$\frac{\partial \ln L}{\partial B} = T\hat{B}'^{-1} - \hat{\Sigma}^{-1}\hat{\tilde{A}}\tilde{W}'Y + \hat{R}'\hat{\Sigma}^{-1}\hat{\tilde{A}}\tilde{W}'Y_{-1} \underset{R}{=} 0, \qquad (7.7.9)$$

$$\frac{\partial \ln L}{\partial C} = -\hat{\Sigma}^{-1}\hat{\tilde{A}}\tilde{W}'X + \hat{R}'\hat{\Sigma}^{-1}\hat{\tilde{A}}\tilde{W}'X_{-1} \underset{R}{=} 0, \tag{7.7.10}$$

$$\frac{\partial \ln L}{\partial R} = \hat{\Sigma}^{-1}\hat{\tilde{A}}\tilde{W}'W_{-1}\hat{A}' = 0, \tag{7.7.11}$$

and

$$\frac{\partial \ln L}{\partial \sigma_{ij}} = -\tfrac{1}{2}T \operatorname{tr}(\hat{\Sigma}^{-1}\,\partial\hat{\Sigma}/\partial\sigma_{ij}) + \tfrac{1}{2}\operatorname{tr}[\hat{\Sigma}^{-1}(\partial\hat{\Sigma}/\partial\sigma_{ij})\,\hat{\Sigma}^{-1}\hat{\tilde{A}}\tilde{W}'\tilde{W}\hat{\tilde{A}}]$$
$$= 0 \tag{7.7.12}$$

for all ij and where $\underset{R}{=}$ denotes that the equality sign holds only for unrestricted elements of B and C.

From (7.7.12) we obtain

$$\hat{\Sigma} = T^{-1}(\hat{\tilde{A}}\tilde{W}'\tilde{W}\hat{\tilde{A}}'), \tag{7.7.13}$$

and from (7.7.11)

$$\hat{\Sigma}^{-1}(\hat{A}W' - \hat{R}\hat{A}W'_{-1})\,W_{-1}\hat{A}' = 0.$$

Hence

$$\hat{R}' = (\hat{A}W'_{-1}W_{-1}\hat{A}')^{-1}\hat{A}W'_{-1}W\hat{A}', \tag{7.7.14}$$

or

$$\hat{R}' = (\hat{U}'_{-1}\hat{U}_{-1})^{-1}\hat{U}'_{-1}\hat{U} \tag{7.7.15}$$

where $\hat{U}' = \hat{A}W'$. In order to solve for $\hat{A}$ we pre-multiply (7.7.13) by $\hat{\Sigma}^{-1}$ and post-multiply by $T\hat{B}'^{-1}$ giving

$$T\hat{B}'^{-1} - \hat{\Sigma}^{-1}\hat{\tilde{A}}\tilde{W}'W\hat{A}'\hat{B}'^{-1} + \hat{\Sigma}^{-1}\hat{\tilde{A}}\tilde{W}'W_{-1}\hat{A}'\hat{R}'\hat{B}^{-1} = 0. \tag{7.7.16}$$

Now the reduced form of (7.7.6) can be written as

$$Y = XP' + W_{-1}\bar{P}' + V = \bar{Y} + V, \tag{7.7.17}$$

with $P' = -C'B'^{-1}$, $\bar{P}' = A'R'B'^{-1}$ and $V = EB'^{-1}$. Hence (7.7.16) becomes

$$T\hat{B}'^{-1} - \hat{\Sigma}^{-1}\hat{\tilde{A}}\tilde{W}'(Y - X\hat{P}') + \hat{\Sigma}^{-1}\hat{\tilde{A}}\tilde{W}'W_{-1}\hat{\bar{P}}' = 0. \tag{7.7.18}$$

Combining (7.7.18) with (7.7.9) we obtain

$$-\hat{R}'\hat{\Sigma}^{-1}\hat{\tilde{A}}\tilde{W}'Y_{-1} + \hat{\Sigma}^{-1}\hat{\tilde{A}}\tilde{W}'X\hat{P}' + \hat{\Sigma}^{-1}\hat{\tilde{A}}\tilde{W}'W_{-1}\hat{\bar{P}}' \underset{R}{=} 0, \tag{7.7.19}$$

or, using (7.7.17),

$$-\hat{R}'\hat{\Sigma}^{-1}\hat{\tilde{A}}\tilde{W}'Y_{-1} + \hat{\Sigma}^{-1}\hat{\tilde{A}}\tilde{W}'\hat{\bar{Y}} \underset{R}{=} 0. \tag{7.7.20}$$

From (7.7.20) and (7.7.10) we find that

$$-\hat{\Sigma}^{-1}\hat{\tilde{A}}\tilde{W}'\bar{W} + \hat{R}'\hat{\Sigma}^{-1}\hat{\tilde{A}}\tilde{W}'W_{-1} \underset{R}{=} 0, \tag{7.7.21}$$

where $\bar{W} = [\hat{\bar{Y}} : X]$. Next, using (7.7.7), we substitute into (7.7.21) to get

$$-\hat{\Sigma}^{-1}\hat{A}W'\bar{W} + \hat{\Sigma}^{-1}\hat{R}\hat{A}W'_{-1}\,\bar{W} + \hat{R}'\hat{\Sigma}^{-1}\hat{A}W'W_{-1}$$
$$-\hat{R}'\hat{\Sigma}^{-1}\hat{R}\hat{A}W'_{-1}W_{-1} \underset{R}{=} 0. \tag{7.7.22}$$

Equation (7.7.22) is seen to be the counterpart of (6.11.14) which was derived for the non-autoregressive error case.

Writing the model (7.7.3) in unrestricted form, as in Question (6.11), we obtain

$$y = Z\delta + u, \tag{7.7.23}$$

where y, Z, δ, u and $\bar{Z}$ are defined in Question (6.11). We can write (7.7.5) in vector notation as

$$u = (R \otimes I) u_{-1} + e. \tag{7.7.24}$$

where $e = \overline{\text{vec}}\,(E)$. By transposing (7.7.22) and vectorising we can write the equation as

$$-[(\hat{\Sigma}^{-1} \otimes \bar{W}^{-1}) + (\hat{R}'\hat{\Sigma}^{-1} \otimes W'_{-1})]\, \hat{u} + [(\hat{\Sigma}^{-1}\hat{R} \otimes \bar{W}')$$
$$- (\hat{R}'\hat{\Sigma}^{-1}\hat{R} \otimes W'_{-1})]\, \hat{u}_{-1} \underset{R}{=} 0 \tag{7.7.25}$$

Substituting (7.7.23) into (7.7.25) and noting that, for instance, $(\hat{\Sigma}^{-1} \otimes \bar{W}') = (I \otimes \bar{W}')\,(\hat{\Sigma}^{-1} \otimes I)$, we can write (7.7.25) in unrestricted form as

$$[\bar{Z}'(\hat{\Sigma}^{-1} \otimes I) - Z'_{-1}(\hat{R}'\hat{\Sigma}^{-1} \otimes I)]\, (y - Z\hat{\delta}) - [\bar{Z}'(\hat{\Sigma}^{-1}\hat{R} \otimes I)$$
$$- Z'_{-1}(\hat{R}'\hat{\Sigma}^{-1}\hat{R} \otimes I)]\, (y_{-1} - Z_{-1}\hat{\delta}) = 0, \tag{7.7.26}$$

where $\bar{Z}$ and Z_{-1} are obtained by eliminating the columns of $-(I \otimes \bar{W})$ and $-(I \otimes W_{-1})$ which correspond to restricted elements of A. Solving (7.7.26) for $\hat{\delta}$ gives us

$$\hat{\delta} = [\hat{\bar{Z}}^{*\prime}(\hat{\Sigma}^{-1} \otimes I)\, \hat{Z}^*]^{-1}\, \hat{\bar{Z}}^{*\prime}(\hat{\Sigma}^{-1} \otimes I)\, \hat{y}^*, \tag{7.7.27}$$

where

$$\hat{Z}^* = Z - (\hat{R} \otimes I) Z_{-1},\ \hat{\bar{Z}}^* = \bar{Z} - (\hat{R} \otimes I) Z_{-1}\ \text{and}$$
$$\hat{y}^* = y - (\hat{R} \otimes I) y_{-1}.$$

The FIML estimators of δ, R and Σ may, therefore, be derived by iterating on (7.7.27), (7.7.14) and (7.7.13) until convergence. But note that $\hat{\delta}$ in (7.7.27) depends on $\hat{R}$, $\hat{\Sigma}$ and $\bar{Y}$ (through the definition of $\bar{Z}$ and $\bar{W}$) so that in order to compute (7.7.27) we will need preliminary estimates of R and Σ and the systematic part of the reduced form $\bar{Y}$ in (7.7.17).

Part (b) Our answer to this part will involve some sacrifice of rigour in the hope that this will make the derivations easier to follow. But, before we commence the formal derivations we will first indicate conditions under which the FIML estimators of δ and R (suitably standardised) do have a limiting (normal) distribution.

In addition to the conditions laid out in the question we will assume that:

(A) the model (7.7.1–2) is stable in the sense that (1) the eigenvalues of R all lie in the unit circle and (2), if we write (7.7.1) as

$$By_t + C^* y_{t-1} + C^{**} x_t^{**} = u_t$$

where x_t^{**} is a vector of non-random exogenous variables, then the equation $\det(\lambda I - B^{-1} C^*) = 0$ has all of its roots inside the unit circle; and
(B) the non-random exogenous variables x_{jt}^{**} $(j = 1, \ldots, m^{**})$ satisfy the following conditions

$$\lim_{T \to \infty} T^{-1} \sum_{t=r+1}^{T} x_t^{**} x_{t-r}^{**\prime}$$

exists for all $r = 0, \pm 1, \ldots$ and is positive definite when $r = 0$.

Remark The above condition (B) is implied by a more general set of conditions on the asymptotic behaviour of the exogenous variables which are known as 'Grenander's conditions' — see Grenander and Rosenblatt (1957, pp. 223–224), Hannan (1970, pp. 77–78) and, in the present context, Hatanaka (1974 and 1976).

The asymptotic distributions of the FIML estimators of δ and R can now be obtained as follows. First from (7.7.23) and (7.7.24) we obtain

$$y - (R \otimes I) y_{-1} = [Z - (R \otimes I) Z_{-1}] \delta + e. \tag{7.7.28}$$

Hence

$$\begin{aligned}
\hat{y}^* &= y - (\hat{R} \otimes I) y_{-1} \\
&= [Z - (\hat{R} \otimes I) Z_{-1}] \delta - [(\hat{R} - R) \otimes I] (y_{-1} - Z_{-1} \delta) + e \\
&= \hat{Z}^* \delta - (I \otimes U_{-1}) (\hat{r} - r) + e, \tag{7.7.29}
\end{aligned}$$

since $[(\hat{R} - R) \otimes I] u_{-1} = \overline{\text{vec}} [U_{-1} (\hat{R} - R)'] = (I \otimes U_{-1}) (\hat{r} - r)$, where $r = \overline{\text{vec}} (R')$ and $\hat{r} = \overline{\text{vec}} (\hat{R}')$. Substituting (7.7.29) into (7.7.27) and after some reorganisation we obtain

$$\begin{aligned}
&[\hat{\bar{Z}}^{*\prime}(\hat{\Sigma}^{-1} \otimes I) \hat{Z}^*] (\hat{\delta} - \delta) + \hat{\bar{Z}}^{*\prime}(\hat{\Sigma}^{-1} \otimes I) (I \otimes U_{-1}) (\hat{r} - r) \\
&= \hat{\bar{Z}}^{*\prime}(\hat{\Sigma}^{-1} \otimes I) e. \tag{7.7.30}
\end{aligned}$$

From (7.7.14)

$$\begin{aligned}
\hat{R}' - R' &= (\hat{A} W_{-1}' W_{-1} \hat{A})^{-1} \hat{A} W_{-1}' (W \hat{A}' - W_{-1} \hat{A}' R') \\
&= (\hat{U}_{-1}' \hat{U}_{-1})^{-1} \hat{U}_{-1}' [W(\hat{A} - A)' - W_{-1} (\hat{A} - A)' + E]. \tag{7.7.31}
\end{aligned}$$

Since $\overline{\text{vec}} [W(\hat{A} - A)'] = (I \otimes W) \overline{\text{vec}} (\hat{A} - A)' = -Z(\hat{\delta} - \delta)$ and $\overline{\text{vec}} [W_{-1} (\hat{A} - A) R'] = (R \otimes W_{-1}) \text{vec} (\hat{A} - A)' = -(R \otimes I) Z_{-1} (\hat{\delta} - \delta)$, we can vectorise (7.7.31) to obtain

$$\hat{r} - r = (I \otimes \hat{U}'_{-1} \hat{U}_{-1})^{-1} (I \otimes \hat{U}'_{-1}) \{-[Z - (R \otimes I) Z_{-1}] (\hat{\delta} - \delta) + e\}$$

$$= (\hat{\Sigma}^{-1} \otimes \hat{U}'_{-1} \hat{U}_{-1})^{-1} (\Sigma^{-1} \otimes \hat{U}'_{-1}) [-Z^*(\hat{\delta} - \delta) + e] = 0,$$

$$(7.7.32)$$

where $Z^* = Z - (R \otimes I) Z_{-1}$. Hence, we can rewrite (7.7.32) as

$$(\hat{\Sigma}^{-1} \otimes \hat{U}'_{-1}) Z^*(\hat{\delta} - \delta) + (\hat{\Sigma}^{-1} \otimes \hat{U}'_{-1} \hat{U}_{-1}) (\hat{r} - r) = (\hat{\Sigma}^{-1} \otimes \hat{U}'_{-1}) e.$$

$$(7.7.33)$$

We can combine (7.7.30) and (7.7.33) in one equation as

$$\left[\begin{array}{c|c} \hat{\bar{Z}}^{*\prime}(\hat{\Sigma}^{-1} \otimes I) Z^* & \hat{\bar{Z}}^{*\prime}(\hat{\Sigma}^{-1} \otimes I) (I \otimes U_{-1}) \\ \hline (\hat{\Sigma}^{-1} \otimes \hat{U}'_{-1}) Z^* & (\hat{\Sigma}^{-1} \otimes \hat{U}'_{-1} \hat{U}_{-1}) \end{array} \right] \left[\begin{array}{c} \hat{\delta} - \delta \\ \hline \hat{r} - r \end{array} \right] = \left[\begin{array}{c} \hat{\bar{Z}}^{*\prime}(\hat{\Sigma}^{-1} \otimes I) e \\ (\hat{\Sigma}^{-1} \otimes \hat{U}'_{-1}) e \end{array} \right].$$

$$(7.7.34)$$

It follows that $[\sqrt{T}(\hat{\delta} - \delta)', \sqrt{T}(\hat{r} - r)']$ has the same limiting distribution as

$$\{\text{plim } T^{-1} [\bar{Z}^* \vdots I \otimes U_{-1}]' (\Sigma^{-1} \otimes I) [\bar{Z}^* \vdots I \otimes U_{-1}]\}^{-1}$$

$$T^{-1/2} [\hat{\bar{Z}}^* \vdots I \otimes \hat{U}_{-1}]' (\hat{\Sigma}^{-1} \otimes I) e \qquad (7.7.35)$$

where $\bar{Z}^* = \bar{Z} - (R \otimes I) Z_{-1}$. Without entering into a rigorous analysis, we can see that the form of (7.7.35) suggests that this limiting distribution is normal with mean zero and covariance matrix

$$[\text{plim } T^{-1} (\bar{Z}^*, I \otimes U_{-1})' (\Sigma^{-1} \otimes I) (\bar{Z}^*, I \otimes U_{-1})]^{-1}. \qquad (7.7.36)$$

Remark If we concentrate the log likelihood function (7.7.8) with respect to the unrestricted elements of A and R (by substituting (7.7.13) into (7.7.8)) and call this concentrated log likelihood ln (L^*) then we can show that the matrix (7.7.36) is the same as

$$\text{plim}_{T \to \infty} \left[-\frac{1}{T} \frac{\partial^2 \ln (L^*)}{\partial \theta \partial \theta'} \right]^{-1} \qquad (7.7.37)$$

where $\theta' = (\delta', r')$ and the derivatives are evaluated at the true value of θ. (7.7.37) is the asymptotic covariance matrix of the full information maximum likelihood estimator of θ in its usual form. The reader is referred to Hatanaka (1976) for the derivation of (7.7.36) using this approach.

Part (c) We can interpret the FIML estimator of δ, (7.7.27), as the instrumental variable estimator

$$\hat{\delta} = (K'\hat{Z}^*)^{-1} K'\hat{y}^* \qquad (7.7.38)$$

where the instrument matrix is

$$K = (\hat{\Sigma}^{-1} \otimes I) \hat{Z}^*. \qquad (7.7.39)$$

However, in contrast to the usual IV estimators, here we must iterate (7.7.38) together with (7.7.13) and (7.7.14) in order to obtain full asymptotic efficiency. An alternative asymptotically efficient estimator which also requires iteration is obtained by replacing (7.7.38) with

$$\delta = (K'\hat{Z}^*)^{-1} K'\hat{y}^*. \qquad (7.7.40)$$

The reader is referred to Hendry (1971 and 1976) for further discussions of the estimation of models such as (7.7.1–2) and references to the recent literature.

Solution 7.8

Part (a) Let $L(\theta; x)$ be the log likelihood function of the parameter vector θ for the sample observations x and suppose $T^{-1} L(\theta; x)$ has continuous partial derivatives with respect to θ up to third order which are bounded and have finite probability limits. Then, given some consistent estimator θ^0 of θ, the estimator θ^L can be obtained as the first iteration of the Newton–Raphson algorithm:

$$\theta^L = \theta^0 - \left[\frac{\partial^2 L}{\partial\theta\partial\theta'}\right]_{\theta=\theta^0} \left[\frac{\partial L}{\partial\theta}\right]_{\theta=\theta^0} \qquad (7.8.2)$$

Rothenberg and Leenders (1964) have proved that θ^L has the same asymptotic distribution as the maximum likelihood estimator. We wish to show that the estimator (7.8.1) can be obtained from (7.8.2).

First, we consider the appropriate form of the likelihood function for the application of this result to the estimation of δ and r. The results of Question (7.7) imply that the FIML estimators of δ, r and Σ can be obtained by maximizing the function

$$L_1 = \text{const} + \tfrac{1}{2} T \ln |\Sigma^{-1}| - \tfrac{1}{2} \text{tr}(E'E\Sigma^{-1}). \qquad (7.8.3)$$

In other words, asymptotically, there is no loss of information in omitting the term $T \ln B$ from (7.7.8). From equation (7.7.28) we can write the model unrestrictedly as

$$y = (R \otimes I) y_{-1} + [Z - (R \otimes I)] \delta + e, \qquad (7.8.4)$$

and (7.8.3) can alternatively be written as

$$L_1 = \text{const} + \tfrac{1}{2} \ln |\Sigma^{-1} \otimes I| - \tfrac{1}{2} e'(\Sigma^{-1} \otimes I) e. \qquad (7.8.5)$$

In large samples the FIML estimator of Σ is distributed independently of the FIML estimators of δ and r. Accordingly we can concentrate L_1 with respect to Σ to obtain

$$L_2 = \text{const} - \tfrac{1}{2} \hat{e}'(\hat{\Sigma}^{-1} \otimes I) \hat{e}, \tag{7.8.6}$$

where $\hat{\Sigma}$ is given by equation (7.7.13) and $\hat{e}$ is derived from equation (7.7.28) with $\hat{Z}$, the predicted value of Z, replacing Z. Thus

$$\hat{e} = y - (R \otimes I) \, y_{-1} - [\hat{Z} - (R \otimes I) \, Z_{-1}] \, \delta. \tag{7.8.7}$$

Alternatively, since $u_{-1} = y_{-1} - Z_{-1} \delta$ and $(R \otimes I) \, u_{-1} = (I \otimes U_{-1}) \, r$, we can write $\hat{e}$ as

$$\hat{e} = y - \hat{Z}\delta - (I \otimes U_{-1}) \, r. \tag{7.8.8}$$

In view of these results we can see that the form of the log likelihood function appropriate for obtaining the maximum likelihood estimators of δ and r is (7.8.6). We shall, therefore, work with this function.

We can now evaluate the terms on the right-hand side of (7.8.2) using (7.8.6). From (7.8.6) and (7.8.7)

$$\frac{\partial L_2}{\partial \delta} = [\hat{Z} - (R \otimes I) \, Z_{-1}]' \, (\hat{\Sigma}^{-1} \otimes I) \, \hat{e}, \tag{7.8.9}$$

and from (7.8.6) and (7.8.8)

$$\frac{\partial L_2}{\partial r} = (I \otimes U_{-1})' \, (\hat{\Sigma}^{-1} \otimes I) \, \hat{e}. \tag{7.8.10}$$

Furthermore,

$$\frac{\partial^2 L_2}{\partial \delta \partial \delta'} = - [\hat{Z} - (R \otimes I) \, Z_{-1}]' \, (\hat{\Sigma}^{-1} \otimes I) \, [\hat{Z} - (R \otimes I) \, Z_{-1}], \tag{7.8.11}$$

$$\frac{\partial^2 L_2}{\partial \delta \partial r'} = - [\hat{Z} - (R \otimes I) \, Z_{-1}]' \, (\hat{\Sigma}^{-1} \otimes I) \, (I \otimes U_{-1}), \tag{7.8.12}$$

and

$$\frac{\partial^2 L_2}{\partial r \partial r'} = - (I \otimes U_{-1})' \, (\hat{\Sigma}^{-1} \otimes I) \, (I \otimes U_{-1}). \tag{7.8.13}$$

Evaluating $\hat{\Sigma}$, and (7.8.9) − (7.8.13) at d_0, r_0 (or equivalently at A_0, R_0) and substituting in (7.8.2) we obtain

$$\begin{bmatrix} \hat{\delta} \\ \hat{r} \end{bmatrix} = \begin{bmatrix} d_0 \\ r_0 \end{bmatrix} + [(\hat{\bar{Z}}^* \vdots I \otimes \hat{U}_{-1})' \, (\hat{\Sigma}^{-1} \otimes I) \, (\hat{\bar{Z}}^* \vdots I \otimes \hat{U}_{-1})]^{-1}$$

$$[(\bar{Z}^* \vdots I \otimes U_{-1})' \, (\hat{\Sigma}^{-1} \otimes I) \, \hat{e}] \tag{7.8.14}$$

where $\hat{\bar{Z}}^* = \hat{Z} - (R_0 \otimes I) \, Z_{-1}$ and, from (7.8.7),

$$\hat{e} = y - (R_0 \otimes I) \, y_{-1} - \hat{\bar{Z}}^* d_0$$
$$= \hat{y}^* - \hat{\bar{Z}}^* d_0.$$
(7.8.15)

Substituting (7.8.15) into (7.8.14) we get

$$\begin{bmatrix} \hat{\delta} \\ \hat{r} \end{bmatrix} = \begin{bmatrix} d_0 \\ r_0 \end{bmatrix} + V^{-1} (\hat{\bar{Z}}^* \vdots I \otimes \hat{U}_{-1})' (\hat{\Sigma}^{-1} \otimes I) \, \hat{y}^* - V^{-1} (\hat{\bar{Z}}^* \vdots I \otimes \hat{U}_{-1})'$$

$$\times \, (\hat{\Sigma}^{-1} \otimes I) \, \hat{\bar{Z}}^* d_0$$
(7.8.16)

where

$$V = (\hat{\bar{Z}}^* \vdots I \otimes \hat{U}_{-1})' (\hat{\Sigma}^{-1} \otimes I) (\hat{\bar{Z}}^* \vdots I \otimes \hat{U}_{-1}).$$

But the last term in (7.7.16) is the first column block of V multiplied by d_0, hence

$$\begin{bmatrix} \hat{\delta} \\ r \end{bmatrix} = \begin{bmatrix} d_0 \\ r_0 \end{bmatrix} + V^{-1} (\hat{\bar{Z}}^* \vdots I \otimes \hat{U}_{-1})' (\hat{\Sigma}^{-1} \otimes I) \, \hat{y}^* - \begin{bmatrix} d_0 \\ 0 \end{bmatrix}$$

$$= \begin{bmatrix} 0 \\ r_0 \end{bmatrix} + V^{-1} (\hat{\bar{Z}}^* \vdots I \otimes \hat{U}_{-1})' (\hat{\Sigma}^{-1} \otimes I) \, \hat{y}^*$$
(7.8.17)

which is identical to (7.8.1) as required.

Remark The reader is referred to Hatanaka (1976) for alternative two step estimators with the same asymptotic properties as (7.8.1). The reader may also profitably refer to Dhrymes (1974) who first demonstrated that this type of two step estimator can be obtained from the Newton–Raphson algorithm after one iteration.

Part (b) The asymptotic efficiency of this estimator follows from the fact that the limiting distribution of $\sqrt{T}(\theta^L - \theta)$ is normal with mean zero and covariance matrix

$$- \left[\text{plim} \, \frac{1}{T} \frac{\partial^2 L}{\partial \theta \partial \theta'} \right]^{-1}$$
(7.8.18)

Substituting (7.8.11) – (7.8.13) into (7.8.17), dividing by T and taking probability limits we find that (7.8.17) becomes (7.7.36), the covariance matrix of the limiting distribution of the (suitably standardised) FIML estimators of δ and r. Consequently, Hatanaka's non-iterative estimator is asymptotically efficient in the sense that it has the same asymptotic covariance matrix as the maximum likelihood estimator.

Solution 7.9

Part (a) First we rewrite equations (7.9.1) and (7.9.2) in matrix form as

$$y_1 = Z_1\delta_1 + u_1,$$ (7.9.3)

and

$$u_1 = \rho_{11}u_{1,-1} + e_1,$$ (7.9.4)

where $Z_1 = (Y_1 : X_1)$, $\delta_1' = (\beta_1', \gamma_1')$ and $u_{1,-1}$ is u_1 lagged one period. Next we combine (7.9.3) and (7.9.4) to eliminate the u's, obtaining

$$y_1 = \rho_{11}y_{1,-1} + (Z_1 - \rho_{11}Z_{1,-1})\,\delta_1 + e_1,$$ (7.9.5)

where $y_{1,-1}$ and $Z_{1,-1}$ are y_1 and Z_1 lagged one period, respectively.

Sargan's estimator Equation (7.9.5) can be rewritten as

$$W\phi = e_1$$ (7.9.6)

where $W = (y_1, y_{1,-1}, Z_1, Z_{1,-1})$ and $\phi' = (1, -\rho_{11}, -\delta_1', \rho_{11}\delta_1')$. Thus $\phi = \phi(\theta)$ where $\theta' = (\delta_1', \rho_{11})$. Let H denote a set of instrumental variables satisfying plim $T^{-1}H'e = 0$ and plim $T^{-1}H'H$ finite and non-singular. Then Sargan's estimator is obtained by minimising

$$L = \phi'W'P_HW\phi$$ (7.9.7)

with respect to θ where $P_H = H(H'H)^{-1}H'$. A necessary condition for a minimum of (7.9.7) is

$$\frac{\partial L}{\partial \theta} = 2\frac{\partial \hat{\phi}'}{\partial \theta}W'P_HW\hat{\phi} = 0,$$ (7.9.8)

or

$$\begin{bmatrix} 0 & 0 & -I & \hat{\rho}_{11}I \\ \hline 0 & -1 & 0 & \hat{\delta}_1' \end{bmatrix} W'P_HW\hat{\phi} = 0.$$ (7.9.9)

Expanding (7.9.9) we obtain the equations

$$(Z_1 - \hat{\rho}_{11}Z_{1,-1})'\,P_H\,[y_1 - \hat{\rho}_{11}y_{1,-1} - (Z_1 - \rho_{11}Z_{1,-1})\hat{\delta}_1] = 0,$$ (7.9.10)

and

$$(y_{1,-1} - Z_{1,-1}\hat{\delta}_1)'P_H\,[y_1 - \hat{\rho}_{11}y_{1,-1} - (Z_1 - \hat{\rho}_{11}Z_{1,-1})\,\hat{\delta}_1] = 0.$$ (7.9.11)

Equations (7.9.10) and (7.9.11) can also be written as

$$\hat{\delta}_1 = [(Z_1 - \hat{\rho}_{11}Z_{1,-1})'\,P_H(Z_1 - \hat{\rho}_{11}Z_{1,-1})]^{-1}$$
$$\times (Z_1 - \hat{\rho}_{11}Z_{1,-1})'\,P_H(y_1 - \hat{\rho}_{11}y_{1,-1}),$$ (7.9.12)

and

$$\hat{\rho}_{11} = (\hat{u}_{1,-1}'P_H\hat{u}_{1,-1})^{-1}\hat{u}_{1,-1}'P_H\hat{u}_1,$$ (7.9.13)

where

$$\hat{u}_1 = y_1 - Z_1\hat{\delta}_1. \tag{7.9.14}$$

To obtain Sargan's estimator we choose an initial consistent estimator of δ_1 and then iterate back and forth between (7.9.12) and (7.9.13) until convergence. The limiting distribution of $\sqrt{T}(\hat{\theta} - \theta)$ is normal with mean zero and covariance matrix

$$V = \sigma^2 \left[\text{plim } T^{-1} \frac{\partial \phi'}{\partial \theta} W' P_H W \frac{\partial \phi}{\partial \theta} \right]^{-1} \tag{7.9.15}$$

$$= \sigma^2 \left[\text{plim } T^{-1} (Z_1 - \hat{\rho}_{11} Z_{1,-1} \vdots \hat{u}_{1,-1})' P_H (Z_1 - \hat{\rho}_{11} Z_{1,-1} \vdots \hat{u}_{1,-1}) \right]^{-1} \tag{7.9.16}$$

The instrumental variables proposed by Sargan consist of all of the lagged endogenous variables, the predetermined variables and the lagged predetermined variables in the complete system of equations, except those variables which are duplicated due to lagging. In the notation of equation (7.7) we have $H = [Y_{-1} \vdots W_{-1}]$. However, if only one equation of the system is specified, namely (7.9.1), and the remaining variables in the system are unknown, a consistent, but asymptotically less efficient estimator, can be obtained by using as instrumental variables $H_1 = [y_{1,-1} \vdots Y_{1,-1} \vdots X_1 \vdots X_{1,-1}]$; again, we exclude those variables which are duplicated due to lagging.

Fair's Estimator This is obtained by first rewriting (7.9.5) as

$$y_1 = \rho_{11} y_{1,-1} + (\hat{Z}_1 - \rho_{11} Z_{1,-1}) \delta_1 + (e_1 + \hat{V}_1 \beta_1) \tag{7.9.17}$$

where

$$\hat{Z}_1 = (\hat{Y}_1 \vdots X_1), \quad Y_1 = \hat{Y}_1 + \hat{V}_1 \quad \text{and} \quad \hat{Y}_1 = P_H \hat{Y}_1;$$

we now estimate (7.9.17) by non-linear least squares. We wish therefore to minimise $\epsilon'\epsilon$ with respect to $\theta' = (\delta_1', \rho_{11})$, where $\epsilon = e_1 + \hat{V}_1 \beta_1$. A necessary condition for a minimum is that

$$\frac{\partial \epsilon' \epsilon}{\partial \theta} = 2 \frac{\partial \epsilon'}{\partial \theta} \cdot \epsilon = 0,$$

or

$$\begin{bmatrix} 0 & -I & \hat{\rho}_{11}I \\ -1 & 0 & \hat{\delta}_1' \end{bmatrix} (y_{1,-1} \vdots \hat{Z}_1 \vdots Z_{1,-1})' [y_1 - \hat{\rho}_{11} y_{1,-1}$$

$$- (\hat{Z}_1 - \hat{\rho}_{11} Z_{1,-1}) \hat{\delta}_1] = 0.$$

This yields the two equations

$$\hat{\delta}_1 = [(\hat{Z}_1 - \hat{\rho}_{11} Z_{1,-1})' (\hat{Z}_1 - \hat{\rho}_{11} Z_{1,-1})]^{-1}$$
$$\times (\hat{Z}_1 - \hat{\rho}_{11} Z_{1,-1})' (y_1 - \hat{\rho}_{11} y_{1,-1}) \tag{7.9.18}$$

and

$$\hat{\rho}_{11} = (\hat{u}'_{1,-1}\hat{u}_{1,-1})^{-1}\hat{u}'_{1,-1}\hat{u}_1, \tag{7.9.19}$$

where $\hat{u}_1 = y_1 - \hat{Z}_1\hat{\delta}_1$. Given an initial consistent estimate of δ_1 we obtain Fair's estimator by iterating back and forth between (7.9.18) and (7.9.19) until convergence.

If we choose the instrumental variables to be H or H_1 then the Fair estimators (7.8.18–19) will be identical to the corresponding Sargan estimators since $P_H y_{1,-1} = y_{1,-1}$, $P_H Z_1 = \hat{Z}_1$, $P_H Z_{1,-1} = Z_{1,-1}$, $P_H \hat{u}_{1,-1} = \hat{u}_{1,-1}$ and

$$P_H \hat{u}_1 = P_H [\hat{u}_1 - (\hat{Z}_1 - Z_1)\hat{\delta}_1] = P_H \hat{u}_1.$$

Replacing P_H by P_{H_1} yields similar results.

Hatanaka's estimator This is obtained by specialising Hatanaka's systems estimator [see equation (7.8.1)] to the case of a single structural equation. For the first structural equation, Hatanaka's estimator simply solves without iteration

$$\begin{bmatrix} \hat{\delta}_1 \\ \hat{\hat{r}}_{11} \end{bmatrix} = [(\hat{\bar{Z}}^*_1 \vdots \hat{u}_{1,-1})'(\bar{Z}^*_1 \vdots \hat{u}_{1,-1})]^{-1}(\bar{Z}^*_1 \vdots \hat{u}_{1,-1})'\hat{y}^*_1, \tag{7.9.20}$$

and

$$\hat{r}_{11} = \hat{\hat{r}}_{11} + \hat{r}^0_{11}, \tag{7.9.21}$$

where

$$\bar{Z}^*_1 = \hat{Z}_1 - r^0_{11}Z_{1,-1}, \hat{y}^*_1 = y_1 - r^0_{11}y_{1,-1}, \hat{u}_{1,-1} = y_{1,-1} - Z_{1,-1}d^0_1,$$

$\hat{Z}_1$ is Z_1 with Y_1 replaced by its reduced form predictions and d^0_1 and r^0_{11} are inital consistent estimators of δ_1 and ρ_{11}.

In comparing Hatanaka's estimator with the Sargan–Fair estimator, we assume the instrument set used in each case is the same, and is either H or H_1.

In the solution to Question (7.8) it was shown that, for a complete system of equations, Hatanaka's estimator involves maximising eqution (7.8.6). But this is equivalent to minimising $\hat{e}'(\hat{\Sigma}^{-1} \otimes I)\hat{e}$. Specialising this to the case of a single structural equation, (7.9.20) aиd (7.9.21) are the first iterations of a Newton–Raphson solution to the minimisation with respect to δ_1 and ρ_{11} of

$$\hat{e}'_1\hat{e}_1 = [y_1 - \rho_{11}y_{1,-1} - (\hat{Z}_1 - \rho_{11}Z_{1,-1})\delta_1]'$$
$$\times [y_1 - \rho_{11}y_{1,-1} - (\hat{Z}_1 - \rho_{11}Z_{1,-1})\delta_1]. \tag{7.9.22}$$

But this is the same minimand as in the Fair estimator. All three estimator's are therefore asymptotically equivalent. Hatanaka's estimator has the advantage of being non-iterative; the Sargan–Fair estimators, it will be recalled, require iteration until convergence.

It can be shown that Hatanaka's estimator is asymptotically equivalent to a LIML estimator of a single structural equation with autocorrelated errors (see Hatanaka, 1976, Hendry, 1976 and Wickens, 1977). Thus Hatanaka's estimator, and hence the Sargan and Fair estimators, are asymptotically efficient among estimators using the same (incomplete) information. The instrumental variable matrix required to attain this efficiency is $H = (Y_{-1} \vdots W_{-1})$. The Hatanaka–Sargan–Fair estimators based on H_1 are asymptotically less efficient. Wickens (1977) has generalised the Hatanaka estimator to the case of a sub-system of dynamic structural equations with autocorrelated errors.

Remark Amemiya (1966) and Fair (1972) have noted that Sargan's estimator based on $H = [Y_{-1} \vdots W_{-1}]$ may present numerical problems in the inversion of the $H'H$ matrix due to the possibly large number of instruments involved. Clearly, when H is used, this problem applies to all three of the estimators above. However, for Fair's estimator we require only initial consistent estimators of Y_1 and ρ_{11} and for Hatanaka's estimator we require initial consistent estimators of Y_1, ρ_{11} and δ_1. These can be obtained even if the $H'H$ matrix cannot be inverted. If $H'H$ is singular (or near singular) we can use the appropriate principal components of H to predict Y_1 (see Question 4.2) and we can use, say, Liviatan's instrumental variable estimator, which has instruments X_1 and $X_{1,-1}$, to obtain initial consistent estimators of δ_1 and ρ_{11}. Alternatively, we can use as instruments all of the current and lagged values of the exogenous variables in the system, namely X and X_{-1}.

Amemiya's solution to the problem is to compute Sargan's estimator using only X and X_{-1} but not Y_{-1} as instruments. The resulting estimator is consistent but asymptotically less efficient than if H is used. Fair proposes two solutions. The first is explained in the context of a two-equation model with a diagonal autoregressive coefficient matrix. In this case, the reduced form equation of the Y_1 variable is obtained and is shown to be a function of H_1 and autoregressive transforms of the remaining predetermined variables. Given an initial consistent estimator of the autoregressive coefficient of the second equation, H_1 can be augmented by estimated autoregressive transforms of these remaining predetermined variables. The resulting matrix of instruments will be fewer in number than H will be. Fair's second alternative estimator is related to his first. It predicts Y_1 using $[H_1 \vdots X_2 - r_0 X_{2,-1}]$ as the instrument matrix where $X = [X_1 \vdots X_2]$ and r_0 is any number. In general, the second of these estimators is less efficient asymptotically than the first which will be asymptotically efficient in the class of LIML estimators.

Part (b) Hatanaka's single equation estimator may be calculated using only a regression program as follows.
1. Using the instrument matrix H_1^*, which may consist of the current and lagged exogenous variables in the system plus any other valid instruments

but not current or lagged endogenous variables, we regress both y_2 and the lagged endogenous variables in X_1 on the variables in H^*. The prediction of y_2 and the lagged endogenous variables in X_1 obtained from these regressions are substituted into Z_1 to form $\hat{Z}_1$.

2. Next we regress y_1 on $\hat{Z}_1$. The resulting regression coefficients are d_1^0, which provides the initial consistent estimator of δ_1.

3. An initial consistent estimator r_{11}^0 of ρ_{11} is chosen to be the regression coefficients from the regression of $\hat{u} = y_1 - Z_1 d_1^0$ on $\hat{u}_{1,-1}$.

4. We form $\hat{Z}_1$ by replacing y_2 in Z_1 with the predictions obtained from the regression of y_2 on $H = [Y_{-1} \vdots W_{-1}]$ or $H_1 = [y_{1,-1} \vdots Y_{1,-1} \vdots X_1 \vdots X_{1,-1}]$.

5. Finally, we form $\hat{\bar{Z}}_1^*$ and $\hat{y}^*$ and regress $\hat{y}^*$ on $\bar{Z}_1^*$ and $\hat{u}_{1,-1}$. The resulting regression coefficients satisfy equation (7.9.20). Substituting $\hat{r}_{11}$ into (7.9.21) we obtain $\hat{r}_{11}$, our final estimator of ρ_{11}.

It should be noted that in practice it would be preferable to replace steps 1 and 2 above by a single instrumental variable estimation of (7.9.3), using H^* as instruments. The resulting estimator of δ would be identical to d_1^0 obtained above.

An estimate of the covariance matrix of the limiting distribution of the Hatanaka estimator is derived from the covariance matrix of the regression coefficients obtained in step 5 above.

Solution 7.10

Part (a) (i) Equations (7.10.1) and (7.10.2) may be written in matrix form as

$$y = X\beta + u, \tag{7.10.3}$$

and

$$\beta = Q\alpha \tag{7.10.4}$$

where

$$y = \begin{bmatrix} y_{n+1} \\ \vdots \\ y_T \end{bmatrix}, X = \begin{bmatrix} x_{n+1} & \cdots & x_1 \\ \cdot & \cdots & \cdot \\ x_T & \cdots & x_{T-n} \end{bmatrix}, u = \begin{bmatrix} u_{n+1} \\ \vdots \\ u_T \end{bmatrix}, \beta = \begin{bmatrix} \beta_0 \\ \vdots \\ \beta_n \end{bmatrix}$$

$$Q = \begin{bmatrix} 1 & 0 & \cdots & 0 \\ 1 & 1 & \cdots & 1 \\ 1 & 2 & \cdots & 2^p \\ \cdot & \cdot & \cdots & \cdot \\ 1 & n & \cdots & n^p \end{bmatrix}, \alpha = \begin{bmatrix} \alpha_0 \\ \vdots \\ \alpha_p \end{bmatrix}.$$

Combining (7.10.3) and (7.10.4) we obtain

$$y = W\alpha + u, \tag{7.10.5}$$

where $W = XQ$. We can now estimate α by OLS on (7.10.5). Substituting this estimator $\hat{\alpha}$ of α into (7.10.4) provides our estimator $\hat{\beta}$ of β. Thus,

$$\hat{\beta} = Q\hat{\alpha}. \tag{7.10.6}$$

Since (7.10.5) is the classical linear model, $E(\hat{\alpha}) = \alpha$ and the covariance matrix of $\hat{\alpha}$ is $\sigma^2 (W'W)^{-1}$. Hence, $E(\hat{\beta}) = Q\alpha$ and the covariance matrix of $\hat{\beta}$ is

$$Q_1 = \sigma^2 Q (W'W)^{-1} Q' = \sigma^2 Q(Q'X'XQ)^{-1} Q'. \tag{7.10.7}$$

(ii) Equations (7.10.2) and (7.10.4) imply that there are $n - p$ linear (inhomogeneous) restrictions imposed on the vector β. These may also be written as the linear homogenous restrictions

$$R\beta = 0 \tag{7.10.8}$$

as follows. We can write (7.10.2) as the pth order polynomial

$$\beta_s = \sum_{j=0}^{P} \alpha_j s^j \qquad (s = 0, \ldots, n) \tag{7.10.9}$$

Hence, the first difference of β_s is

$$\Delta\beta_s = \beta_s - \beta_{s-1} = \sum_{j=0}^{P} \alpha_j [s^j - (s-1)^j]$$

$$= \sum_{j=0}^{P-1} \theta_j s^j \tag{7.10.10}$$

which is a $(p - 1)$th order polynomial. We can continue this process of differencing until we find that the $(p + 1)$th difference of β_s is

$$\Delta^{p+1} \beta_s = 0 \qquad (s = p + 1, \ldots, n) \tag{7.10.11}$$

We may, therefore, construct the matrix R above with rows consisting of the coefficients of L in the $(p + 1)$th difference polynomial $(I - L)^{p+1}$; the remaining $n - p - 1$ elements in the row will be zero. There will be $n - p$ rows in the matrix. Thus R is an $(n - p) \times (n + 1)$ matrix whose $(i, i + j)$th element is the coefficient of L^j in the expansion of $(I - L)^{p+1}$ for $i = 1, \ldots, n - p$ and $j = 0, \ldots, p + 1$; the remaining elements are zero (see Shiller, 1975).

We can now estimate (7.10.3) by restricted least squares (see Question 2.5). Our estimator of β is then

$$\hat{\beta} = (X'X)^{-1} X'y - (X'X)^{-1} R' [R(X'X)^{-1}R']^{-1} R(X'X)^{-1} X'y. \tag{7.10.12}$$

$E(\hat{\beta}) = \beta$ and the covariance matrix of $\hat{\beta}$ is

$$V_2 = \sigma^2 \{(X'X)^{-1} - (X'X)^{-1} R' [R(X'X)^{-1} R']^{-1} R(X'X)^{-1}\}.$$

$$(7.10.13)$$

Part (b) The importance of performing this test arises from the fact that if H_1 is correct, then the estimates of β_s on H_0 will be biased (if H_1 is true, then (7.10.2) imposes invalid restrictions on the distributed lag coefficients β_s).

A test based on unrestricted estimates of β_s is performed as follows. If the approximating polynomial (7.10.2) is valid then the linear restrictions (7.10.8) are correct. Thus, a test of H_0 is equivalent to a test of (7.10.8). In Solution 2.5 it was shown how a test of linear restrictions of the coefficients of the classical linear model can be made. The test statistic is

$$F = \frac{b'R'[R(X'X)^{-1}R']^{-1}Rb}{s^2} \cdot \frac{T-n-1}{n-p}, \qquad (7.10.14)$$

where b is the unrestricted OLS estimator of β from (7.10.3), s^2 is the estimate of the error variance and R is defined in (7.10.8). F is distributed as an $F_{n-p, T-n-1}$ variate when H_0 is true.

An alternative test using estimates of α_s on H_1 is the following. On H_1 the vector α, defined in equation (7.10.4), becomes $\alpha^* = (\alpha_0, \ldots, \alpha_n)'$ and Q becomes an $(n+1) \times (n+1)$ non-singular matrix Q^*, say. Thus, $R\beta = RQ^*\alpha^* = H\alpha^*$, say. Now, on H_0, $R\beta = 0$ so that $H\alpha^* = 0$. To test H_0 against H_1, therefore, we can perform a test of the linear restrictions $H\alpha^* = 0$ using the equation

$$y = W^*\alpha^* + u \qquad (7.10.15)$$

where $W^* = XQ^*$. The test statistic is

$$F^* = \frac{a^{*'}H'[H(W^{*'}W^*)^{-1}H']^{-1}Ha^*}{s^2} \cdot \frac{T-n-1}{n-p} \qquad (7.10.16)$$

where a^* is the OLS estimator of α^* from (7.10.15). As $H = RQ^*$ and Q^* is non-singular, $R = HQ^{*-1}$. Moreover, as b is the unrestricted OLS estimator of β and Q^* is non-singular it follows that $b = Q^*a^*$ and $a^* = Q^{*-1}b$. Thus,

$$F^* = \frac{b'Q^{*'-1}H'[H(Q^{*'}X'XQ^*)^{-1}H']^{-1}HQ^{*-1}b}{s^2} \cdot \frac{T-n-1}{n-p}$$

$$= \frac{b'R'[R(X'X)^{-1}R']^{-1}Rb}{s^2} \cdot \frac{T-n-1}{n-p}$$

which is identical to F in equation (7.10.14). F^* was proposed by Godfrey and Poskitt (1975).

The third and, in practice, probably the simplest way of testing H_0 against H_1 is obtained by first noting that on H_1 (7.10.15) can be written as

$$y = W\alpha + \tilde{W}\tilde{\alpha} + u, \qquad (7.10.17)$$

where

$$\alpha^{*\prime} = (\alpha', \tilde{\alpha}') = (\alpha_0, \ldots, \alpha_p : \alpha_{p+1}, \ldots, \alpha_n),$$

$$Q^* = (Q, \tilde{Q}) = \begin{bmatrix} 1 & 0 & \cdots & 0 & 0 & \cdots & 0 \\ 1 & 1 & \cdots & 1 & 1 & \cdots & 1 \\ \cdot & & \cdots & \cdot & \cdot & \cdots & \cdot \\ 1 & n & n & n^p & n^{p+1} & & n^n \end{bmatrix},$$

$$W = XQ \quad \text{and} \quad \tilde{W} = X\tilde{Q}.$$

Thus, on H_0, $\tilde{\alpha} = 0$. We can now test H_0 by a conventional test of significance from zero of the subset of regression coefficients $\tilde{\alpha}$ (see Question 2.3 for further details).

Solution 7.11

Part (a) A rational distributed lag model takes the form

$$y_t = \frac{A(L)}{B(L)} x_t + u_t \qquad (7.11.3)$$

where $A(L) = a_1 + a_1 L + \ldots + a_M L^M$, $B(L) = 1 + b_1 L + \ldots b_N L^N$ and $L^r z_t = z_{t-r}$ (see Jorgensen, 1965). We are required, therefore, to show that

$$\beta(L) = \frac{A(L)}{B(L)}, \qquad (7.11.4)$$

where $\beta(L) = \beta_0 + \beta_1 L + \ldots + \beta_n L^n$, as given in (7.11.2).

In Question (7.10) it was argued that the pth order approximating polynomial (7.11.2) imposes $n - p$ linear constraints which can be written as

$$(1 - L)^{p+1} \beta_s = 0 \qquad (s = p + 1, \ldots, n) \qquad (7.11.5)$$

Applying this result to (7.11.2) we have

$$(1 - L)^2 \beta_s = 0 \qquad (s = 2, 3, \ldots, n) \qquad (7.11.6)$$

Consider, therefore,

$$(1-L)^2 \beta(L) = \beta_0 + \beta_1 L + \beta_2 L^2 + \ldots + \beta_n L^n \qquad (7.11.7)$$
$$- 2\beta_0 L - 2\beta_1 L^2 - 2\beta_2 L^3 - \ldots - 2\beta_n L^{n+1}$$
$$+ \beta_0 L^2 + \beta_1 L^3 + \beta_2 L^4 + \ldots + \beta_n L^{n+2}.$$

Using (7.11.6) we find that

$$(1-L)^2 \beta(L) = \beta_0 + (\beta_1 - 2\beta_0) L + (\beta_{n-1} - 2\beta_n) L^{n+1} + \beta_n L^{n+2}.$$
$$(7.11.8)$$

Consequently we can write

$$\beta(L) = \frac{\beta_0 + (\beta_1 - 2\beta_0) L + (\beta_{n-1} - 2\beta_n) L^{n+1} + \beta_n L^{n+2}}{(1-L)^2} \qquad (7.11.9)$$

$$= \frac{A(L)}{B(L)},$$

as required. Thus, $A(L)$ is a restricted polynomial of order $n + 2$ and $B(L) = (1-L)^2$.

Part (b) As $n \to \infty$, (7.11.9) becomes

$$\beta(L) = \frac{\beta_0 + (\beta_1 - 2\beta_0) L}{(1-L)^2} \qquad (7.11.10)$$

Thus, $A(L)$ becomes an unrestricted polynomial of order 1. Generalising this result, if (7.11.2) is a pth order polynomial and $n = \infty$, we can show that $A(L)$ is an unrestricted polynomial of order p and $B(L)$ involves differencing $p + 1$ times.

It is often claimed that an advantage of using polynomial distributed lags is their flexibility. The results above suggest that this flexibility may be less than is thought. These results can be generalised to the case where the approximating polynomial (7.11.2) is of order greater than one.

Solution 7.12

Part (a) We define the new variables

$$y_1(t) = x_1(t) - x_1(t-1)$$
$$y_2(t) = x_2(t) - x_2(t-1)$$
$$y_3(t) = x_3(t) - x_3(t-1)$$
$$y_4(t) = [x_1(t) + x_1(t-1)]/2$$
$$y_5(t) = [x_2(t) + x_2(t-1)]/2$$
$$y_6(t) = [x_3(t) + x_3(t-1)]/2$$

and we notice that these variables are related according to the identities

$$y_1(t) = 2y_4(t) - 2x_1(t-1) \tag{7.12.4}$$

$$y_2(t) = 2y_5(t) - 2x_2(t-1) \tag{7.12.5}$$

$$y_3(t) = 2y_6(t) - 2x_3(t-1) \tag{7.12.6}$$

We now write the system (7.12.1–3) as

$$y_1(t) = \lambda_1 \alpha y_5(t) - \lambda_1 y_4(t) + \eta_1(t)$$

$$y_2(t) = \lambda_2 \beta y_6(t) - \lambda_2 y_5(t) + \eta_2(t)$$

$$y_3(t) = \lambda_3 \gamma y_4(t) + \lambda_3 \delta y_5(t) - \lambda_3 y_6(t) + \eta_3(t)$$

and combining these equations with the identities (7.12.4–6) we obtain the complete system

$$
\begin{bmatrix}
1 & 0 & 0 & -\lambda_1 & \lambda_1\alpha & 0 \\
0 & 1 & 0 & 0 & -\lambda_2 & \lambda_2\beta \\
0 & 0 & 1 & \lambda_3\gamma & \lambda_3\delta & -\lambda_3 \\
1 & 0 & 0 & -2 & 0 & 0 \\
0 & 1 & 0 & 0 & -2 & 0 \\
0 & 0 & 1 & 0 & 0 & -2
\end{bmatrix}
\begin{bmatrix}
y_1(t) \\
y_2(t) \\
y_3(t) \\
y_4(t) \\
y_5(t) \\
y_6(t)
\end{bmatrix}
$$

$$
=
\begin{bmatrix}
0 & 0 & 0 \\
0 & 0 & 0 \\
0 & 0 & 0 \\
-2 & 0 & 0 \\
0 & -2 & 0 \\
0 & 0 & -2
\end{bmatrix}
\begin{bmatrix}
x_1(t-1) \\
x_2(t-1) \\
x_3(t-1)
\end{bmatrix}
+
\begin{bmatrix}
\eta_1(t) \\
\eta_2(t) \\
\eta_3(t) \\
0 \\
0 \\
0
\end{bmatrix}
\tag{7.12.7}
$$

which is in the conventional simultaneous equations framework.

Part (b) We write the complete matrix of coefficients of the endogenous and predetermined variables as

$$P = \begin{bmatrix} 1 & 0 & 0 & -\lambda_1 & \lambda_1\alpha & 0 & 0 & 0 & 0 \\ 0 & 1 & 0 & 0 & -\lambda_2 & \lambda_2\beta & 0 & 0 & 0 \\ 0 & 0 & 1 & \lambda_3\gamma & \lambda_3\delta & -\lambda_3 & 0 & 0 & 0 \\ 1 & 0 & 0 & -2 & 0 & 0 & 2 & 0 & 0 \\ 0 & 1 & 0 & 0 & -2 & 0 & 0 & 2 & 0 \\ 0 & 0 & 1 & 0 & 0 & -2 & 0 & 0 & 2 \end{bmatrix}$$

$$= \begin{bmatrix} 1 & 0 & 0 & p_{14} & p_{15} & 0 & 0 & 0 & 0 \\ 0 & 1 & 0 & 0 & p_{25} & p_{26} & 0 & 0 & 0 \\ 0 & 0 & 1 & p_{34} & p_{35} & p_{36} & 0 & 0 & 0 \\ 1 & 0 & 0 & -2 & 0 & 0 & 2 & 0 & 0 \\ 0 & 1 & 0 & 0 & -2 & 0 & 0 & 2 & 0 \\ 0 & 0 & 1 & 0 & 0 & -2 & 0 & 0 & 2 \end{bmatrix}$$

say; and it follows from the equations

$$p_{14} = -\lambda_1 \quad p_{25} = -\lambda_2 \quad p_{34} = \lambda_3\gamma$$
$$p_{15} = \lambda_1\alpha \quad p_{26} = \lambda_2\beta \quad p_{35} = \lambda_3\delta$$
$$p_{36} = -\lambda_3$$

that the underlying parameters $\alpha, \beta, \gamma, \delta, \lambda_1, \lambda_2$ and λ_3 will be identifiable if (i) the coefficients $p_{14}, p_{15}, p_{25}, p_{26}, p_{34}, p_{35}$ and p_{36} are identifiable and (ii) $p_{14} \neq 0$, $p_{25} \neq 0$ and $p_{36} \neq 0$. Indeed, the underlying parameters are then defined by the equations

$$\lambda_1 = -p_{14}, \quad \alpha = -p_{15}/p_{14},$$
$$\lambda_2 = -p_{25}, \quad \beta = -p_{26}/p_{25},$$
$$\lambda_3 = -p_{36}, \quad \gamma = -p_{34}/p_{36} \quad \text{and} \quad \delta = -p_{35}/p_{36}.$$

To determine whether the coefficients are themselves identifiable we can apply the usual criteria (see Solutions 6.1 and 6.2 above). We take each equation in turn.

First equation The matrix of restrictions is

$$\Phi_1 = \begin{bmatrix} 0 & 0 & 0 & 0 & 0 & 0 \\ 1 & 0 & 0 & 0 & 0 & 0 \\ 0 & 1 & 0 & 0 & 0 & 0 \\ 0 & 0 & 0 & 0 & 0 & 0 \\ 0 & 0 & 0 & 0 & 0 & 0 \\ 0 & 0 & 1 & 0 & 0 & 0 \\ 0 & 0 & 0 & 1 & 0 & 0 \\ 0 & 0 & 0 & 0 & 1 & 0 \\ 0 & 0 & 0 & 0 & 0 & 1 \end{bmatrix}$$

and

$$P\Phi_1 = \begin{bmatrix} 0 & 0 & 0 & 0 & 0 & 0 \\ 1 & 0 & p_{26} & 0 & 0 & 0 \\ 0 & 1 & p_{36} & 0 & 0 & 0 \\ 0 & 0 & 0 & 2 & 0 & 0 \\ 1 & 0 & 0 & 0 & 2 & 0 \\ 0 & 1 & -2 & 0 & 0 & 2 \end{bmatrix}$$

which has rank = 5 (for instance, the first two and last three columns are linearly independent). There are 6 equations in the complete system (7.12.7) above and it follows that the coefficients in the first eqution are identifiable by the rank condition.

Remark Notice that the inclusion of identities in the system does not affect the usual way in which the rank condition for identifiability is applied. We need only treat the stochastic equations and identities together as a single system (see Malinvaud, 1970b, ch. 18 and, in particular, theorem 1 on p. 658).

Second equation In this case, we have

$$P\Phi_2 = \begin{bmatrix} 1 & 0 & p_{14} & 0 & 0 & 0 \\ 0 & 0 & 0 & 0 & 0 & 0 \\ 0 & 1 & p_{34} & 0 & 0 & 0 \\ 1 & 0 & -2 & 2 & 0 & 0 \\ 0 & 0 & 0 & 0 & 2 & 0 \\ 0 & 1 & 0 & 0 & 0 & 2 \end{bmatrix}$$

which has rank = 5 for all values of p_{14} and p_{34} (the first two and last three columns are linearly independent). It follows that the coefficients in the second equation are identifiable.

Third equation In this case, we have

$$
P\Phi_3 = \begin{bmatrix}
1 & 0 & 0 & 0 & 0 \\
0 & 1 & 0 & 0 & 0 \\
0 & 0 & 0 & 0 & 0 \\
1 & 0 & 2 & 0 & 0 \\
0 & 1 & 0 & 2 & 0 \\
0 & 0 & 0 & 0 & 2
\end{bmatrix}
$$

which has rank = 5. Hence, the coefficients in the third equation are identifiable.

Since the coefficients in every equation are identifiable it follows from our earlier argument that the parameters $\alpha, \beta, \gamma, \delta, \lambda_1, \lambda_2$ and λ_3 will be identifiable in all structures for which $p_{14} \neq 0, p_{25} \neq 0$ and $p_{16} \neq 0$. That is, in all structures for which $\lambda_1 \neq 0, \lambda_2 \neq 0$ and $\lambda_3 \neq 0$.

Remark When the condition $\lambda_i \neq 0$ for all i is not satisfied it is clear from the form of the model (7.12.1–3) that some (or all) of the equations now contain no information about the structural parameters α, β, γ and δ. Take, for instance, the case where $\lambda_1 = 0$. We then have

$$x_1(t) = x_1(t-1) + \eta_1(t) \tag{7.12.8}$$

and this equation, which is often referred to as a random walk (c.f. Bartlett 1955), can provide us with no information concerning the parameter α. The earlier specification (7.21.1) suggested that, when $\lambda_1 \neq 0$, then the change $x_1(t) - x_1(t-1)$ in $x_1(t)$ would be greater the greater the excess of $\alpha[x_2(t) + x_2(t-1)]/2$ over $[x_1(t) + x_1(t-1)]/2$. When $\lambda_1 = 0$ the change $x_1(t) - x_1(t-1)$ in $x_1(t)$ is purely random [according to the specification of the $\eta_i(t)$] and in no way depends on α.

Part (c) Consider the following system of stochastic differential equations:

$$dx_1(t)/dt = \lambda_1[\alpha x_2(t)] + \zeta_1(t) \tag{7.12.9}$$

$$dx_2(t)/dt = \lambda_2[\beta x_3(t) - x_2(t)] + \zeta_2(t) \tag{7.12.10}$$

$$dx_3(t)/dt = \lambda_3[\gamma x_1(t) + \delta x_2(t) - x_3(t)] + \zeta_3(t) \tag{7.12.11}$$

[we leave until Solution 7.13 a discussion of the proper interpretation of a stochastic model such as (7.12.9–11)]. If we now integrate each equation of the above system over a unit time interval such as $(s - 1, s)$, we find that on the left side of the equations we have terms such as

$$\int_{s-1}^{s} \frac{dx_i(t)}{dt} dt = x_i(s) - x_i(s - 1)$$

and on the right hand side of the equations we have terms such as

$$\int_{s-1}^{s} x_i(t) dt$$

which we can approximate (using the trapezoidal rule) by the average

$$[x_i(s) + x_i(s - 1)]/2.$$

In this way we obtain the model (7.12.1–3) as a *discrete approximation* to (7.12.9–11). The disturbance terms $\eta_i(t)$ in (7.12.1–3) are then related to the corresponding terms $\zeta_i(t)$ in (7.12.9–11) by the equations

$$\eta_i(t) = \int_{t-1}^{t} \zeta_i(r) dr.$$

The reader is referred (i) to Bergstrom (1966) and (1967, ch. 9) for a discussion of this type of approximation and some of its implications in econometric work and (ii) to Sargan (1976) for a wide ranging analysis of the mis-specification bias that results from the use of the approximate system (7.12.1–3) when the true underlying system is given by (7.12.9–11).

Solution 7.13

Part (a) The model (7.13.1) is known as a *stochastic differential equation* and the proper interpretation of such an equation has been the subject of much discussion in the literature on stochastic processes (see, for instance, Doob, 1953, Bartlett, 1955, Edwards and Moyal, 1955 and Yaglom, 1962; a thorough discussion has recently been given by Wong, 1971). Models of this type have also been a subject of discussion among econometricians in recent years and the reader is referred, in particular, to two books by Bergstrom (1967, ch. 9; and 1976) for some of the literature in this area.

In the formulation of (7.13.1) $y(t)$ and $\zeta(t)$ are random functions of time, which is taken to be a continuous variable; and one of the mathematical difficulties that arise in treating (7.13.1) as it stands is due to the fact that $\zeta(t)$ does not have a finite variance and is a highly erratic process which we often call pure noise. Roughly speaking, we can see from (7.13.3) that the variance of the mean value of $\zeta(t)$ over the interval (t_1, t_2) tends to infinity as $t_2 - t_1 \to 0$; and from (7.13.4) it appears that

$\zeta(t)$ is uncorrelated with $\zeta(s)$ no matter how close t and s are in time. It follows that realisations of the process $\zeta(t)$ will be erratic and display a high degree of variation. On the other hand, the integral or smoothed process

$$\int_{t_1}^{t} \zeta(t)\, dt \qquad\qquad (7.13.5)$$

has properties which appear more regular, as is clear from (7.13.2–4). For this reason, the proper interpretation of (7.13.1) is as a *stochastic integral equation* or, more precisely, as

$$y(t) - y(a) = \alpha \int_{a}^{t_2} y(s)\, ds + \int_{a}^{t} \zeta(s)\, ds \qquad\qquad (7.13.6)$$

which holds for any interval (a, t); and the last term on the right side of (7.13.6) satisfies (7.13.2–4). Since (7.13.5) has regular properties, it is clear from (7.13.6) that the same is true of the process $y(t)$. And it is the process $y(t)$ which attracts our main interest because it usually represents an economic variable which is observable at discrete points in time.

If, in (7.13.6), we let the interval (a, t) grow smaller we can in the limit as $t - a \to 0$ write (7.13.6) in terms of differentials as

$$dy(t) = \alpha y(t)\, dt + \zeta(t)\, dt \qquad\qquad (7.13.7)$$

and some authors (e.g. Doob, 1953 or, in the economic literature, Wymer, 1972) prefer to use the slightly different form

$$dy(t) = \alpha y(t)\, dt + du(t) \qquad\qquad (7.13.7)$$

where $u(t)$ is known as a homogeneous random process with stationary increments (see, for instance, Yaglom, 1962, p. 67). This means that $u(t)$ is a process of independent, stationary increments for which

$$E\{[u(t) - u(s)]\ [u(t) - u(s)]\} = \sigma^2 |t - s|. \qquad\qquad (7.13.8)$$

(For the definition of a stationary process, the reader is referred to Yaglom, 1962, Malinvaud, 1970b, pp. 418–420, or Dhrymes, 1970, p. 385.)

Remarks Since the model (7.13.1) is driven by a disturbance, $\zeta(t)$, whose realisations are normally very erratic, it is natural to ask whether the conditions (7.13.2–4) imposed on $\zeta(t)$ are unrealistic. Certainly, the conditions are strong and they have recently been criticised by Sims (1971 and 1973) as inappropriate in the context of an econometric model. But, while agreeing that the grounds for criticism are substantial, we should also bear in mind that the specification of (7.13.1) is quite different from that of conventional econometric models formulated in discrete time. For, the endogenous variable $y(t)$ refers to a precise instant in time t and

(7.13.1) is an equation of motion of this variable. Frequently, economic variables (particularly at the aggregate level) represent the outcome of a large number of decisions by different individuals; and it is reasonable to suppose that the number of individuals involved in these decisions may itself vary considerably from one instant in time to another. Under these conditions, the random elements entering individual decisions which lead, when aggregated over individuals, to the random disturbance $\zeta(t)$ are not exposed to the type of aggregation where conventional central limit theorems apply. Whereas in the conventional central limit argument the *number* of random elements entering into aggregation is non-random and is allowed to tend to infinity, it is reasonable to suppose that the number of random elements resulting from individual decisions that underlies $\zeta(t)$ is itself random because of the nature of the continuous time specification of (7.13.1). Notice that in a discrete time formulation the same argument will not apply because the number of individuals involved in a particular type of decision over a certain *period of time* (like a month or a quarter) will be much less subject to random influences. The main impact of this remark is that when the *number* or random elements in aggregation is itself random we can expect more erratic behaviour in $\zeta(t)$ and, in particular, the fact that $\zeta(t)$ does not possess a finite variance should not be unexpected [$\zeta(t)$ then corresponds more closely to what is known as a subordinated stochastic process — see Clark (1973, pp. 137—138)].

We may also remark in connection with (7.13.1) that $y(t)$ frequently represents a flow variable in economics. It may, for instance, measure the rate of aggregate consumption at a particular instant in time. When this is the case, we can clearly expect a good deal of high frequency variation in the process; there will, for example, be considerable variation in the process from hour to hour and certainly between day-time and night-time. It is this high frequency variation that we are less interested in exploring in the systematic component of a model. It then becomes absorbed in the disturbance and is, therefore, consistent with the implication of the conditions (7.13.2—4).

In spite of the above arguments in support of the assumed stochastic properties of $\zeta(t)$, it is of great interest to consider methods which are applicable in a more general context. Recent work with Fourier methods by Robinson (1976a and b) is promising in this respect.

Part (b) When the initial conditions of (7.13.1) are in the infinite past, this equation has a solution given by

$$y(t) = \int_{-\infty}^{t} e^{\alpha(t-s)} \zeta(s) \, ds \qquad (7.13.9)$$

(c.f. Bergstrom, 1967, p. 114). We write (7.13.9) as

$$y(t) = e^\alpha \int_{-\infty}^t e^{\alpha(t-1-s)} \zeta(s) \, ds$$

$$= e^\alpha \int_{-\infty}^{t-1} e^{\alpha(t-1-s)} \zeta(s) \, ds + \int_{t-1}^t e^{\alpha(-s)} \zeta(s) \, ds$$

$$= e^\alpha y(t-1) + \xi(t) \tag{7.13.10}$$

say, and we notice that according to our conditions on the process $\zeta(t)$

$$E[\xi(t)] = 0$$

$$E[\xi(t)^2] = E\left[\int_{t-1}^t e^{\alpha(t-1-s)} \zeta(s) \, ds \cdot \int_{t-1}^t e^{\alpha(t-r)} \zeta(r) \, dr \right]$$

$$= \int_{t-1}^t \int_{t-1}^t e^{\alpha(t-s)} E[\zeta(s) \, ds \, \zeta(r) \, dr] \, e^{\alpha(t-r)}$$

$$= \int_{t-1}^t \int_{t-1}^t e^{\alpha(t-s)} E[du(s) \, du(r)] \, e^{\alpha(t-r)}$$

in the notation of (7.13.7) and (7.13.8). But $u(s)$ has independent increments with variance given by (7.13.8) so that

$$E[du(s) \, du(r)] = \begin{cases} 0 & s \neq r \\ \sigma^2 ds & s = r \end{cases}$$

and, therefore,

$$E[\xi(t)^2] = \int_{t-1}^t e^{\alpha(t-s)} \sigma^2 e^{\alpha(t-s)} \, ds$$

$$= \sigma^2 \int_0^1 e^{2\alpha r} \, dr$$

$$= \sigma^2 \left[\frac{e^{2\alpha r}}{2\alpha} \right]_0^1$$

$$= \frac{\sigma^2}{2\alpha} (e^{2\alpha} - 1).$$

Finally, we note that $\{\xi(t): t = \ldots -1, 0, 1, \ldots\}$ is serially uncorrelated because of condition (7.13.4).

It follows that (7.13.10) is a conventional stochastic difference equation with coefficient given by $\beta = e^\alpha$. We can obtain a consistent estimator of β by ordinary least squares regression; and if we denote this estimator by $\hat{\beta}$ then we can extract a consistent estimator of α from the equation

$$\hat{\alpha} = \ln(\hat{\beta}) \tag{7.13.11}$$

Note that $e^\alpha > 0$ and, since $\hat{\beta}$ is consistent, we will certainly have $\hat{\beta} > 0$ for large enough T. So, $\hat{\alpha}$ will be well defined by (7.13.11) at least for large enough T.

Part (c) Under the assumption that $\alpha < 0$ it is clear that $0 < e^\alpha < 1$ and the model (7.13.10) is stable. It follows that $\sqrt{T}(\hat{\beta} - \beta)$ has a limiting normal distribution as $T \to \infty$ with zero mean and variance given by

$$\sigma_{\hat{\beta}}^2 = \frac{\sigma_{\xi}^2}{\operatorname{plim}_{T \to \infty} T^{-1} \sum_{t=1}^{T} y(t)^2} = \frac{\sigma_{\xi}^2}{E[y(t)^2]} \tag{7.13.12}$$

where

$$\sigma_{\xi}^2 = E[\xi(t)^2] = \frac{\sigma^2}{2\alpha}(e^{2\alpha} - 1).$$

From (7.13.10) we obtain

$$E[y(t)^2] = e^{2\alpha} E[y(t-1)^2] + E[\xi(t)^2]$$

so that

$$E[y(t)^2] = \frac{E[\xi(t)^2]}{1 - e^{2\alpha}} = -\frac{\sigma^2}{2\alpha}$$

Hence, (7.13.12) becomes

$$\sigma_{\hat{\beta}}^2 = \frac{\sigma^2}{2\alpha}(e^{2\alpha} - 1) \Big/ \left(-\frac{\sigma^2}{2\alpha}\right) = 1 - e^{2\alpha}.$$

But, from (7.13.11) we have

$$\hat{\alpha} = \ln(\hat{\beta}) = \ln(\beta) + \frac{1}{\beta}(\hat{\beta} - \beta) - \frac{1}{\tilde{\beta}^2}(\hat{\beta} - \beta)^2$$

where $\tilde{\beta}$ lies between $\hat{\beta}$ and β. We write this equation as

$$T^{1/2}(\hat{\alpha} - \alpha) = \frac{1}{\beta} T^{1/2}(\hat{\beta} - \beta) - \frac{1}{T^{1/2} \tilde{\beta}}[T^{1/2}(\hat{\beta} - \beta)]^2$$

and since the second term on the right side tends to zero in probability [as $T^{1/2}(\hat{\beta} - \beta)$ has a limiting distribution and $1/(T^{1/2} \tilde{\beta}) \to 0$ in probability as $T \to \infty$] it follows that $T^{1/2}(\hat{\alpha} - \alpha)$ has the same limiting distribution as

$$\frac{1}{\beta} T^{1/2}(\hat{\beta} - \beta) = e^{-\alpha} T^{1/2}(\hat{\beta} - \beta);$$

that is, normal with zero mean and variance given by

$$e^{-2\alpha} \sigma_{\hat{\beta}}^2 = e^{-2\alpha}(1 - e^{2\alpha}) = e^{-2\alpha} - 1$$

Hence, the variance of the limiting distribution of $T^{1/2}(\hat{\alpha} - \alpha)$ when $\alpha = -1$ is $e^2 - 1 = 6.389$.

Solution 7.14

Part (a) When we observe that $\Delta P_t < 0$ we can infer that $D_t < S_t$ and hence that $Q_t = D_t$. In this case market observations will satisfy the demand function, which can be written

$$Q_t = X_{1t}\beta_1 + P_{t-1}\beta_2 + u_{1t}. \tag{7.14.4}$$

Similarly when $\Delta P_t > 0$ it follows that $D_t > S_t$ and $Q_t = S_t$, implying that we can observe the supply function:

$$Q_t = X_{2t}\beta_3 + P_{t-1}\beta_4 + u_{2t}. \tag{7.14.5}$$

Only when $\Delta P_t = 0$ is the market in equilibrium. In this case both demand and supply functions are observable. In figure 7.14.1 the bold line indicates the parts of the demand function DD and the supply function SS that are observable

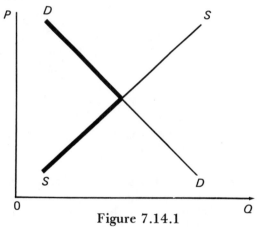

Figure 7.14.1

The lagged price term in each function implies that the *ex ante* quantities demanded and supplied depend on price in the previous period. The *ex post* quantitites demanded and supplied depend upon the relative sizes of the *ex ante* quantities. If $D_t < S_t$ then *ex ante* demand is satisfied. It is not clear, however, what happens to the excess supply $S_t - Q_t$. If $D_t > S_t$ then all *ex ante* supply is sold but not all *ex ante* demands are satisfied. There is no explanation of how price is determined in this model and hence, when $D_t < S_t$, there is no way of knowing how sales are allocated over competing firms or, when $D_t > S_t$, how output is allocated over competing demands. In an alternative model Fair and Kelejian (1974) attempt to overcome some of these difficulties by introducing an additional equation

$$\Delta P_t = \gamma(D_t - S_t) \qquad (\gamma > 0) \tag{7.14.6}$$

Part (b) Equations (7.14.4) and (7.14.5) can be estimated directly by OLS provided the number of observations on each equation is greater than or equal to the number of coefficients to be estimated in that equation. The set of observations at time t $\{Q_t, X_{1t}, X_{2t}, P_{t-1}\}$ is allocated to equation (7.14.4) if $\Delta P_t \leqslant 0$ and to (7.16.5) if $\Delta P_t \geqslant 0$.

Part (c) These OLS estimates are inconsistent because the disturbances u_{it} $(i = 1, 2)$ are correlated with the regressor variables even in large samples. To see this, consider

$$E(u_{1t}|X_t, \Delta P_t \leqslant 0) = E(u_{1t}|X_t, D_t \leqslant S_t) \tag{7.14.7}$$

$$= E(u_{1t}|X_t, u_{1t} - u_{2t} \leqslant S_t^* - D_t^*) \tag{7.14.8}$$

where $X_t = (X_{1t}, X_{2t}, P_{t-1})$, $D_t^* = X_{1t}\beta_1 + P_{t-1}\beta_2$ and $S_t^* = X_{2t}\beta_3 + P_{t-1}\beta_4$. From the joint density of u_{1t} and u_{2t} given X_t we can derive the density of $u_{1t} - u_{2t}$ given X_t and the joint density of u_{1t} and $u_{1t} - u_{2t}$ given X_t. Denote these by $f_1(Z_t|X_t)$ and $f_2(u_{1t}, Z_t|X_t)$, where $Z_t = u_{1t} - u_{2t}$. Then

$$E(u_{1t}|X_t, u_{1t} - u_{2t} \leqslant S_t^* - D_t^*) = \frac{\int_{-\infty}^{\infty} \int_{-\infty}^{S_t^*-D_t^*} u_{1t} f_2(u_{1t}, Z_t|X_t)\, dZ_t du_{1t}}{\int_{-\infty}^{S_t^*-D_t^*} f_1(Z_t|X_t)\, dZ_t}$$

$$\tag{7.14.9}$$

The expectation in (7.14.9) will in general be dependent on X_t unless u_{1t} and Z_t are independent, when the density $f_2(\ ,\ )$ factors. Thus, the use of OLS will lead to inconsistent estimates.

Part (d) The demand and supply functions, (7.14.4) and (7.14.5), can be consistently estimated by maximum likelihood estimation. Let $f_3(u_{1t}|X_t, \Delta P_t \leqslant 0)$ be the conditional density of u_{1t} given X_t and $\Delta P_t \leqslant 0$ and $f_4(u_{2t}|X_t, \Delta P_t \geqslant 0)$ be the conditional density of u_{2t} given X_t and $\Delta P_t \geqslant 0$. In view of the earlier results these densities can also be written as $f_3(u_{1t}|X_t, Z_t \leqslant S_t^* - D_t^*)$ and $f_4(u_{2t}|X_t, Z_t \geqslant S_t^* - D_t^*)$, respectively. The likelihood function can now be written as

$$L(\beta_1, \beta_2, \beta_3, \beta_4, \sigma_{11}, \sigma_{22}, \sigma_{12}) \tag{7.14.10}$$

$$= \prod_{\Delta P_t < 0} f_3(u_{1t}|X_t, Z_t \leqslant S_t^* - D_t^*) \prod_{\Delta P_t > 0} f_4(u_{2t}|X_t, Z_t \geqslant S_t^* - D_t^*)$$

where $u_{1t} = Q_t - X_{1t}\beta_1 - P_{t-1}\beta_2$ and $u_{2t} = Q_t - X_{2t}\beta_3 - P_{t-1}\beta_4$. Recall that for continuous distributions prob $\{\Delta P_t = 0\} = 0$ and hence only inequalities appear in (7.14.10)

$$f_3\left(u_{1t}\,|\,X_t,\,Z_t\leqslant S_t^*-D_t^*\right)\;=\;\frac{\int_{-\infty}^{S_t^*-D_t^*}f_2\left(u_{1t},\,Z_t\,|\,X_t\right)dZ_t}{\int_{-\infty}^{S_t^*-D_t^*}f_1\left(Z_t\,|\,X_t\right)dZ_t}\qquad(7.14.11)$$

and, similarly, we can write

$$f_4\left(u_{2t}\,|\,X_t,\,Z_t\geqslant S_t^*-D_t^*\right)\;=\;\frac{\int_{S_t^*-D_t^*}^{\infty}f_5\left(u_{2t},\,Z_t\,|\,X_t\right)dZ_t}{\int_{S_t^*-D_t^*}^{\infty}f_1\left(Z_t\,|\,X_t\right)dZ_t}\qquad(7.14.12)$$

where $f_5\left(u_{2t},\,Z_t\,|\,X_t\right)$ is the joint density of u_{2t} and Z_t given X_t. Substituting (7.14.11) and (7.14.12) into (7.14.10) we obtain the likelihood function as a function of normal integrals. The remaining step is to maximise the likelihood function with respect to $\beta_1,\beta_2,\beta_3,\beta_4,\sigma_{11}$, σ_{22} and σ_{12} using a suitable non-linear optimisation algorithm.

Solution 7.15

This question is concerned with the asymptotic distribution of multi-period forecasts obtained from the reduced form of an econometric model. The results we obtain in this solution were recently derived by Schmidt (1974) and our treatment will follow the lines of his paper (although our use of the vec operator rather than the $\overline{\text{vec}}$ operator — as in Schmidt — will lead to some difference in our notation but provides some simplification of the argument).

Part (a) Since $\hat{y}_{N+h}$ in (7.15.2) is already a vector we can write

$$\hat{y}_{N+h}\;=\;\text{vec}\left(\hat{P}^h y_N\right)+\sum_{j=0}^{h-1}\text{vec}\left(\hat{P}^j\hat{Q}x_{N+h-j}\right)$$

$$=\;\left(I\otimes y_N'\right)\text{vec}\left(\hat{P}^h\right)+\sum_{j=0}^{h-1}\left(I\otimes x_{N+h-j}'\right)\text{vec}\left(\hat{P}^j\hat{Q}\right)$$

$$=\;W_h\hat{a}_h$$

as required in (7.15.3) since

$$\hat{a}_h\;=\;\text{vec}\left(\hat{A}_h\right)\;=\;\begin{bmatrix}\text{vec}\left(\hat{P}^h\right)\\[4pt]\text{vec}\left(\hat{P}^{h-1}\hat{Q}\right)\\[4pt]\text{vec}\left(\hat{Q}\right)\end{bmatrix}.\qquad(7.15.6)$$

Part (b) From the definition of $\bar{y}_{N+h}$ it follows that

$$T^{1/2}\left(\hat{y}_{N+h}-\bar{y}_{N+h}\right)\;=\;W_h T^{1/2}\left(\hat{a}_h-a_h\right)\qquad(7.15.7)$$

and, since we are concerned with the conditional distribution of forecasts given $y_N,x_N,\ldots,x_{N+h}$ (and, hence, given W_h), we are concerned to derive the limiting distribution of $T^{1/2}(\hat{a}_h - a_h)$. The limiting distribution of $T^{1/2}(\hat{y}_{N+h} - y_{N+h})$ will then follow directly from the transformation (7.15.7).

We see from (7.15.6) and the definition of a_h that

$$
\hat{a}_h - a_h = \begin{bmatrix} \text{vec}(\hat{P}^h - P^h) \\ \text{vec}(\hat{P}^{h-1}\hat{Q} - P^{h-1}Q) \\ \vdots \\ \text{vec}(\hat{Q} - Q) \end{bmatrix} \tag{7.15.8}
$$

and we now attempt to write this vector as a transformation of the vector

$$
\begin{bmatrix} \text{vec}(\hat{P} - P) \\ \text{vec}(\hat{Q} - Q) \end{bmatrix} = \hat{\alpha} - \alpha
$$

To do this we note first that

$$
\begin{aligned}
\hat{P}^i - P^i &= \hat{P}^i + \sum_{j=1}^{i-1} \hat{P}^j P^{i-j} - \sum_{k=1}^{i-1} \hat{P}^k P^{i-k} - P^i \tag{7.15.9} \\
&= \hat{P}^i + \sum_{s=0}^{i-2} \hat{P}^{s+1} P^{i-s-1} - \sum_{r=0}^{i-1} \hat{P}^r P^{i-r}
\end{aligned}
$$

where we have taken $-P^i$ into the summation in the third term on the right side of (7.15.9) and changed the index of summation in the second term on the right side of (7.15.9). Consequently

$$
\begin{aligned}
\hat{P}^i - P^i &= \sum_{s=0}^{i-1} \hat{P}^{s+1} P^{i-s-1} - \sum_{r=0}^{i-1} \hat{P}^r P^{i-s} \\
&= \sum_{s=0}^{i-1} \hat{P}^s (\hat{P} - P) P^{i-s-1}
\end{aligned}
$$

It follows that

$$
\begin{aligned}
\text{vec}(\hat{P}^i - P^i) &= \sum_{s=0}^{i-1} \text{vec}[\hat{P}^s(\hat{P} - P)P^{i-s-1}] \\
&= \sum_{s=0}^{i-1} (\hat{P}^s \otimes P'^{i-s-1})\, \text{vec}(\hat{P} - P). \tag{7.15.10}
\end{aligned}
$$

we also have

$$
\hat{P}^i\hat{Q} - P^iQ = (\hat{P}^i - P^i)\hat{Q} + P^i(\hat{Q} - Q)
$$

so that

$$\text{vec}(\hat{P}^i\hat{Q}-P^iQ) = (I \otimes \hat{Q}') \, \text{vec}(\hat{P}^i - P^i)$$
$$+ (P^i \otimes I) \, \text{vec}(\hat{Q} - Q)$$

$$= [C_i : D_i] \begin{bmatrix} \text{vec}(\hat{P} - P) \\ \text{vec}(\hat{Q} - Q) \end{bmatrix} \qquad (7.15.11)$$

where

$$C_i = (I \otimes \hat{Q}') \sum_{s=0}^{i-1} (\hat{P}^s \otimes P'^{i-s-1})$$

$$= \sum_{s=0}^{i-1} (\hat{P}^s \otimes \hat{Q}'P'^{i-s-1})$$

and
$$D_i = P^i \otimes I.$$

It follows from (7.15.10) and (7.15.11) that we can write (7.15.8) in the form

$$\hat{a}_h - a_h = \begin{bmatrix} \sum_{s=0}^{h-1} (\hat{P}^s \otimes P'^{h-s-1}) & 0 \\ \hline C_{h-1} & D_{h-1} \\ \vdots & \vdots \\ \hline C_1 & D_1 \\ \hline 0 & I \end{bmatrix} \begin{bmatrix} \text{vec}(\hat{P} - P) \\ \text{vec}(\hat{Q} - Q) \end{bmatrix} \qquad (7.15.12)$$

$$= Q_h (\hat{\alpha} - \alpha),$$

say. Since the elements of Q_h are simple functions of the elements of $\hat{P}$, $\hat{Q}$, P and Q and since $\hat{P}$ and $\hat{Q}$ converge in probability to P and Q (by assumption), it follows that the matrix Q_h has a finite limit in probability as $T \to \infty$, which we denote by $\bar{Q}$.

From (7.15.7) and (7.15.12) we obtain

$$T^{1/2} (\hat{y}_{N+h} - \bar{y}_{N+h}) = W_h Q_h T^{1/2} \begin{bmatrix} \text{vec}(\hat{P} - P) \\ \text{vec}(\hat{Q} - Q) \end{bmatrix} = W_h Q_h T^{1/2} (\hat{\alpha} - \alpha)$$

which has the same limiting distribution (conditional on W_h) as

$$W_h \bar{Q} T^{1/2} (\hat{\alpha} - \alpha)$$

But, by assumption, $T^{1/2} (\hat{\alpha} - \alpha)$ has a limiting $N(0, \Psi)$ distribution so that the limiting distribution of $T^{1/2} (\hat{y}_{N+h} - \bar{y}_{N+h})$, conditional on the elements of W_h, is normal with zero mean vector and covariance matrix

$$W_h \bar{Q} \Psi \bar{Q}' W_h'. \qquad\qquad\qquad\qquad (7.15.13)$$

Remark The limiting distribution of $T^{1/2}(\hat{y}_{N+h} - \bar{y}_{N+h})$ is obtained as $T \to \infty$ where T is the size of the sample of (independent) data available for the estimation of P and Q. We note that h and N remain fixed throughout this derivation and we emphasize that the result is conditional on the given values of $y_N, x_N, \ldots, x_{N+h}$. In practice, of course, the assumption of independent data used to construct the estimators $\hat{P}$ and $\hat{Q}$ is quite unrealistic in an econometric context. If we do not have independent data available to us then we need to condition, also, the distribution of the estimators $\hat{P}$ and $\hat{Q}$. If the correlation between the sample used to estimate P and Q (say $\{y_1, \ldots, y_T; x_1, \ldots, x_T\}$) and y_N, $x_N, \ldots, x_{N+h}$ is small, then the effect of this conditioning can be expected to be small. This is most likely to be the case when the sample $\{y_1, \ldots, y_T\}$ is separated from y_N by a reasonable length of data (so that, for example, the observations $y_{T+1}, \ldots, y_N$ are neglected in the estimation of P and Q). But, when the sample size T is small this is unlikely to be the case. An adequate treatment in this case would therefore require us to consider not only the small sample distribution of $\hat{P}$ and $\hat{Q}$ but also the effect of making this distribution conditional on certain initial values used for forecasting.

An analysis along these lines is contained in Phillips (1978).

Part (c) Since Y_{N+h} is the realised value of y in period $N + h$ we have, from (7.15.1),

$$
\begin{aligned}
y_{N+h} &= P y_{N+h-1} + Q x_{N+h} + v_{N+h} \\
&= P^h y_N + \sum_{j=0}^{h-1} P^j Q x_{N+h-j} \\
&\quad + \sum_{j=0}^{h-1} P^j v_{N+h-j}
\end{aligned}
$$

But, by definition,

$$
\begin{aligned}
\bar{y}_{N+h} &= W_h a_h \\
&= (I_n \otimes y_N') \operatorname{vec}(P^h) + (I_n \otimes x_{N+1}') \operatorname{vec}(P^{h-1} Q) \\
&\quad + \ldots + (I_n \otimes x_{N+h}') \operatorname{vec}(Q) \\
&= P^h y_N + \sum_{j=0}^{h-1} P^j Q x_{N+h-j}
\end{aligned}
$$

(once again, because if x is a vector then $\operatorname{vec}(x) = x$). Thus

$$y_{N+h} = \bar{y}_{N+h} + \sum_{j=0}^{h-1} P^j v_{N+h-j}$$

and

$$\hat{y}_{N+h} - y_{N+h} = (\hat{y}_{N+h} - \bar{y}_{N+h}) - \sum_{j=0}^{h-1} P^j v_{N+h-j} \qquad (7.15.14)$$

Now the covariance matrix of the last term on the right side of (7.15.14) is given by

$$\sum_{j=0}^{h-1} P^j \Omega P'^j \qquad (7.15.15)$$

and this matrix does not depend on T. Moreover, from (7.15.13) the asymptotic covariance matrix of the first term on the right side of (7.15.14) is

$$T^{-1} W_h \bar{Q} \Psi \bar{Q}' W_h' \qquad (7.15.16)$$

Finally, $\hat{P}$ and $\hat{Q}$ are, by assumption, statistically independent of the disturbances v_t in (7.15.1) for all values of t. Hence, $\hat{y}_{N+h} - \bar{y}_{N+h}$ is statistically independent of $\sum_{j=0}^{h-1} P^j v_{N+h-j}$ and the asymptotic covariance matrix is just the sum of (7.15.15) and (7.15.16). That is

$$\sum_{j=0}^{h-1} P^j \Omega P'^j + T^{-1} W_h \bar{Q} \Psi \bar{Q}' W_h'. \qquad (7.15.17)$$

Remark The first term of (7.15.17) is essentially the mean square error (or, strictly, covariance matrix) of what is known in the statistical literature as the best linear predictor of y_{N+h} (see, for instance, Hannan, 1970, p 127, Box and Jenkins, 1970, or Malinvaud, 1970, pp. 435–438). For in the present case, the optimal predictor of y_{N+h} (conditional on $y_N, x_N, \ldots, x_{N+h}$) is just $\bar{y}_{N+h}$ and the mean square covariance matrix of prediction is just

$$E[(y_{N+h} - \bar{y}_{N+h})(y_{N+h} - \bar{y}_{N+h})'|y_N, x_N, \ldots, x_{N+h}]$$

$$= E\left[\left(\sum_{j=0}^{h-1} P^j v_{N+h-j}\right)\left(\sum_{k=0}^{h-1} v_{N+h-k}' P'^k\right)\right]$$

$$= \sum_{j=0}^{h-1} P^j \Omega P'^k$$

The second term of (7.15.17) measures the effect of the sampling error of estimating P and Q and $\hat{P}$ and $\hat{Q}$. We note that this term is of $O(T^{-1})$ so that as $T \to \infty$ the effect of the sampling error on the mean square error of prediction decreases. This squares with the assumption that $\hat{P}$ and $\hat{Q}$ are consistent estimators; for, as $T \to \infty$, $\hat{P}$ and $\hat{Q}$ will differ from the true values by very little and, correspondingly, $\hat{y}_{N+h}$ will differ by very little from the optimal predictor $\bar{y}_{N+h}$.

Solution 7.16

Before we turn to discuss Part (a) of this question it will be helpful if we first consider the nature of the model (7.16.1) and the conditions under which the identification of the parameters in such models have been derived in the literature.

The model (7.16.1) is an example of a multiple equation model with moving average errors or disturbances. We notice that lagged values of the endogenous variables as well as lagged values of the errors occur in the specification — so there are system dynamics as well as error dynamics. And an exogenous input also enters the specification. For these reasons, the model belongs to the class of vector autoregressive moving average models with exogenous inputs (or, as they are sometimes called, ARMAX systems). The general form of this type of equation system is written as

$$\sum_{j=0}^{p} B(j) y_{t-j} + \sum_{k=0}^{q} C(k) x_{t-k} = \sum_{l=0}^{r} A(l) u_{t-l} \qquad (7.16.2)$$

where the $B(j)$, $C(k)$ and $A(l)$ ($j = 0, \ldots, p; k = 0, \ldots, q; l = 0, \ldots, r$) are matrices of unknown parameters, y is an n-vector of endogenous variables, x is an m-vector of exogenous variables and u is a vector of random disturbances.

The problem of identification in the context of systems such as (7.16.2) has recently been examined by Hannan (1971). The reader is also referred to an earlier paper by Hannan (1969) dealing with the same problem for models in which there are no exogenous inputs $C(k) = 0$ for all k, as well as the very useful discussion of the problem in Preston and Wall (1973) and the more recent papers by Deistler (1975 and 1976).

To complete the stochastic specification of (7.16.2) we add the following assumptions:

Assumption A

and
$$E(u_t) = 0, E(u_t u_t') = I_n \qquad \text{for all } t$$
$$E(u_t u_s') = 0 \qquad \text{for all } t \neq s$$

Assumption B

$$E(x_t u_s') = 0 \qquad \text{for all } t \text{ and } s$$

Assumption C x_t is a second order (or covariance) stationary process, so that the sequence of covariance matrices $E(x_t x_s') = R(t - s)$ depends only on the time difference $t - s$. (See, for example, Dhrymes, 1971, pp. 385–386, Malinvaud, 1970b, pp. 418–419, and Fishman, 1969, for a discussion of stationary processes). Moreover, the spectral density matrix of x_t, defined by

$$f_x(\lambda) = \frac{1}{2\pi} \sum_{n=-\infty}^{\infty} R(n) \, e^{-in\lambda} \qquad \lambda \epsilon(-\pi, \pi]$$

satisfies the condition

$$\det[f_x(\lambda)] > 0$$

for all λ in a non-negligible set in $(-\pi, \pi]$; an example of such a set would be $[-\epsilon, \epsilon]$ where $\pi > \epsilon > 0$. (By a non-negligible set we mean here, strictly speaking, a set that is not of Lebesgue measure zero i.e. a set of positive Lebesgue measure — see, for instance, Tichmarsh (1964), Rudin (1964) or Dieudonné (1969) for the definition of Lebesgue measure.)

We now introduce the following generating functions (as in Hannan, 1971)

$$G(\zeta) = \sum_{l=0}^{r} A(l) \, \zeta^l, \quad H(\zeta) = \sum_{j=0}^{p} B(j) \, \zeta^j, \quad J(\zeta) \stackrel{\cdot}{=} \sum_{k=0}^{q} C(k) \, \zeta^k$$

(7.16.3)

which are polynomials in ζ whose coefficients are the matrices occurring in (7.16.2). We can then write (7.16.2) in operator form as

$$H(L) \, y_t + J(L) \, x_t = G(L) \, u_t \tag{7.16.4}$$

where L is the lag operator for which $Ly_t = y_{t-1}$; and we assume the following about the polynomial operators $H(\ )$ and $G(\ )$:

Assumption D *The roots of the two equations*

$$\det[H(\zeta)] = 0 \quad and \quad \det[G(\zeta)] = 0 \tag{7.16.5}$$

all have absolute value greater than unity.

Discussion of Assumptions A–D Assumption A implies that u_t is a serially uncorrelated random disturbance and the requirement that $E(u_t u_t') = I$ is a normalisation condition. We write

$$v_t = \sum_{l=0}^{r} A(l) \, u_{t-l}$$

and assume that $A(0)$ is non-singular. We then have

$$E(v_t v_t') = \sum_{l=0}^{r} A(l) \, IA(l)'$$

$$= \sum_{l=0}^{r} A(l) \, A(0)^{-1} A(0) \, A(0)' \, A(0)'^{-1} A(l)'$$

and, setting $\Omega = A(0) \, A(0)'$ This becomes

$$\sum_{l=0}^{r} A(l) A(0)^{-1} \Omega A(0)'^{-1} A(l)'$$

$$= \sum_{l=0}^{r} \bar{A}(l) \Omega \bar{A}(l)'$$

which can be regarded as the covariance matrix of the new disturbance $\bar{v}_t$ defined by

$$\bar{v}_t = \sum_{l=0}^{r} \bar{A}(l) \bar{u}_{t-l} \qquad (7.16.6)$$

where
$$\bar{A}(0) = I,$$
$$\bar{A}(l) = A(l) A(0)^{-1} \qquad (l = 1, \ldots, r)$$

and $\bar{u}_t = A(0) u_t$ so that $\bar{u}_t$ has zero mean and covariance matrix $E(\bar{u}_t \bar{u}_t')$ $= \Omega = A(0) A(0)'$ for all t. Thus, an alternative specification of (7.16.2) would replace v_t by $\bar{v}_t$ as in (7.16.6) and this specification would involve the alternative normalisation $A(0) = I$.

Assumption B corresponds to the usual condition that the exogenous variables are *truly* exogenous, being uncorrelated with the disturbances in all time periods.

Assumption C imposes conditions on the nature of the exogenous variable vector x_t. In the first place, it requires that x_t belong to the class of stationary random processes; and, secondly, the spectral density matrix of this process must be non-singular in a non-negligible set of $(-\pi, \pi]$. The first requirement can be relaxed and ways of doing this are discussed in Hannan (1971) (see, also, Deistler, 1976, for an examination of the identification problem in this context *without* the assumption of stationarity). The second requirement is more difficult to interpret and we refer the reader to the discussions of this requirement in Hannan (1971, pp. 754—55) and in Preston and Wall (1973, p. 5).

The main effect of Asssumption D is to ensure that the model is stable and that the solution or final form of (7.16.4) which we write as

$$y_t = -H(L)^{-1} J(L) x_t + H(L)^{-1} G(L) u_t \qquad (7.16.7)$$

gives us a representation of y_t as an infinite linear combination of the vectors $x_t, x_{t-1}, \ldots$ and $u_t, u_{t-1}, \ldots$ (see, for instance, Anderson, 1971, p. 170). In this way, y_t can be regarded as a linear filter of the process x_t and the process u_t (see Fishman, 1969, pp. 41—44, or Hannan, 1970, pp. 51—76, for discussions of linear filters and their properties).

Let us now assume that the general model (7.16.2), or equivalently (7.16.4), satisfies Assumptions A, B, C and D. On the basis of Theorem 4 in Hannan (1971, p. 761) and Theorem B in Preston and Wall (1973, p. 9) we have the following sufficient conditions for the identifiability of the parameters of the model:

(i) The degrees p, q and r of the matrix polynomials $H(\zeta)$, $J(\zeta)$ and $G(\zeta)$ are prescribed *a priori* and

$$\text{rank}\,[H(\zeta) \vdots J(\zeta) \vdots G(\zeta)] \; = \; n \qquad\qquad (7.16.8)$$

for all (complex) ζ.

(ii) rank $[B(p) \vdots C(q) \vdots A(r)] = n$

(iii) If we define

$$\Lambda \; = \; [B(0) \vdots \cdots \vdots B(p) \vdots C(0) \vdots \cdots \vdots C(q) \vdots A(0) \vdots \cdots \vdots A(r)]$$

then there are at least $n - 1$ zeros prescribed in each row of Λ and one element in each row of $B(0)$ is prescribed as unity. Moreover, if Λ_1 denotes the matrix obtained by taking the columns of Λ containing prescribed zeros in row i then

$$\text{rank}\,[\Lambda_i] \; = \; n - 1$$

for all $i = 1, \ldots, n$.

Discussion of Conditions (i) —(iii) The first requirement of (i) is that p, q and r be known *a priori*. Hence, the form of the specification of (7.16.2) is known up to the order of the lags in the system dynamics and the error dynamics. Turning to the rank condition (7.16.8), we know that this condition is necessary and sufficient for there to be no common left divisors of $H(\zeta)$, $J(\zeta)$ and $G(\zeta)$ other than unimodular matrices (see, for instance, Lemma 1 of Deistler, 1976, p. 36, or MacDuffee, 1933, p. 35). We define the terms 'unimodular matrix' and 'common left divisor' as follows (see, also, Hannan, 1971, pp. 755—756): a *unimodular matrix* is a polynomial matrix $U(\zeta)$, say, whose determinant is a constant for all values of ζ; a *common left divisor* of $H(\zeta)$, $J(\zeta)$ and $G(\zeta)$ is a polynomial matrix $K(\zeta)$ for which we have

$$H(\zeta) \; = \; K(\zeta)\,H_1(\zeta)$$

$$J(\zeta) \; = \; K(\zeta)\,J_1(\zeta) \quad\text{and}\quad G(\zeta) \; = \; K(\zeta)\,G_1(\zeta)$$

If such a matrix as $K(\zeta)$ exists then it is clear that (7.16.4) is equivalent to the system

$$H_1(L)\,y_t + J_1(L)\,x_t \; = \; G_1(L)\,u_t \qquad\qquad (7.16.9)$$

in the sense that, given realisations of the processes $\{x_t\}$ and $\{u_t\}$, both (7.16.4) and (7.16.9) will generate the data we observe. Hence, in terms of our observations, (7.16.4) would in this case be indistinguishable from a system of the same form but in which $K(\zeta)$ were replaced by another polynomial matrix of the same degree. It is this type of indeterminacy which condition (7.16.8) removes. We note finally that (7.16.8) is given by Preston and Wall (1973, p. 9) and Deistler (1976, p. 36), whereas Hannan states the condition explicitly in terms of left divisors. The effect of (7.16.8) is, therefore, to restrict the admissible left divisors $K(\zeta)$ to the class of unimodular matrices. The prescription of the degrees p, q and r *a priori* then restricts this class further and *together with* condition (ii) reduces the class of admissible $K(\zeta)$ to the class of non-singular constant matrices.

Condition (iii) closely resembles the rank condition and usual normalisation rule in the classical identification problem of simultaneous equations. This final condition reduces the class of non-singular constant matrices, up to which (7.16.2) is determined, to the identity matrix. Preston and Wall (1973) call condition (iii) Hannan's *extended rank condition*.

Part (a) We recall from our discussion in Solution 6.2 (see, also, Malinvaud, 1970b, ch. 18, and Rothenberg, 1971) that, in the context of the linear simultaneous equations model, a structure is a set of hypotheses which determine the joint probability distribution of the model's endogenous variables (in the case of a separate stochastic hypothesis about the disturbances in the model, a structure reduces simply to a set of parameter values). Two structures are then observationally equivalent if they imply the same joint distribution of the model's endogenous variables (compare Definition 1 in Malinvaud, 1970b, p. 650, or Definition 1' in Rothenberg, 1971, p. 578).

In the context of the model (7.16.1), or the more general case (7.16.4), our notion of observational equivalence is similar but not quite the same. We assume that all the information about the model that we can extract from our data is contained in the second moments of the endogenous and exogenous variables; that is in

$$R_x(n) = E[x(t)\,x(t+n)'], R_y(n) = E[y(t)\,y(t+n)'],$$
$$R_{yx}(n) = E[y(t)\,x(t+n)'].$$
$$(7.16.10)$$

This information is, alternatively, contained in the spectral density matrices defined as the transforms

$$f_x(\lambda) = \frac{1}{2\pi}\sum_{n=-\infty}^{\infty} R_x(n)\,e^{-in\lambda}, \quad f_y(\lambda) = \frac{1}{2\pi}\sum_{n=-\infty}^{\infty} R_y(n)\,e^{-in\lambda},$$
$$f_{yx}(\lambda) = \frac{1}{2\pi}\sum_{n=-\infty}^{\infty} R_{yx}(n)\,e^{-in\lambda}.$$
$$(7.16.11)$$

We now characterise a structure of the model (7.16.4) as the triplet of specified parameter values

$$\{B(j): j = 0, \ldots, p; \quad C(k): k = 0, \ldots, q; \quad A(l): l = 0, \ldots, r\}$$
$$(7.16.12)$$

Two such structures are then *observationally equivalent* if they generate the same second moments $\{R_x(n),\,R_y(n)\,R_{yx}(n): n = 0, 1, \ldots\}$ or, alternatively, the same spectral density matrices $f_x(\lambda)$, $f_y(\lambda)$ and $f_{yx}(\lambda)$.

A particular structure is identifiable if there is no other structure in the set of all feasible structures of the model which is observationally equivalent. This means, in the present context, that a structure such as (7.16.12) above is identifiable if values of the matrices in (7.16.12) can be uniquely determined from the knowledge of the second moments (7.16.10) or, alternatively, the spectral density matrices (7.16.11). But we know that the spectral density matrices satisfy the relations

$$f_y(\lambda) = \frac{1}{2\pi} H(e^{i\lambda})^{-1} G(e^{i\lambda}) G^*(e^{i\lambda}) H^*(e^{i\lambda})^{-1} \qquad (7.16.13)$$

$$+ H(e^{i\lambda})^{-1} J(e^{i\lambda}) f_x(\lambda) J^*(e^{i\lambda}) H^*(e^{i\lambda})^{-1}$$

$$f_{yx}(\lambda) = H(e^{i\lambda})^{-1} J(e^{i\lambda}) f_x(\lambda) \qquad (7.16.14)$$

(see, for instance, Hannan, 1971, p. 754, or Hannan, 1970, p. 67) where we use * to denote the complex conjugate transpose of a matrix. The problem of identification in this context can then be viewed as the problem of whether equations (7.16.13) and (7.16.14) allow us to determine uniquely the coefficient matrices in the matrix polynomials $H(\ )$, $G(\ )$ and $J(\ )$ when we are given the spectral density matrices $f_y(\lambda)$, $f_x(\lambda)$ and $f_{yx}(\lambda)$.

Remark The reader is referred to Hannan (1971) and Deistler (1976) for further discussion of the concepts of observational equivalence and identification in this type of model.

Part (b) We can now apply Conditions (i)–(iii) above to the stated model (7.16.1). We check, first of all, the Assumptions A–D under which the conditions operate. We see that A holds from the information given in the question; but B, C and D do not necessarily hold on the given information. We, therefore, require that the exogenous variable x_{1t} in (7.16.1) satisfies Assmptions B and C. Turning to D, we have

$$H(\zeta) = \begin{bmatrix} 1 + b_{11}^1 \zeta & b_{12}^0 + b_{12}^1 \zeta \\ b_{21}^0 & 1 \end{bmatrix} \quad \text{and}$$

$$G(\zeta) = \begin{bmatrix} a_{11}^0 + a_{11}^1 \zeta & a_{12}^1 \\ 0 & a_{22}^0 + a_{22}^1 \zeta \end{bmatrix}$$

so that

$$\det[H(\zeta)] = 0 \quad \text{and} \quad \det[G(\zeta)] = 0$$

imply that

$$\zeta = \frac{b_{12}^0 b_{21}^0 - 1}{b_{11}^1 - b_{12}^1 b_{21}^0} \quad \text{and} \quad \zeta = -\frac{a_{11}^0}{a_{11}^1}, -\frac{a_{22}^0}{a_{22}^1}$$

Assumption D now holds when

$$|b_{12}^0 b_{21}^0 - 1| > |b_{11}^1 - b_{12}^1 b_{21}^0| \tag{7.16.15}$$

$$|a_{11}^0| > |a_{11}^1| \tag{7.16.16}$$

and

$$|a_{22}^0| > |a_{22}^1|. \tag{7.16.17}$$

Remark If $b_{11}^1 = b_{12}^1 = 0$ we see that there are no system dynamics in (7.16.1). The model is then a model with truly exogenous variables, serially correlated errors and no lagged endogenous variables. If the classical rank condition for identification holds, then we will be able to identify the structural parameters (c.f. Hannan, 1971, p. 751).

Before we proceed to check the Conditions (i), (ii) and (iii) for identification we therefore tighten our specification of (7.16.1) so that B and C hold and the parameters satisfy (7.16.15), (7.16.16) and (7.16.17). We now check the identification conditions in turn.

Condition (i) From the specification of (7.16.1) we have the degrees of the lag polynomials prescribed as $p = 1$, $q = 0$ and $r = 1$. Now

$$[H(\zeta) \vdots J(\zeta) \vdots G(\zeta)] = \begin{bmatrix} 1 + b_{11}^1 \zeta & b_{12}^0 + b_{12}^1 \zeta & c_{11} \\ b_{21}^0 & 1 & c_{21} \end{bmatrix}$$

$$\begin{matrix} a_{11}^0 + a_{11}^1 \zeta & a_{12}^1 \\ 0 & a_{22}^0 + a_{22}^1 \zeta \end{matrix} \Bigg] \tag{7.16.18}$$

and this matrix has rank = 2 for all values of ζ provided $\det[H(\zeta)] \neq 0$ when $\det[G(\zeta)] = 0$; that is, provided

$$\frac{b_{12}^0 b_{21}^0 - 1}{b_{11}^1 - b_{12}^1 b_{21}^0} \neq -\frac{a_{11}^0}{a_{11}^1} \tag{7.16.19}$$

and

$$\frac{b_{12}^0 b_{21}^0 - 1}{b_{11}^1 - b_{12}^1 b_{21}^0} \neq -\frac{a_{22}^0}{a_{22}^1} \tag{7.16.20}$$

We can, of course, find other sufficient conditions for (7.16.18) to have full rank. A complete set of necessary conditions is obtained by looking at the determinant of every 2×2 submatrix of (7.16.18). We will not bother to do this because it is clear, at any rate from (7.16.19) and (7.16.20), that most structures of the model (7.16.1) lead to a matrix (7.16.18) of rank 2.

Condition (ii) In the present case we have $p = 1, q = 0, r = 1$ and

$$[B(1) \vdots C(0) \vdots A(1)] = \begin{bmatrix} b^1_{11} & b^1_{12} & c_{11} & a^1_{11} & a^1_{12} \\ 0 & 0 & c_{21} & 0 & a^1_{22} \end{bmatrix}$$

which has rank $= 2$ unless

$$c_{21} = a^1_{22} = 0$$

or

$$c_{11}a^1_{22} = c_{21}a^1_{12} \quad \text{and} \quad b^1_{11} = b^1_{12} = a^1_{11} = 0.$$

Condition (iii) We have

$$\Lambda = \begin{bmatrix} 1 & b^0_{12} & b^1_{11} & b^1_{21} & c_{11} & a^0_{11} & 0 & a^1_{11} & a^1_{12} \\ b^0_{21} & 1 & 0 & 0 & c_{21} & 0 & a^0_{22} & 0 & a^1_{22} \end{bmatrix}$$

and we notice that the normalisation rule is already applied. Now

$$\Lambda_1 = \begin{bmatrix} 0 \\ a^0_{22} \end{bmatrix}$$

and

$$\Lambda_2 = \begin{bmatrix} b^1_{11} & b^1_{21} & a^0_{11} & a^1_{11} \\ 0 & 0 & 0 & 0 \end{bmatrix}$$

It follows that

$$\text{rank}(\Lambda_1) = 1 \quad \text{unless} \quad a^0_{22} = 0$$

and

$$\text{rank}(\Lambda_2) = 1 \quad \text{unless} \quad b^1_{11} = b^1_{21} = a^0_{11} = a^1_{11} = 0.$$

From this examination of the separate conditions (i), (ii) and (iii) it is clear that there are many alternative requirements on the parameters which are sufficient for (i), (ii) and (iii) to hold and hence for the model to be identifiable. We will not enumerate all these alternatives but we note that all structures which satisfy the following simple requirements in addition to (7.16.15–17) will be identifiable:

$$\frac{b^0_{12}b^0_{21} - 1}{b^1_{11} - b^1_{12}b^0_{21}} \neq -\frac{a^0_{11}}{a^1_{11}}, \quad \frac{b^0_{12}b^0_{21} - 1}{b^1_{11} - b^1_{12}b^0_{21}} \neq -\frac{a^0_{22}}{a^1_{22}},$$

$$a^0_{22} \neq 0 \quad \text{and} \quad b^1_{11} \neq 0. \tag{7.16.21}$$

Part (c) It is easy to verify that the given structure I satisfies (7.16.15–17) and (7.16.21) above. It follows that this structure will be identifiable in the model (7.16.1) where x_{1t} satisfies Assumptions B and C.

Structure II yields the following system of equations:

$$\begin{bmatrix} 1 & -1 \\ 2 & 1 \end{bmatrix} y_t + \begin{bmatrix} -1 & -1 \\ 0 & 0 \end{bmatrix} y_{t-1} + \begin{bmatrix} 1 \\ 0 \end{bmatrix} x_{1t} \tag{7.16.22}$$

$$= \begin{bmatrix} 2 & 0 \\ 0 & 2 \end{bmatrix} u_t + \begin{bmatrix} 1 & -1 \\ 0 & 0 \end{bmatrix} u_{t-1}$$

We see that Condition (ii) is not satisfied for this structure. We have, in fact,

$$[B(1) \vdots C(0) \vdots A(1)] = \begin{bmatrix} -1 & -1 & 1 & 1 & -1 \\ 0 & 0 & 0 & 0 & 0 \end{bmatrix}$$

which has rank unity. Since Condition (ii) does not hold we cannot assert that the structure is identifiable; but since Conditions (i)—(iii) are sufficient conditions and not always necessary conditions for identifiability it does *not* follow immediately that structure II is not identifiable.

However, if we can find an equivalent structure which satisfies all the *a priori* restrictions of the model (7.16.1) then we will be able to deduce from this that structure II is not identifiable. We recall from our introductory discussion of Conditions (i)—(iii) that the effect of Condition (ii) is to restrict the class of admissible left divisors $K(L)$ of the system to the class of non-singular constant matrices. If Condition (ii) does not hold then this suggests to us that there may well be a unimodular matrix $K(L)$ which is an admissible left divisor. The word 'admissible' is used here to mean that the new system (obtained after the divisor has been extracted) satisfies the *a priori* restrictions (including both the parameters restrictions *and* the prescribed degrees of the polynomials in (7.16.4) — here $p = 1$, $q = 0$ and $r = 1$).

In an attempt to construct an alternative structure which is equivalent to II we consider the unimodular matrix

$$K(\zeta) = \begin{bmatrix} 1 & \zeta \\ 0 & 1 \end{bmatrix}$$

(note that $\det[K(\zeta)] = 1$ for all ζ). We premultiply the system (7.16.22) by the lag operator $K(L)$ and obtain

$$\begin{bmatrix} 1 & L \\ 0 & 1 \end{bmatrix} \begin{bmatrix} 1-L & -1-L \\ 2 & 1 \end{bmatrix} y_t + \begin{bmatrix} 1 & L \\ 0 & 1 \end{bmatrix} \begin{bmatrix} 1 \\ 0 \end{bmatrix} x_{1t} \tag{7.16.23}$$

$$= \begin{bmatrix} 1 & L \\ 0 & 1 \end{bmatrix} \begin{bmatrix} 2+L & -L \\ 0 & 2 \end{bmatrix} u_t$$

or

$$\begin{bmatrix} 1+L & -1 \\ 2 & 1 \end{bmatrix} y_t + \begin{bmatrix} 1 \\ 0 \end{bmatrix} x_{1t} = \begin{bmatrix} 2+L & L \\ 0 & 2 \end{bmatrix} u_t$$

which we write out as

$$\begin{bmatrix} 1 & -1 \\ 2 & 1 \end{bmatrix} y_t + \begin{bmatrix} 1 & 0 \\ 0 & 0 \end{bmatrix} y_{t-1} + \begin{bmatrix} 1 \\ 0 \end{bmatrix} x_{1t}$$

$$= \begin{bmatrix} 2 & 0 \\ 0 & 2 \end{bmatrix} u_t + \begin{bmatrix} 1 & 1 \\ 0 & 0 \end{bmatrix} u_{t-1} \qquad (7.16.24)$$

We notice that the new structure (7.16.24) satisfies the *a priori* parameter restrictions imposed on (7.16.1) and the prescribed lags implied by $p = 1$, $q = 0$ and $r = 1$. We note also that the parameter values in (7.16.24) satisfy the preliminary stability requirements (7.16.15—17). It follows that the new structure (7.16.24) is certainly feasible, according to all our prior conditions on the system. But (7.16.24) is observationally equivalent to (7.16.22). For, if we write (7.16.22) as

$$H(L)\, y_t + J(L)\, x_t = G(L)\, u_t$$

then it is clear from (7.16.23) that (7.16.24) can be written as

$$K(L)\, H(L)\, y_t + K(L)\, J(L)\, x_t = K(L)\, G(L)\, u_t$$

or

$$\bar{H}(L)\, y_t + \bar{J}(L)\, x_t = \bar{G}(L)\, u_t$$

Both these systems now lead to the same set of equations (7.16.13) and (7.16.14) since

$$\bar{H}(e^{i\lambda})^{-1}\, \bar{G}(e^{i\lambda}) = H(e^{i\lambda})^{-1} K(e^{i\lambda})^{-1} K(e^{i\lambda})\, G(e^{i\lambda})$$

$$= H(e^{i\lambda})^{-1} G(e^{i\lambda})$$

and similarly

$$\bar{H}(e^{i\lambda})^{-1}\, \bar{J}(e^{i\lambda}) = H(e^{i\lambda})^{-1} J(e^{i\lambda})$$

It then follows that we will not be able to determine uniquely the coefficient matrices of $H(L), J(L)$ and $G(L)$ from equations (7.16.13) and (7.16.14) and our knowledge of the prior restrictions on (7.16.1). Structure II is, therefore, not identifiable.

Solution 7.17

The model given by $(7.17.1-2)$ is an example of a simultaneous equations model with lagged endogenous variables as regressors and disturbances generated according to a vector autoregressive system. The problem of identification that arises in the context of such systems is in many respects similar to that in systems with moving average disturbances such as $(7.16.1)$. We have already discussed some aspects of this problem in Solution 7.6, where we distinguished between the concepts of local and global identification in such models. The subject has also been treated recently in Sargan (1972) Deistler (1976) and Hatanaka (1970). The present question deals only with one aspect of the problem and the reader is, therefore, referred to these articles for a more detailed discussion.

Part (a) If $K(\zeta)$ is a common left divisor of $H(\zeta)$ and $J(\zeta)$, then we can write

$$H(\zeta) = K(\zeta) H_1(\zeta), \quad J(\zeta) = K(\zeta) J_1(\zeta)$$

for some polynomial matrices $H_1(\zeta)$ and $J_1(\zeta)$ (compare Solution 7.16 and the references given there). We also say that $H(\zeta)$ and $J(\zeta)$ are right multiples of $K(\zeta)$. Then $K(\zeta)$ is a greatest common left divisor (g.c.l.d.) if it is a right multiple of all left divisors (c.f. Hannan, 1971, MacDuffee, 1933, and Preston and Wall, 1973).

Clearly, the identity matrix is a common left divisor of $H(\zeta)$ and $J(\zeta)$. It will, in fact, be a g.c.l.d. if and only if

$$\operatorname{rank} [H(\zeta) \vdots J(\zeta)] = 2$$

for all complex ζ. (see Lemma 1 of Deistler, 1976, and Preston and Wall, 1973). In the present case we have

$$[H(\zeta) \vdots J(\zeta)] = \begin{bmatrix} 1 - \frac{1}{2}\zeta & \frac{1}{2} & 4 \\ -\frac{1}{4} & 1 - \frac{1}{4}\zeta & 2 \end{bmatrix}$$

and when $\zeta = 3$ this matrix becomes

$$\begin{bmatrix} -\frac{1}{2} & \frac{1}{2} & 4 \\ -\frac{1}{4} & \frac{1}{4} & 2 \end{bmatrix}$$

which has rank unity. So the identity matrix is *not* a g.c.l.d. of $H(\zeta)$ and $J(\zeta)$.

To find a g.c.l.d. in this case we can use the general procedure described in MacDuffee (1933, p. 35) and Gantmacher (1959, pp. 135−136) (see also Preston and Wall, 1973). The idea behind the procedure is to transform the matrix $[H(\zeta) \vdots J(\zeta)]$ by elementary column operations into the form $[D(\zeta) \vdots 0]$ where $D(\zeta)$ is a lower triangular matrix of the form

$$D(\zeta) = \begin{bmatrix} d_{11}(\zeta) & 0 \\ d_{21}(\zeta) & d_{22}(\zeta) \end{bmatrix}$$

and where $d_{21}(\zeta)$ has degree less than that of $d_{22}(\zeta)$ provided $d_{22}(\zeta) \neq 0$ and is identically zero if $d_{22}(\zeta) = \text{const} \neq 0$ (Gantmacher, 1959, pp. 135–136). The fact that the matrix polynomial $D(\zeta)$ constructed in this way is a g.c.l.d. of $H(\zeta)$ and $J(\zeta)$ then follows from the result in MacDuffee (1933, p. 35).

To construct $D(\zeta)$ in our example we need to be clear about the nature of elementary operations on a matrix polynomial. These operations allow for the following:

1. multiplication of all the elements in a column by a non-zero scalar;

2. addition to any column of any other column multiplied by an arbitrary polynomial $a(\lambda)$;

3. interchange of any two columns.

Indicating our operations at the head of each column that is changed, we now have

$$\begin{bmatrix} 1 - \tfrac{1}{2}\zeta & \tfrac{1}{2} & 4 \\ -\tfrac{1}{4} & 1 - \tfrac{1}{4}\zeta & 2 \end{bmatrix} \sim \overset{C_1 + (\zeta/8)\, C_3 \quad C_2 - \tfrac{1}{8} C_3}{\begin{bmatrix} 1 & 0 & 4 \\ -\tfrac{1}{4} + \tfrac{1}{4}\zeta & \tfrac{3}{4} - \tfrac{1}{4}\zeta & 2 \end{bmatrix}}$$

$$\sim \overset{C_1 + C_2}{\begin{bmatrix} 1 & 0 & 4 \\ \tfrac{1}{2} & \tfrac{3}{4} - \tfrac{1}{4}\zeta & 2 \end{bmatrix}}$$

$$\sim \overset{C_3 - 4C_1}{\begin{bmatrix} 1 & 0 & 0 \\ \tfrac{1}{2} & \tfrac{3}{4} - \tfrac{1}{4}\zeta & 0 \end{bmatrix}}$$

Hence

$$D(\zeta) = \begin{bmatrix} 1 & 0 \\ \tfrac{1}{2} & \tfrac{3}{4} - \tfrac{1}{4}\zeta \end{bmatrix}$$

is a g.c.l.d. of $[H(\zeta) \vdots J(\zeta)]$ and we note that

$$\begin{bmatrix} 1 - \tfrac{1}{2}\zeta & \tfrac{1}{2} & 4 \\ -\tfrac{1}{4} & 1 - \tfrac{1}{4}\zeta & 2 \end{bmatrix} = \begin{bmatrix} 1 & 0 \\ \tfrac{1}{2} & \tfrac{3}{4} - \tfrac{1}{4}\zeta \end{bmatrix} \begin{bmatrix} 1 - \tfrac{1}{2}\zeta & \tfrac{1}{2} & 4 \\ -1 & 1 & 0 \end{bmatrix} \qquad (7.17.3)$$

Part (b) The model with structure I is just

$$\begin{bmatrix} 1 & \frac{1}{2} \\ -\frac{1}{4} & 1 \end{bmatrix} y_t + \begin{bmatrix} -\frac{1}{2} & 0 \\ 0 & -\frac{1}{4} \end{bmatrix} y_{t-1} + \begin{bmatrix} 4 \\ 2 \end{bmatrix} x_{1t} = u_t \qquad (7.17.4)$$

where

$$u_t = \begin{bmatrix} \frac{1}{3} & 0 \\ \frac{1}{9} & 0 \end{bmatrix} u_{t-1} + \epsilon_t \qquad (7.17.5)$$

and we have used the vectors $y_t' = (y_{1t}, y_{2t})$, $u_t' = (u_{1t}, u_{2t})$ and $\epsilon_t' = (\epsilon_{1t}, \epsilon_{2t})$. We now write (7.17.4) as

$$\begin{bmatrix} 1 - \frac{1}{2}L & \frac{1}{2} & 4 \\ -\frac{1}{4} & 1 - \frac{1}{4}L & 2 \end{bmatrix} \begin{bmatrix} y_t \\ x_{1t} \end{bmatrix} = u_t$$

and from (7.17.5) we have

$$u_t = \begin{bmatrix} 1 - \frac{1}{3}L & 0 \\ -\frac{1}{9}L & 1 \end{bmatrix}^{-1} \epsilon_t$$

From (7.17.3) it now follows that

$$\begin{bmatrix} 1 & 0 \\ \frac{1}{2} & \frac{3}{4} - \frac{1}{4}L \end{bmatrix} \begin{bmatrix} 1 - \frac{1}{2}L & \frac{1}{2} & 4 \\ -1 & 1 & 0 \end{bmatrix} \begin{bmatrix} y_t \\ x_{1t} \end{bmatrix} = \begin{bmatrix} 1 - \frac{1}{3}L & 0 \\ -\frac{1}{9}L & 1 \end{bmatrix}^{-1} \epsilon_t$$

so that

$$\begin{bmatrix} 1 - \frac{1}{2}L & \frac{1}{2} & 4 \\ -1 & 1 & 0 \end{bmatrix} \begin{bmatrix} y_t \\ x_{1t} \end{bmatrix} = \begin{bmatrix} 1 & 0 \\ \frac{1}{2} & \frac{3}{4} - \frac{1}{4}L \end{bmatrix}^{-1} \begin{bmatrix} 1 - \frac{1}{3}L & 0 \\ -\frac{1}{9}L & 1 \end{bmatrix}^{-1} \epsilon_t \ (7.17.6)$$

Writing

$$v_t = \begin{bmatrix} 1 & 0 \\ \frac{1}{2} & \frac{3}{4} - \frac{1}{4}L \end{bmatrix}^{-1} \begin{bmatrix} 1 - \frac{1}{3}L & 0 \\ -\frac{1}{9}L & 1 \end{bmatrix}^{-1} \epsilon_t \qquad (7.17.7)$$

we have

$$\begin{bmatrix} 1 - \frac{1}{3}L & 0 \\ -\frac{1}{9}L & 1 \end{bmatrix} \begin{bmatrix} 1 & 0 \\ \frac{1}{2} & \frac{3}{4} - \frac{1}{4}L \end{bmatrix} v_t = \epsilon_t$$

or

$$\begin{bmatrix} 1 - \frac{1}{3}L & 0 \\ \frac{1}{2} - \frac{1}{9}L & \frac{3}{4} - \frac{1}{4}L \end{bmatrix} v_t = \epsilon_t$$

That is

$$\begin{bmatrix} 1 & 0 \\ \frac{1}{2} & \frac{3}{4} \end{bmatrix} v_t = \begin{bmatrix} \frac{1}{3} & 0 \\ \frac{1}{9} & \frac{1}{4} \end{bmatrix} v_{t-1} + \epsilon_t$$

and, alternatively,

$$v_t = \begin{bmatrix} 1 & 0 \\ \frac{1}{2} & \frac{3}{4} \end{bmatrix}^{-1} \begin{bmatrix} \frac{1}{3} & 0 \\ \frac{1}{9} & \frac{1}{4} \end{bmatrix} v_{t-1} + \eta_t \tag{7.17.8}$$

where

$$\eta_t = \begin{bmatrix} 1 & 0 \\ \frac{1}{2} & \frac{3}{4} \end{bmatrix}^{-1} \epsilon_t = \begin{bmatrix} 1 & 0 \\ -\frac{2}{3} & \frac{4}{3} \end{bmatrix} \epsilon_t$$

has the same properties assumed of ϵ_t. From (7.17.6), (7.17.7) and (7.17.8) we obtain the new structure

$$\begin{bmatrix} 1 & \frac{1}{2} \\ -1 & 1 \end{bmatrix} y_t + \begin{bmatrix} -\frac{1}{2} & 0 \\ 0 & 0 \end{bmatrix} y_{t-1} + \begin{bmatrix} 4 \\ 0 \end{bmatrix} x_{1t} = v_t \tag{7.17.9}$$

where

$$v_t = \begin{bmatrix} \frac{1}{3} & 0 \\ -\frac{2}{27} & \frac{1}{3} \end{bmatrix} v_{t-1} + \eta_t \tag{7.17.10}$$

We notice that this structure is admissible in that it satisfies the *a priori* restrictions implied by the form of (7.17.1), the prescribed lag orders are satisfied and η_t has the same properties assumed of ϵ_t. But (7.17.9–10) is obtained essentially by taking out the g.c.l.d.

$$K(L) = \begin{bmatrix} 1 & 0 \\ \frac{1}{2} & \frac{3}{4} - \frac{1}{4}L \end{bmatrix}$$

as a common factor from each term of (7.17.4); and this common factor will not influence the spectral density matrices $f_y(\lambda)$ and $f_{yx}(\lambda)$ of y_t and y_t and x_t. It follows, as in Solution 7.16, that the two structures given by (7.17.4–5) and (7.17.9–10) (or I and II in the question) are observationally equivalent (the reader is referred to Solution 7.16 for a discussion of the use of this term).

To see this we need only write (7.17.4—5) in the form

$$H(L) y_t + J(L) x_t = u_t, \quad R(L) u_t = \epsilon_t$$

so that

$$R(L) H(L) y_t + R(L) J(L) x_t = \epsilon_t$$

and we have (see, for instance, Hannan, 1970, p. 67)

$$f_y(\lambda) = H(e^{i\lambda})^{-1} J(e^{i\lambda}) f_x(\lambda) J^*(e^{i\lambda})^{-1} H^*(e^{i\lambda})^{-1}$$

$$+ H(e^{i\lambda})^{-1} R(e^{i\lambda})^{-1} \frac{\Omega}{2\pi} R^*(e^{i\lambda})^{-1} H^*(e^{i\lambda})^{-1}$$

$$f_{yx}(\lambda) = H(e^{i\lambda})^{-1} J(e^{i\lambda}) f_x(\lambda)$$

where $\Omega = E(\epsilon_t \epsilon_t')$. On the other hand, (7.17.9—10) can be written as

$$K(L) H_1(L) y_t + K(L) J_1(L) x_t = u_t, \quad R(L) u_t = \epsilon_t$$

so that

$$R(L) K(L) H_1(L) y_t + R(L) K(L) J_1(L) x_t = \epsilon_t$$

and then we obtain the same spectral density matrices $f_y(\lambda)$ and $f_{yx}(\lambda)$ as given above.

Solution 7.18

Part (a) We first clarify the meaning of the term optimal linear predictor: $\hat{x}_t(k)$ is said to be the optimal linear predictor of x_{t+k} if it is that linear function of $x_t, x_{t-1}, \ldots$ which best approximates x_{t+k} in the mean square sense, i.e. we can write $\hat{x}_t(k)$ as the linear function

$$\hat{x}_t(k) = \sum_{s=0}^{\infty} a_s x_{t-s}$$

and the coefficients $\{a_s : s = 0, 1, \ldots\}$ here are such that they minimise the mean square error of prediction

$$E\left(x_{t+k} - \sum_{s=0}^{\infty} a_s x_{t-s}\right)^2$$

The predictor $\hat{x}_t(k)$ can be interpreted geometrically as a projection onto an appropriate linear space and for a development of the theory of linear prediction along these lines the reader is referred to Anderson (1971, pp. 414—424).

In the ARMA model (7.18.1) we normally assume that the u_t are serially independent, identically distributed random variates with zero mean and variance $\sigma^2 > 0$. The random sequence $\{u_t\}$ is then often referred to as 'white noise' and has the constant spectral density $\sigma^2/2\pi$ (see, for instance, Fishman, 1969, p. 40). We can then write the spectral density of the process x_t defined by (7.18.1) as

$$f_x(\lambda) = \frac{\sigma^2}{2\pi} \frac{|\Sigma_{k=0}^q \beta_k e^{ik\lambda}|^2}{|\Sigma_{j=0}^p \alpha_j e^{ij\lambda}|^2} \qquad (\alpha_0 = \beta_0 = 1) \qquad (7.18.7)$$

(see, for instance, Anderson, 1971, p. 409). We notice that $f_x(\lambda)$ is a rational function of $e^{i\lambda}$.

The theory of linear prediction for random processes with rational spectral densities such as (7.18.7) is well developed in the literature (see, in particular, Hannan, 1970, pp. 127–136) and recursion formulae are available to calculate optimal linear predictors (and update them as new data become available). In the present case, the general formula for the calculation of $\hat{x}_t(k)$ is given by

$$\hat{x}_t(k) = -[\alpha_1 \hat{x}_t(k-1) + \ldots + \alpha_p \hat{x}_t(k-p)] \qquad (7.18.8)$$
$$+ \beta_k[x_t - \hat{x}_{t-1}(1)] + \ldots + \beta_q[x_{t-q+1} - \hat{x}_{t-q}(1)]$$

and

$$\hat{x}_t(1) = -[\alpha_1 x_t + \ldots + \alpha_p x_{t-p}] + \beta_1[x_t - \hat{x}_{t-1}(1)] \qquad (7.18.9)$$
$$+ \ldots + \beta_q[x_{t-q+1} - \hat{x}_{t-q}(1)]$$

(see, in particular, Hannan, 1970, p. 135) where we use the convention that $\hat{x}_s(j) = x_{s+j}$ if $j \leqslant 0$. The optimal linear predictors $\{\hat{x}_t(k): k = 1, 2, \ldots\}$ are then obtained iteratively as follows:

(1) We compute $\hat{x}_t(1)$ using (7.18.9) and we note from the formula that this in itself requires the computation of the earlier one-step predictors $\hat{x}_{t-1}(1), \ldots, \hat{x}_{t-q}(1)$; we can start, perhaps, with $\hat{x}_{t-q}(1)$ and, neglecting earlier prediction errors, write

$$\hat{x}_{t-q}(1) = \alpha_1 x_{t-q} + \ldots + \alpha_p x_{t-q-p}.$$

Then

$$\hat{x}_{t-q+1}(1) = \alpha_1 x_{t-q+1} + \ldots + \alpha_p x_{t-q-p+1}$$
$$+ \beta_1[x_{t-q+1} - \hat{x}_{t-q}(1)]$$

and we continue until, by successive substitution in (7.18.9), we have $\hat{x}_t(1)$.

(2) We can now compute $\hat{x}_t(2), \hat{x}_t(3), \ldots$ iteratively using (7.18.8) together with the one step predictors $\hat{x}_{t-1}(1), \ldots, \hat{x}_{t-q}(1)$ obtained in (1).

Remark 1 We should emphasize that in the notation of this question $\hat{x}_t(k)$

is a prediction of x_{t+k} using the observations $x_t, x_{t-1}, \ldots$. This means that $\hat{x}_t(k)$ is a predictor k steps ahead or, as we sometimes say, with lead time k. Some authors use the notation $\hat{x}_t^{(n)}$ to indicate a predictor of x_t n steps ahead, i.e. a predictor of x_t based on $x_{t-n}, x_{t-n-1}, \ldots$. In this notation, we see that $\hat{x}_t(k)$ would be written as $\hat{x}_{t+k}^{(k)}$ and equations (7.18.8) and (7.18.9), which define the recursion formulae, would become

$$\hat{x}_{t+k}^{(k)} = -(\alpha_1 \hat{x}_{t+k-1}^{(k-1)} + \ldots + \alpha_p \hat{x}_{t+k-p}^{(k-p)}) \tag{7.18.10}$$
$$+ \beta_k (x_t - \hat{x}_t^{(1)}) + \ldots + \beta_q (x_{t-q+1} - \hat{x}_{t-q+1}^{(1)})$$

and

$$\hat{x}_{t+1}^{(1)} = -(\alpha_1 x_t + \ldots + \alpha_p x_{t-p+1})$$
$$+ \beta_1 (x_t - \hat{x}_t^{(1)}) + \ldots + \beta_q (x_{t-q+1} - \hat{x}_{t-q+1}^{(1)})$$

Note that (7.18.10) holds for all values of t so we can replace $t + k$ by s and this gives us the alternative form

$$\hat{x}_s^{(k)} = -(\alpha_1 \hat{x}_{s-1}^{(k-1)} + \ldots + \alpha_p \hat{x}_{s-p}^{(k-p)})$$
$$+ \beta_k (x_{s-k} - \hat{x}_{s-k}^{(1)}) + \ldots + \beta_q (x_{s-k-q+1} - \hat{x}_{x-k-q+1}^{(1)})$$

which corresponds with the formula in Hannan (1970, p. 135) — but note that the summation Σ_1^s in Hannan's formula for $x^\nu(n)$ should read Σ_ν^s,

Remark 2 We observe from formula (7.18.8) that when $k > q$ (i.e. the lead time of prediction is greater than the order of the moving average in the model) this formula reduces to

$$\hat{x}_t(k) = -[\alpha_1 \hat{x}_t(k-1) + \ldots + \alpha_p \hat{x}_t(k-p)]$$

so that forecasts are obtained from forecasts for earlier preiods using only the autoregressive component of the model.

Part (b) The optimal linear one-step predictor for the general ARMA model (7.18.1) is given by (7.18.9). Hence, in order to identify the ARMA model for which (7.18.2) is an optimal linear predictor, we need only write (7.18.2) in the form of (7.18.9). We have

$$\hat{x}_t(1) = \alpha(x_t + \beta x_{t-1} + \beta^2 x_{t-2} + \ldots)$$

so that

$$\beta \hat{x}_{t-1}(1) = \alpha(\beta x_{t-1} + \beta^2 x_{t-2} + \ldots)$$

and

$$\hat{x}_t(1) = \alpha x_t + \beta \hat{x}_{t-1}(1)$$

or

$$\hat{x}_t(1) = \alpha x_t + \beta x_t - \beta\{x_t - \hat{x}_{t-1}(1)\}$$

which reproduce exactly the form of (7.18.9). We see that $p = 1, q = 1$ and the underlying ARMA model for x_t is

$$x_t - (\alpha + \beta) x_{t-1} = u_t - \beta u_{t-1}. \tag{7.18.11}$$

Remark We can derive (7.18.11) in an alternative way as follows. We note first that we can write $\hat{x}_t(1)$ as

$$\hat{x}_t(1) = \alpha(1 - \beta L)^{-1} x_t$$

where L is the lag operator for which $L x_t = x_{t-1}$. If the process $\{x_t\}$ is Gaussian (i.e. the joint distribution of $x_t, \ldots, x_{t-s}$ is multivariate normal for any positive integer s) then the optimal linear predictor is just the conditional expectation of x_{t+1} given $x_t, x_{t-1}, \ldots$; i.e. $\hat{x}_t(1) = E(x_{t+1}|x_t, x_{t-1}, \ldots)$ (see, for instance, Anderson, 1971, p. 147). We can then write

$$\begin{aligned} x_{t+1} &= E(x_{t+1}|x_t, x_{t-1}, \ldots) + u_{t+1} \\ &= \alpha(1 - \beta L)^{-1} x_t + u_{t+1} \end{aligned} \tag{7.18.12}$$

where u_{t+1} is uncorrelated with $x_t, x_{t-1}, \ldots$ [otherwise, $E(u_{t+1}|x_t, x_{t-1}, \ldots)$ would not be zero]. From (7.18.12) we now have

$$(1 - \beta L) x_{t+1} = \alpha x_t + (1 - \beta L) u_{t+1}$$

and, therefore,

$$x_{t+1} - (\alpha + \beta) x_t = u_{t+1} - \beta u_t$$

as in (7.18.11).

Part (c) Since p_t^e is the optimal linear predictor of p_t using $p_{t-1}, p_{t-2}, \ldots$ we can write, in the notation of Parts (a) and (b),

$$p_t^e = \hat{p}_{t-1}(1).$$

We know that p_t is determined so that the market clears and it follows that p_t must satisfy

$$\alpha p_t = \beta p_t^e + u_t.$$

Now

$$\rho \alpha p_{t-1} = \rho \beta p_{t-1}^e + \rho u_{t-1}$$

and, thus, using (7.18.6) we have the equation

$$\alpha p_t - \alpha \rho p_{t-1} = \beta p_t^e - \beta \rho p_{t-1}^e + \epsilon_t \tag{7.18.13}$$

Taking expectations of (7.18.13) conditional on $p_{t-1}, p_{t-2}, \ldots$ and, noting that

$$p_t^e = \hat{p}_{t-1}(1) = E(p_t|p_{t-1}, p_{t-2}, \ldots)$$

because of the Gaussian assumption, we have

$$\alpha p_t^e - \alpha \rho p_{t-1} = \beta p_t^e - \beta \rho p_{t-1}^e.$$

Rearranging, we obtain

$$p_t^e \;=\; \frac{\alpha\rho}{\alpha-\beta}\, p_{t-1} - \frac{\beta\rho}{\alpha-\beta}\, p_{t-1}^e \tag{7.18.14}$$

$$=\; \frac{\alpha\rho}{\alpha-\beta}\, p_{t-1} - \frac{\beta\rho}{\alpha-\beta}\, p_{t-1} + \frac{\beta\rho}{\alpha-\beta}\,(p_{t-1} - p_{t-1}^e)$$

$$=\; \rho p_{t-1} + \frac{\beta\rho}{\alpha-\beta}\,(p_{t-1} - p_{t-1}^e)$$

or, replacing p_t^e by the notation $\hat{p}_{t-1}(1)$,

$$\hat{p}_{t-1}(1) \;=\; \rho p_{t-1} + \frac{\beta\rho}{\alpha-\beta}\,[p_{t-1} - \hat{p}_{t-2}(1)] \tag{7.18.15}$$

We see that (7.18.15) corresponds exactly in form to (7.18.9) with $p = 1$ and $q = 1$. The underlying ARMA model can then be deduced from (7.18.15) using the correspondence between (7.18.9) and the model (7.18.1). We obtain in this way the following ARMA model for p_t:

$$p_t - \rho p_{t-1} \;=\; v_t + \frac{\beta\rho}{\alpha-\beta}\, v_{t-1} \tag{7.18.16}$$

where v_t has the same properties as ϵ_t.

To find the relationship between v_t and ϵ_t we can proceed as follows. From (7.18.14) we have the relation

$$\left(1 + \frac{\beta\rho}{\alpha-\beta}\, L\right) p_t^e \;=\; \frac{\alpha\rho}{\alpha-\beta}\, L p_t$$

and substituting into

$$\alpha p_t \;=\; \beta p_t^e + u_t$$

we obtain

$$\alpha \left(1 + \frac{\beta\rho}{\alpha-\beta}\, L\right) p_t \;=\; \beta\,\frac{\alpha\rho}{\alpha-\beta}\, L p_t + \left(1 + \frac{\beta\rho}{\alpha-\beta}\, L\right) u_t$$

or, rearranging,

$$\alpha p_t \;=\; \left(1 + \frac{\beta\rho}{\alpha-\beta}\, L\right) u_t.$$

But, it follows from (7.18.6) that

$$u_t \;=\; (1 - \rho L)^{-1} \epsilon_t$$

so that

$$p_t = \frac{1}{\alpha}\left(1 + \frac{\beta\rho}{\alpha - \beta}L\right)(1 - \rho L)^{-1}\epsilon_t$$

or

$$(1 - \rho L)\,p_t = \left(1 + \frac{\beta\rho}{\alpha - \beta}L\right)\left(\frac{\epsilon_t}{\alpha}\right) \qquad (7.18.17)$$

comparing (7.18.16) and (7.18.17) it is clear that $v_t = \epsilon_t/\alpha$.

Solution 7.19

Part (a) We are required to maximise (7.19.2) with respect to L_t subject to (7.19.1). A necessary condition for a maximum is the familiar marginal productivity equation

$$\frac{w_t}{p_t} = \frac{\partial Q_t}{\partial L_t}$$

$$= A^{-\theta}\,\delta Q_t^{1+\theta}\,L_t^{-(1+\theta)}.$$

Hence the desired level of output per manhour is

$$\left(\frac{Q_t}{L_t}\right)^* = (A^{-\theta}\,\delta)^{-1/(1+\theta)}\left(\frac{w_t}{p_t}\right)^{1/1+\theta}$$

or

$$\ln\left(\frac{Q_t}{L_t}\right)^* = \alpha + \frac{1}{1+\theta}\ln\left(\frac{w_t}{p_t}\right) = \alpha + \sigma\ln\left(\frac{w_t}{p_t}\right). \qquad (7.19.9)$$

Thus, in (7.19.3) $\beta = 1/(1 + \theta) = \sigma$.

Part (b) On the hypothesis H_0, $(Q_t/L_t)^*$ adjusts instantly to Q_t/L_t and $u_t = e_t$ $(t = 1, \ldots, T)$, which are independent $N(0, \sigma^2)$ variables. Thus, the estimating equation is

$$\ln(Q_t/L_t) = \alpha + \sigma\ln(w_t/p_t) + e_t, \qquad (7.19.10)$$

which corresponds to (7.19.6)

On hypothesis H_1, $\ln(Q_t/L_t)^*$ is related to actual $\ln(Q_t/L_t)$ by the partial adjustment mechanism (7.19.5) and $u_t = e_t$. In this case we obtain the model

$$\Delta\ln\frac{Q_t}{L_t} = \lambda\left(\alpha + \sigma\ln\frac{w_t}{p_t} + e_t - \ln\frac{Q_{t-1}}{L_{t-1}}\right),$$

or

$$\ln \frac{Q_t}{L_t} = \lambda\alpha + \lambda\sigma \ln \frac{w_t}{p_t} + (1-\lambda) \ln \frac{Q_{t-1}}{L_{t-1}} + \lambda e_t, \qquad (7.19.11)$$

which corresponds to equation (7.19.7).

On hypothesis H_2, (Q_t/L_t) adjusts instantly to $(Q_t/L_t)^*$ but u_t is generated by (7.19.4). In this case, our model is

$$\ln (Q_t/L_t) = \alpha + \sigma \ln (w_t/p_t) + u_t,$$

or, eliminating u_t,

$$\ln (Q_t/L_t) = \alpha(1-\rho) + \sigma \ln (w_t/p_t) + \rho \ln (Q_{t-1}/L_{t-1})$$
$$- \sigma\rho \ln (w_{t-1}/p_{t-1}) + e_t. \qquad (7.19.12)$$

This corresponds to equation (7.19.8). Since equations (7.19.10) − (7.19.12) have serially independent errors and, assuming the given price and wage variables are exogenous, these equations can be estimated consistently by ordinary least squares.

Of the three hypotheses, H_2 is the least restrictive (although we ignore the parameter restriction on the coefficients of (7.19.12)). H_1 implies that the variable $\ln (w_{t-1}/p_{t-1})$ should have a zero coefficient and H_0 implies that $\ln (w_{t-1}/p_{t-1})$ and $\ln (Q_{t-1}/L_{t-1})$ should both have zero coefficients. H_0, H_1 and H_2 are, therefore, a set of nested hypotheses with $H_0 < H_1 < H_2$. Comparing H_0 with H_1 we can reject H_0 in favour of H_1 as $\ln (Q_{t-1}/L_{t-1})$ is significant in (7.19.7). But, comparing H_1 with H_2 we can reject H_1 in favour of H_2 as $\ln (w_{t-1}/p_{t-1})$ is significant in (7.19.8). In each case we note that the coefficients of the other variables are also significant, as required. Moreover, from (7.19.12) we see that, if H_2 is correct then the coefficient of $\ln (w_{t-1}/p_{t-1})$ in (7.19.8) is minus the product of the coefficients of $\ln (w_t/p_t)$ and $\ln (Q_{t-1}/L_{t-1})$. In fact, the product is $1.056 \times 0.855 = 0.903$ which is very close to 0.900, the unrestricted estimate of the product, and well within one standard error of this estimate. On this evidence, therefore, we prefer H_2 to both H_0 and H_1.

Using equation (7.19.8) as our preferred equation, we obtain a point estimate of σ of 1.056 which is not significantly different from unity.

If H_2 is correct, equations (7.19.6) and (7.19.7) are mis-specified. Notice, however, that the implied estimate of σ from (7.19.6) is close to that from (7.19.8) but its standard error is lower in (7.19.6). This result is a typical consequence of neglecting to take account of autocorrelation in the error term of an equation with fixed regressors. In theory, this neglect does not introduce biases but does tend to underestimate the true variances of the regression estimates. The mis-specification of (7.19.7) through the omission of $\ln (w_{t-1}/p_{t-1})$ had a pronounced effect on the coefficient of $\ln (w_t/p_t)$ and the implied estimate of σ which is $0.233/(1 - 0.827) = 1.35$. Thus, trying to eliminate serial correlation by adding a lagged dependent variable, rather than by using the appropriate error structure, can have serious consequences. It should be remarked, however, that if the model is mis-specified in some other more fundamental way (any or all of the equations (7.20.3–5) could be incorrect) then the consequences noted may not be as severe. In this case more extensive tests, perhaps involving a detailed analysis of the residuals from the several regressions, are required.

Solution 7.20

Part (a) Introducing the lag operator $L^r x_t = x_{t-r}$ we can rewrite equation (7.20.1) as

$$\Delta p_t = \frac{\gamma(1-\xi)}{1-\xi L} e_t, \tag{7.20.4}$$

and (7.20.2) as

$$d_t = \frac{(1-\mu) L}{1-\mu L} e_t. \tag{7.20.5}$$

From (7.20.5) we deduce that

$$e_t = \left(\frac{1-\mu L}{1-\mu}\right) d_{t+1} \tag{7.20.6}$$

Substituting (7.20.6) into (7.20.4) we obtain

$$\begin{aligned}
\Delta p_t &= \frac{\gamma(1-\xi)(1-\mu L)}{(1-L\xi)(1-\mu)} d_{t+1} \\
&= \frac{\gamma(1-\xi)}{1-\mu} d_{t+1} - \frac{\mu\gamma(1-\xi)}{1-\mu} d_t + \xi\Delta p_{t-1},
\end{aligned} \tag{7.20.7}$$

which has the same form as (7.20.3). Using the estimates in (7.20.3), it follows that

$$\hat{\xi} = 0.814,$$

$$\hat{\mu} = \frac{\hat{\mu}\hat{\gamma}(1-\hat{\xi})/(1-\hat{\mu})}{\hat{\gamma}(1-\hat{\xi})/(1-\hat{\mu})} = \frac{3.200}{3.914} = 0.818,$$

$$\hat{\gamma} = \frac{1-\hat{\mu}}{1-\hat{\xi}} \times 3.914 = 3.830.$$

Part (b) First, given the transformations we have used, it is somewhat unlikely that the disturbances influencing (7.20.7) will be serially independent. As there is a lagged dependent variable among the regressors, this is likely to affect the large sample (and, in particular, the consistency) properties of the OLS estimator. For example, if we add serially independent disturbances ϵ_{1t} and ϵ_{2t} to equations (7.20.1) and (7.20.3) respectively, then the disturbance influencing (7.20.7) is

$$v_t = \epsilon_{1t} - \xi\epsilon_{1,\,t-1} - \frac{\gamma(1-\xi)}{1-\mu}(\epsilon_{2,\,t+1} - \mu\epsilon_{2t}), \qquad (7.20.8)$$

which is not, in general, serially independent.

Second, for v_t defined as in (7.20.8), d_{t+1} and d_t will generally be correlated with v_t through ϵ_{2t+1} and ϵ_{2t}, resulting in further sources of large sample biases. Finally, it is possible that ϵ_{1t} will be correlated with ϵ_{2t}. Thus Δp_t and d_t are likely to be endogenous and jointly dependent, hence giving rise to simultaneous equation bias. For these reasons, ordinary least squares is unlikely to be a suitable estimator.

Part (c) A major policy implication of equation (7.20.1) is that, in order to control product price changes, it is necessary to pursue policies which affect excess demand in the product market. Presumably this can be achieved by inducing shifts in either (or both) the product demand or supply function. Conventional fiscal and monetary policy measures would, therefore, appear to be appropriate. The estimate of ξ of 0.814 implies that the average lag of price changes to excess demand is

$$\frac{\partial}{\partial L}\left(\frac{1-\xi}{1-\xi L}\right)\Bigg|_{L=1} = \frac{\xi}{1-\xi} = \frac{0.814}{0.186} = 4.38 \text{ quarters.}$$

In other words, the mean of the lag distribution is approximately one year. This implies that a policy of, say, reducing inflation from one steady state level to another by inducing a once-for-all reduction in excess demand would take effect fairly slowly. In order to reduce inflation more quickly, it might be preferable to reduce excess demand more sharply in the short run and then allow excess demand to rise in the longer run to a level consistent with the desired steady state inflation rate. The precise policy timing is really a problem in the theory of optimal control and will depend upon the government's target rates of inflation and unemployment. For an exposition of the application of the theory of optimal control in econometrics the reader is referred to the recent book by Chow (1976).

Equation (7.20.2) implies that excess demand in the labour market is influenced by excess demand in the product market. Therefore, an inflation policy based on the control of excess demand in the product market will, according to (7.20.2), have side effects for the labour market. These may or may not be desirable. Since $\mu = 0.818$, the average lag of d to changes in e is 5.33 quarters. Again this is quite a slow response rate.

Although excess demand in the labour market has no direct influence on prices in this model, it may have an indirect influence through excess demand in the product market. If e can be controlled and if price inflation is the sole target, then this indirect effect can be ignored. It is apparent that knowledge of (7.20.3) without knowledge of the underlying equations (7.20.1) and (7.20.2) may lead to incorrect policy inferences arising from a mistaken belief that there is direct causal link between Δp_t and d_t.

Solution 7.21

Part (a) We can rewrite equation (7.21.4) as

$$(1 + \alpha_2 L)\,\pi_t = (1 + \alpha_1 + \alpha_2)\,p_t - \alpha_1 p_{t-1} \qquad (7.21.6)$$

where $L^r \pi_t = \pi_{t-r}$. Combining (7.21.1) and (7.21.6) we obtain

$$m_t = \beta_0 + \beta_1 y_t + \beta_2 r_t + \frac{\beta_3}{1 + \alpha_2 L}[(1 + \alpha_2)\,p_t + \alpha_1 \Delta p_t]$$

$$+ \beta_4 m_{t-1} + u_t,$$

$$= \beta_0(1 + \alpha_2) + \beta_1 y_t + \beta_1 \alpha_2 y_{t-1} + \beta_2 r_t + \beta_2 \alpha_2 r_{t-1} + \beta_3(1 + \alpha_2)p_t$$

$$+ \beta_3 \alpha_1 \Delta p_t + (\beta_4 - \alpha_2)\,m_{t-1} + \beta_4 \alpha_2 m_{t-2} + u_t + \alpha_2 u_{t-1}. \qquad (7.21.7)$$

Assuming that m_t, y_t r_t and p_t are all endogenous variables, equation (7.21.7) is a single structural equation, non-linear in its parameters and with a first order moving average disturbance term whose parameter appears elsewhere in the equation. Notice that equation (7.21.7) involves only observable variables and hence is estimable, whereas (7.21.5) which contains the unobservable variable π_{t-1} cannot be estimated directly.

In order to see how (7.21.7) can be estimated, first we write the equation as

$$X\,\phi(\alpha, \beta) = e \qquad (7.21.8)$$

where $X' = (x_3, \ldots, x_T)$, $x_t' = (m_t, 1, y_t, y_{t-1}, r_t, r_{t-1}, p_t, \Delta p_t, m_{t-1},$ $m_{t-2})$, $e' = (e_3, \ldots, e_T)$, $e_t = u_t + \alpha_2 u_{t-1}$ and $\phi(\alpha, \beta)$ is a vector of the coefficients of x_t which is non-linear in $\alpha' = (\alpha_1, \alpha_2)$ and $\beta' = (\beta_0, \ldots, \beta_4)$. For $t = 3, \ldots, T$ the covariance matrix of e is

$$\sigma^2 \Sigma = \sigma^2 \begin{bmatrix} (1 + \alpha_2)^2 & \alpha_2 & 0 & \cdots & 0 \\ \alpha_2 & (1 + \alpha_2)^2 & \alpha_2 & \cdots & 0 \\ 0 & \alpha_2 & (1 + \alpha_2)^2 & \cdots & 0 \\ \cdot & \cdot & \cdot & \cdots & \cdot \\ 0 & \cdot & \cdot & \cdots & (1 + \alpha_2)^2 \end{bmatrix}$$

Assuming that we have a matrix of valid instruments Z for X which may include $y_{t-1}, r_{t-1}, p_{t-1}, m_{t-1}$ and m_{t-2}, we estimate (7.21.8) as follows (the final choice of which instruments are appropriate will depend, in part, on the properties of the errors affecting the equations for y_t, r_t and p_t). First, for a given α_2 in the interval $|\alpha_2| < 1$, we can construct Σ and ϕ by replacing α_2 in Σ and ϕ with the given value of α_2. Next we choose α_1 and β to minimise

$$\hat{\phi}' X' \hat{\Sigma}^{-1} Z (Z' \hat{\Sigma}^{-1} Z)^{-1} Z' \hat{\Sigma}^{-1} X \hat{\phi} \tag{7.21.10}$$

(see Theil, 1958, p. 345, and Wickens, 1969, for a discussion of the use of this minimand).

A necessary condition for a minimum is

$$\frac{\partial \phi'}{\partial \begin{bmatrix} \alpha_1 \\ \beta \end{bmatrix}} X' \hat{\Sigma}^{-1} Z (Z' \hat{\Sigma}^{-1} Z)^{-1} Z' \hat{\Sigma}^{-1} X \hat{\phi} = 0. \tag{7.21.11}$$

(7.21.11) can be solved without iteration for the estimators of α_1 and β. These estimators will, of course, depend upon the choice of α_2. In order to find the value of α_2 that minimises (7.21.10) we can search in the interval $|\alpha_2| < 1$; for each α_2 we construct Σ and $\hat{\phi}$, and then minimise (7.21.10) with respect to α_1 and β. The money demand function (7.21.5) can be interpreted as just one equation from a macroeconometric model. The estimation procedure proposed here ignores the information contained in these other equations; consequently, the estimator of α_2 that minimises (7.21.10) and the corresponding estimators of α_1 and β are limited information maximum likelihood estimators.

If α_2 had been known then Σ would be known and hence the estimators of α_1 and β, namely $\hat{\alpha}_1$ and $\hat{\beta}$, could be obtained without (additional) iteration from (7.21.11). Under assumptions similar to those in Question 7.8 (see also Hatanaka, 1974 and 1976), the limiting distribution of $T^{1/2}(\hat{\alpha}_1 - \alpha_1, \hat{\beta} - \beta)$ would be normal with mean zero and covariance matrix

$$\sigma^2 \text{ plim } T \left[\left(\begin{matrix} \dfrac{\partial \phi'}{\partial \alpha_1} \\ \dfrac{\partial \phi'}{\partial \beta} \end{matrix} \right) X' \Sigma^{-1} Z (Z' \Sigma^{-1} Z)^{-1} Z' \Sigma^{-1} X \left(\begin{matrix} \dfrac{\partial \phi'}{\partial \alpha_1} \\ \dfrac{\partial \phi'}{\partial \beta} \end{matrix} \right)' \right]^{-1} \tag{7.21.12}$$

where σ^2 could be consistently estimated by $T^{-1} \phi'(\hat{\alpha}_1, \hat{\alpha}_2, \hat{\beta}) X' X \phi(\hat{\alpha}_1, \hat{\alpha}_2, \hat{\alpha}_2, \hat{\beta})$. But since α_2 is unknown and both ϕ and Σ are functions of α_2 we cannot use this result. Instead, we must proceed in a different way.

We can write

$$\phi' X' \Sigma^{-1} Z (Z' \Sigma^{-1} Z)^{-1} Z' \Sigma^{-1} X \phi = \phi' A \phi \tag{7.21.13}$$

where $\phi = \phi(\theta)$, $\theta' = (\alpha_1, \alpha_2, \beta')$ and $A = A(\alpha_2)$. The necessary conditions for a minimum of (7.21.13) are

$$\frac{\partial \phi'}{\partial \theta} A \phi + \tfrac{1}{2} D \phi' \frac{\partial A}{\partial \alpha_2} \phi' = H(\theta) = 0 \tag{7.21.14}$$

where D is a column vector with zero elements apart from the second which is unity. Expanding (7.21.14) in a Taylor series in the neighbourhood of θ^0, the true value of θ, we obtain the approximation

$$0 = H(\theta) = H(\theta^0) + \frac{\partial H(\theta^0)}{\partial \theta} (\theta - \theta^0) + \tfrac{1}{2} (\theta - \theta^0)' \frac{\partial^2 H(\theta^*)}{\partial \theta \partial \theta'} (\theta - \theta^0) \tag{7.21.15}$$

where θ^* lies in the interval (θ, θ^0).

We make the following assumptions: θ is consistent for θ^0, $T^{-1} \partial H(\theta^0)/\partial \theta$ has probability limit $\bar{H}$ which is finite non-singular, the elements of $T^{-1} \partial^2 H(\theta^*)/\partial \theta \partial \theta'$ are bounded in probability as $T \to \infty$ and $T^{-1/2} Z' \Sigma^{-1} e$ evaluated at θ^0 has a limiting normal distribution with mean zero and covariance matrix

$$V_e = \sigma^2 \text{ plim } T^{-1} Z' \Sigma^{-1} Z \tag{7.21.16}$$

It follows that $[T^{-1} \partial H(\theta^0)/\partial \theta] T^{1/2} (\theta - \theta^0)$ has the same limiting distribution as $- T^{-1/2} H(\theta^0)$. But

$$T^{-1/2} H(\theta^0) = \frac{\partial \phi(\theta^0)'}{\partial \theta} \frac{X' \Sigma^{-1} Z}{T} \left(\frac{Z' \Sigma^{-1} Z}{T} \right)^{-1} \frac{Z' \Sigma^{-1} e}{T^{1/2}}$$

$$+ \tfrac{1}{2} D \phi(\theta^0) \frac{\partial A(\alpha_2^0)}{\partial \alpha_2^0} A^{-1}(\alpha_2^0) \frac{X' \Sigma^{-1} Z}{T} \left(\frac{Z' \Sigma^{-1} Z}{T} \right)^{-1} \frac{Z' \Sigma^{-1} e}{T^{1/2}}$$

$$= T^{-1/2} G Z' \Sigma^{-1} e \tag{7.21.17}$$

where

$$G = \left[2 \frac{\partial \phi(\theta_0)}{\partial \theta} + \tfrac{1}{2} D\phi(\theta^0) \frac{\partial A(\alpha_2^0)}{\partial \alpha_2^0} A^{-1}(\alpha_2^0) \right] \frac{X'\Sigma^{-1}Z}{T} \left(\frac{Z'\Sigma^{-1}Z}{T} \right)^{-1} \tag{7.21.18}$$

and $A(\alpha_2^0)$ is assumed to be non-singular. Note that in obtaining the last line in the above expression we have used the fact that

$$A^{-1}A\phi = A^{-1}(X'\Sigma^{-1}Z)(Z'\Sigma^{-1}Z)^{-1}(Z'\Sigma^{-1}X)\phi$$
$$= A^{-1}(X'\Sigma^{-1}Z)(Z'\Sigma^{-1}Z)^{-1}(Z'\Sigma^{-1}e)$$

when ϕ is evaluated at θ^0. If we now let $\operatorname{plim}_{T \to \infty} G = \bar{G}$, then we can show that the limiting distribution of $T^{1/2}(\theta - \theta^0)$ is the same as that of $-T^{-1/2}\bar{H}^{-1}\bar{G}Z'\Sigma^{-1}e$ which is normal with mean zero and covariance matrix

$$V_\theta = \bar{H}^{-1}\bar{G}V_e\bar{G}'\bar{H}^{-1}{}'. \tag{7.21.18}$$

We notice that when α_2 is known we can drop the terms in (7.21.14), (7.21.17) and (7.21.18) corresponding to α_2. In this case we find that

$$\bar{H} = \operatorname*{plim}_{T \to \infty} \left[\frac{\partial \phi'}{\partial \binom{\alpha_1}{\beta}} \frac{X'\Sigma^{-1}Z}{T} \left(\frac{Z'\Sigma^{-1}Z}{T} \right)^{-1} \frac{X'\Sigma^{-1}Z}{T} \frac{\partial \phi}{\partial \binom{\alpha_1}{\beta}'} \right]$$

and

$$\bar{G} = \operatorname*{plim}_{T \to \infty} \left[\frac{\partial \phi'}{\partial \binom{\alpha_1}{\beta}} \frac{X'\Sigma^{-1}Z}{T} \left(\frac{Z'\Sigma^{-1}Z}{T} \right)^{-1} \right]$$

Hence, (7.21.18) becomes

$$V^* = \sigma^2 \bar{H}^{-1} \operatorname{plim} \left\{ \left[\frac{\partial \phi'}{\partial \binom{\alpha_1}{\beta}} \frac{X'\Sigma^{-1}Z}{T} \left(\frac{Z'\Sigma^{-1}Z}{T} \right)^{-1} \right] \frac{Z'\Sigma^{-1}Z}{T} \right.$$
$$\left. \times \left[\left(\frac{Z'\Sigma^{-1}Z}{T} \right)^{-1} \frac{Z'\Sigma^{-1}X}{T} \frac{\partial \phi}{\partial \binom{\alpha_1}{\beta}'} \right] \right\}$$

$$= \sigma^2 \bar{H}^{-1}$$

which is equal to (7.21.12).

Part (b) If (7.21.2) is the correct expectations generating process, then in equation (7.21.4) we have $\alpha_1 = \theta_1$ and $\alpha_2 = 0$. But if (7.21.3) is the correct process, then $\alpha_1 = \theta_2$ and $\alpha_2 = -1$. In order to test which process is the more compatible with the data we can, therefore, test $H_0: \alpha_2 = 0$ against $H_1: \alpha_2 = -1$. From equation (7.21.5), which has been obtained by first substituting (7.21.4) directly into (7.21.1) and then replacing the unknown coefficients by their estimates, our estimate of α_2 is 0.730 with t statistic 1.15. Hence the standard error of this estimate is 0.635. A 95% confidence interval for α_2 is the interval $(-0.515, 1.975)$. On this evidence, therefore, we can accept H_0 in preference to H_1; that is, the expectations generating process (7.21.2) is more compatible with these data than is (7.21.3).

It should be noted, however, that if we accept the process (7.21.2), then our estimate of θ_1 is 0.363, which is not significantly different from zero. This implies that we cannot reject the hypothesis that $\pi_t = p_t$, that is, that expected equals actual inflation. However, given the probable high correlation between Δp_t and $p_t - \pi_{t-1}$, before we finally 'accept' that $\theta_1 = 0$, it would be preferable to omit $p_t - \pi_{t-1}$, to re-estimate the model and then to re-test θ_1.

Part (c) Consider the model

$$A(L) y_t = B(L) x_t$$

where L is the lag operator, $A(L) = \Sigma_{i=0}^I a_i L^i$, $a_0 = 1$, $B(L) = \Sigma_{j=0}^J b_j L^j$ and y_t and x_t are scalars, then the long-run multiplier of y with respect to x is given by $C(1)$ and the average lag by $[\partial C(1)/\partial L]/C(1)$, where $C(L) = B(L)/A(L)$. In the present example, $C(L) = -27.1(1.363 - 0.363L)/(1 - 0.859L)$. Hence, $C(1) = -27.1/(1 - 0.859) = -192$. Furthermore

$$\frac{\partial C(L)}{\partial L} = \frac{\partial}{\partial L} \left[\frac{-27.1(1.363 - 0.363L)}{1 - 0.859L} \right]$$

$$= \frac{27.1 \times 0.363}{1 - 0.859L} + \frac{C(L) \times 0.859}{1 - 0.859L}.$$

Hence

$$\frac{1}{C(1)} \cdot \frac{\partial C(1)}{\partial L} = -0.363 + 0.859/0.141 = 5.73$$

implying that the average lag of m to p is 5.73 periods.

Appendix

A. THE VEC( ) OPERATOR

Definition *If A is an $n \times m$ matrix and a_i' denotes the ith row of A then we write*

$$\text{vec}(A) = \begin{bmatrix} a_1 \\ a_2 \\ \cdot \\ \cdot \\ \cdot \\ a_n \end{bmatrix}.$$

Clearly $\text{vec}(A)$, which is an $nm \times 1$ vector, is an alternative representation of the elements of the matrix A. This alternative representation is particularly useful in algebraic manipulations when A is a random matrix, for the second moment properties of the elements of A can often be more conveniently analysed when these elements are arranged in vector form (so that there is a matrix of second moments) than when the elements are arranged in a rectangular array. A simple example is the least squares estimator $A^* = M_{yx} M_{xx}^{-1}$ of A in the multiple equation regression model $y_t = A x_t + u_t$ (see Solutions 3.1, 3.2 and 3.3). In this case, the covariance matrix of $\text{vec}(A^*)$ is given by

$$E[\text{vec}(A^*) - \text{vec}(A)][\text{vec}(A^*) - \text{vec}(A)]' = T^{-1}\, \Omega \otimes M_{xx}^{-1}$$

where Ω is the covariance matrix of the disturbance vector u_t (see Goldberger, 1964, p. 209, and Malinvaud, 1970, p. 209).

The main properties of the vec operation which we find useful are as follows:

Property (i) $\quad \text{vec}(ABC) = (A \otimes C')\, \text{vec}(B)$

where A, B and C are rectangular arrays of dimension $n \times m$, $m \times p$ and $p \times q$ respectively.

Proof We let $D = ABC$ and write $A = [(a_{ij})]$, $B = [(b_{ij})]$, $C = [(c_{ij})]$ and $D = [(d_{ij})]$. Then

$$d_{ij} = \sum_{k=1}^{m} \sum_{l=1}^{p} a_{ik} b_{kl} c_{lj}$$

$$= \sum_{k} \sum_{l} a_{ik} c'_{jl} b_{kl}$$

where c'_{jl} is the (j, l)th element of C'. The matrix D has dimension $n \times q$ so that there are q elements in each row of D and therefore the $(iq + j)$th element of vec(D) is $d_{ij} = \Sigma_k \Sigma_l a_{ik} c'_{jl} b_{kl}$. But

$$A \otimes C' = \begin{bmatrix} a_{11} C' & a_{12} C' & \cdots & a_{1m} C' \\ a_{21} C' & a_{22} C' & \cdots & a_{2m} C' \\ \cdot & \cdot & \cdots & \cdot \\ a_{nl} C' & a_{n2} C' & \cdots & a_{nm} C' \end{bmatrix}$$

so that the $(iq + j)$th row of $A \otimes C'$ is the jth row of

$$[a_{i1} C' a_{i2} C' \ldots a_{im} C']$$

That is

$$[a_{i1} (c'_{j1}, c'_{j2}, \ldots, c'_{jp}), \ldots, a_{im} (c'_{j1}, c'_{j2}, \ldots, c'_{jp})] \qquad (A.1)$$

Now since

$$B = \begin{bmatrix} b_{11} & b_{12} & \cdots & b_{1p} \\ \cdot & \cdot & & \cdot \\ \cdot & \cdot & & \cdot \\ \cdot & \cdot & & \cdot \\ b_{m1} & b_{m2} & & b_{mp} \end{bmatrix}$$

$$\text{vec}(B) = \begin{bmatrix} b_{11} \\ b_{12} \\ \cdot \\ \cdot \\ b_{1p} \\ b_{21} \\ \cdot \\ \cdot \\ b_{mp} \end{bmatrix} \qquad (A.2)$$

and the $(iq + j)$th element of $(A \otimes C')\,\text{vec}(B)$ is the scalar product of (A.1) and (A.2). That is

$$\sum_k \sum_l a_{ik} c'_{jl} b_{kl}$$

Thus $\text{vec}(D)$ and $(A \otimes C')\,\text{vec}(B)$ have the same $(iq + j)$th elements and since this holds for all i and j we have

$$\text{vec}(D) = (A \otimes C')\,\text{vec}(B)$$

Remark It follows immediately from Property (i) that

$$\text{vec}(AB) = (A \otimes I)\,\text{vec}(B)$$

and

$$\text{vec}(BC) = (I \otimes C')\,\text{vec}(B)$$

Property (ii) $\quad \text{tr}(A'C) = [\text{vec}(A)]'\,[\text{vec}(C)]$

Proof

$$\text{tr}(A'C) = \sum_i \sum_j a'_{ij} c_{ji}$$

where a'_{ij} is the (i, j)th element of A' and c_{ji} is the (j, i)th element of C. Hence

$$\text{tr}(A'C) = \sum_i \sum_j a_{ji} c_{ji}$$

$$= [\text{vec}(A)]'\,[\text{vec}(C)]$$

where a_{ji} is the (j, i)th element of A.

Property (iii) $\quad \text{tr}(A'BCD) = [\text{vec}(A)]'(B \otimes D')\,\text{vec}(C)$

where A', B, C and D are conformable matrices.

Proof From (ii) above it follows that

$$\text{tr}(A'BCD) = [\text{vec}(A)]'\,\text{vec}(BCD)$$

$$= [\text{vec}(A)]'\,(B \otimes D')\,\text{vec}(C)$$

and the last line follows from (i) above.

Final Remark The vec( ) operation as defined above is not the only way of rearranging the elements of a matrix into a long vector. Another way which is in common use (c.f. Marcus, 1964) is to stack the columns of a matrix. Thus, if A is $n \times m$ and we write A in the form $A = [A_1, A_2, \ldots, A_m]$, where A_i denotes the ith column of A we can define

$$\overline{vec}\,(A)\;=\;\begin{bmatrix} A_1 \\ A_2 \\ \vdots \\ A_m \end{bmatrix}\;=\;\begin{bmatrix} a_{11} \\ a_{21} \\ \vdots \\ a_{n1} \\ a_{12} \\ a_{22} \\ \vdots \\ a_{nm} \end{bmatrix}$$

Since the columns of A are the rows of A' and $vec\,(A')$ stacks the rows of A' it follows immediately that

$$\overline{vec}\,(A)\;=\;vec\,(A')$$

From this relationship between the $\overline{vec}\,(\;)$ and $vec\,(\;)$ operations we can deduce the main rules for operating with $\overline{vec}\,(\;)$ on matrix products. For example, the rule corresponding to Property (i) above is

$$\overline{vec}\,(ABC)\;=\;(C'\otimes A)\,\overline{vec}\,(B)$$

since

$$\begin{aligned}
\overline{vec}\,(ABC)\;=\;vec\,[(ABC)']\;&=\;vec\,(C'B'A') \\
&=\;(C'\otimes A)\,vec\,(B') \\
&=\;(C'\otimes A)\,\overline{vec}\,(B).
\end{aligned}$$

B. MATRIX CALCULUS NOTATION

Definition *If α is a $p \times 1$ vector then by $\partial/\partial\alpha$ (sometimes written $d/d\alpha$) we mean the $p \times 1$ vector operator $(\partial/\partial\alpha_i)$.*

If $a = a(\alpha)$ is a sçalar function of the elements of α, $b = b(\alpha)$ is an n-vector $[b_i(\alpha)]$ whose elements $b_i(\alpha)$ are functions of α and $A = A(\alpha)$ is an $n \times m$ matrix $[a_{ij}(\alpha)]$ whose elements $a_{ij}(\alpha)$ are functions of α, then we use the following notation

$$\frac{\partial a}{\partial\alpha}\;=\;\begin{bmatrix} \dfrac{\partial a(\alpha)}{\partial\alpha_1} \\ \vdots \\ \dfrac{\partial a(\alpha)}{\partial\alpha_p} \end{bmatrix},\;\frac{\partial a}{\partial\alpha'}\;=\;\begin{bmatrix} \dfrac{\partial a(\alpha)}{\partial\alpha_1}, & \cdots, & \dfrac{\partial a(\alpha)}{\partial\alpha_p} \end{bmatrix}$$

$$\frac{\partial^2 a}{\partial \alpha \partial \alpha'} = \left[\left(\frac{\partial^2 a(\alpha)}{\partial \alpha_i \partial \alpha_j} \right)_{ij} \right]_{p \times p}$$

$$\frac{\partial b}{\partial \alpha_i} = \begin{bmatrix} \dfrac{\partial b_1(\alpha)}{\partial \alpha_i} \\ \dfrac{\partial b_n(\alpha)}{\partial \alpha_i} \end{bmatrix}, \frac{\partial b'}{\partial \alpha_i} = \left[\frac{\partial b_1(\alpha)}{\partial \alpha_i}, \dots, \frac{\partial b_n(\alpha)}{\partial \alpha_i} \right],$$

$$\frac{\partial b'}{\partial \alpha} = \left[\left(\frac{\partial b_j(\alpha)}{\partial \alpha_i} \right)_{ij} \right]_{p \times n}, \frac{\partial b}{\partial \alpha'} = \left[\left(\frac{\partial b_i(\alpha)}{\partial \alpha_j} \right)_{ij} \right]_{n \times p},$$

$$\frac{\partial A}{\partial \alpha_i} = \left[\left(\frac{\partial a_{kl}(\alpha)}{\partial \alpha_i} \right)_{kl} \right]_{n \times m},$$

$$\frac{\partial \, \text{vec}(A)}{\partial \alpha_i} = \begin{bmatrix} \dfrac{\partial a_{11}(\alpha)}{\partial \alpha_i} \\ \dfrac{\partial a_{12}(\alpha)}{\partial \alpha_i} \\ \cdot \\ \cdot \\ \cdot \\ \dfrac{\partial a_{1m}(\alpha)}{\partial \alpha_i} \\ \dfrac{\partial a_{21}(\alpha)}{\partial \alpha_i} \\ \cdot \\ \cdot \\ \cdot \\ \dfrac{\partial a_{nm}(\alpha)}{\partial \alpha_i} \end{bmatrix}_{nm \times 1}, \qquad \frac{\partial \, [\text{vec}(A)]'}{\partial \alpha} = \begin{bmatrix} \dfrac{\partial \, \text{vec}(A)}{\partial \alpha_1}' \\ \cdot \\ \cdot \\ \cdot \\ \dfrac{\partial \, \text{vec}(A)}{\partial \alpha_p}' \end{bmatrix}_{p \times nm}$$

and

$$\frac{\partial \, \text{vec}(A)}{\partial \alpha'} = \left[\frac{\partial \, \text{vec}(A)}{\partial \alpha_1}, \dots, \frac{\partial \, \text{vec}(A)}{\partial \alpha_n} \right]$$

Most of the rules for operating in matrix calculus can be found in the main econometrics texts and will not be discussed here. We refer the reader to Goldberger (1964, pp. 39—44), Theil (1971, pp. 30—33), Malinvaud (1970b, pp. 196—198) and Fisk (1967, pp. 144—154). Dwyer (1967) and Neudecker (1968) are also useful references in this area. One rule we will find it useful to derive here is the following:

If $A = A(\lambda)$ is a square non-singular matrix of order n whose elements are differentiable functions of the scalar λ then

$$\frac{\partial}{\partial \lambda} \ln \det[A(\lambda)] = \text{tr}\left[A^{-1}(\lambda) \frac{\partial A(\lambda)}{\partial \lambda}\right] \tag{B.1}$$

Proof We set $A = [(a_{pq})]$. Then

$$\frac{\partial \ln \det[A(\lambda)]}{\partial \lambda} = \frac{\partial \ln \det[A(\lambda)]}{\partial \det A(\lambda)} \frac{\partial \det A(\lambda)}{\partial \lambda}$$

$$= \frac{1}{\det A(\lambda)} \frac{\partial \det[A(\lambda)]}{\partial \lambda}$$

$$= \frac{1}{\det A(\lambda)} \sum_{p=1}^{n} \sum_{q=1}^{n} \frac{\partial \det[A(\lambda)]}{\partial a_{pq}} \frac{\partial a_{pq}}{\partial \lambda}$$

$$= \frac{1}{\det A(\lambda)} \sum_{p} \sum_{q} A_{pq} \frac{\partial a_{pq}}{\partial \lambda}$$

where A_{pq} is the cofactor of a_{pq} in A. Note that the last line follows because we have

$$\det A = \sum_{q=1}^{n} a_{iq} A_{iq}$$

and thus

$$\frac{\partial \det A}{\partial a_{pq}} = A_{pq}.$$

But

$$\frac{A_{pq}}{\det A} = (A^{-1})_{qp} \quad \text{and} \quad \frac{\partial a_{pq}}{\partial \lambda} = \left(\frac{\partial A}{\partial \lambda}\right)_{pq}$$

so that

$$\frac{\partial \ln \det[A(\lambda)]}{\partial \lambda} = \sum_{p} \sum_{q} (A^{-1})_{qp}\left(\frac{\partial A}{\partial \lambda}\right)_{pq} = \text{tr}\left[A^{-1}(\lambda) \frac{\partial A(\lambda)}{\partial \lambda}\right]$$

as required.

Remark It is important to realise that rule (B.1) holds whether or not $A(\lambda)$ is a symmetric matrix. But, note that if $A(\lambda)$ is not symmetric and we set $\lambda = a_{ij}$, the (i,j)th element of A, then $\partial A(\lambda)/\partial\lambda$ has unity in the (i,j)th position and zeros elsewhere. The rule then tells us that

$$\frac{\partial \ln(\det A)}{\partial a_{ij}} = a^{ji}$$

the (i,j)th element of A'^{-1}. Thus

$$\frac{\partial \ln(\det A)}{\partial A} = A'^{-1}.$$

Bibliography

Aigner D.J. and Goldfeld S.M. (1974), 'Estimation and prediction from aggregate data when aggregates are measured more accurately than their components', *Econometrica*, 42, 113–134.

Amemiya T. (1966), 'Specification analysis in the estimation of parameters of a simultaneous equation model with autoregressive residuals', *Econometrica*, 34, 283–306.

Amemiya T. (1974), 'The nonlinear two-stage least-squares estimator', *Journal of Econometrics*, 2, 105–110.

Amemiya T. (1977), 'The maximum likelihood and the nonlinear three-stage least squares estimator in the general nonlinear simultaneous equation model', *Econometrica*, 45, 955–968.

Anderson T.W. (1971), *The Statistical Analysis of Time Series*, John Wiley, New York.

Anderson T.W. (1974), 'An asymptotic expansion of the distribution of the limited information maximum likelihood estimate of a coefficient in a simultaneous equation system', *Journal of the American Statistical Association*, 69, 565–573.

Ashenfelter O. and Heckman J. (1974), 'The estimation of income and substitution effects in a model of family labor supply', *Econometrica*, 42, 73–86.

Bahadur R.R. (1964), 'On Fisher's bound for asymptotic variances', *Annals of Mathematical Statistics*, 35, 1545–1552.

Barnett W.A. (1976), Maximum likelihood and iterated Aitken estimation of nonlinear systems of equations', *Journal of the American Statistical Association*, 71, 354–360.

Barten A.P. and Bronsard L.S. (1970), 'Two-stage least squares estimators with shifts in the structural form', *Econometrica*, 38, 938–941.

Bartlett M.S. (1966), *An Introduction to Stochastic Processes with Special Reference t Methods and Applications*, Cambridge University Press, London (2nd edn).

Basmann R.L. (1960), 'On finite sample distributions of generalised classical linear identifiability test statistics', *Journal of the American Statistical Association*, 55, 650–659.

Basmann R.L. (1974), 'Exact finite sample distributions of some econometric estimators and test statistics: a survey and appraisal', in Intriligator M.D. and Kendrick D. (eds) *Frontiers of Quantitative Economics* Vol II, North Holland, Amsterdam, Chap. 4, pp 209–271.

Bentzel R. and Hansen B. (1954), 'On recursiveness and interdependency in economic models', *Review of Economic Studies*, 22, 153–168.

Bergstrom A.R. (1962), 'The exact sampling distributions of least squares and maximum likelihood estimators of the marginal propensity to consume', *Econometrica*, 30, 480–490.

Bergstrom A.R. (1966), 'What is econometrics?', *The University of Auckland Gazette*, 8, 1–3.

Bergstrom A.R. (1967), *'The Construction and Use of Economic Models'*, English Universities Press, London.

Berndt E.R. and Savin N.E. (1977), 'Conflict among criteria for testing hypotheses in the multivariate regression model', *Econometrica*, **45**, 1263–1278.

Box G.E.P. and Jenkins G.M. (1970), *'Time Series Analysis Forecasting and Control'*, Holden Day, San Francisco.

Braithwaite R.B. (1968), *Scientific Explanation*, Cambridge University Press, London.

Breuch T. (1976), 'The relationship among three statistics for testing hypotheses in the linear regression model — an expository note', unpublished paper, Australian National University.

Brissimis S.N. (1976), 'Multiplier effects for higher than first-order linear dynamic econometric models', *Econometrica*, **44**, 593–596.

Brown J.T. and Manson C.W. (1950), *'The Elements of Analytical Geometry'*, Macmillan, London.

Byron R.P. (1970), 'The restricted Aitken estimation of sets of demand relations', *Econometrica*, **38**, 816–830.

Chatfield C. and Prothero D.L. (1973), 'Box—Jenkins seasonal forecasting: problems in a case study', *Journal of the Royal Statistical Society*, Series A, **136**, 295–315.

Chow G.C. (1960), 'Tests of equality between sets of coefficients in two linear regressions', *Econometrica*, **28**, 591–605.

Chow G.C. (1976), *Analysis and Control of Dynamic Economic Systems*, John Wiley, New York.

Christ C. (1975), 'Judging the performance of econometric models of the US', *International Economic Review*, **16**, 54–74.

Clark P. (1973), 'A subordinated stochastic process model with finite variance for speculative prices', *Econometrica*, **41**, 135–156.

Cochrane D. and Orcutt G. (1949), 'Application of least squares regression to relationships containing autocorrelated error terms', *Journal of the American Statistical Association*, **44**, 32–61.

Cooper R.L. (1972), 'The predictive performance of quarterly econometric models of the United States', in Hickman B.G. (ed.) *Econometric Models of Cyclical Behaviour*, Columbia University Press, New York, pp 813–916.

Court R.H. (1974), 'Three-stage least squares and some extensions where the structural disturbance covariance matrix may be singular', *Econometrica*, **42**, 547–558.

Cramer H. (1946), *Mathematical Methods of Statistics*, Princeton University Press, Princeton NJ.

Daniels H.E. (1956), 'The approximate distribution of serial correlation coefficients', *Biometrika*, **43**, 169–185.

Deistler M. (1975), 'z—Transform and identification of linear econometric models with autocorrelated errors', *Metrika*, **22**, 13–25.

Deistler M. (1976), 'The identifiability of linear econometric models with autocorrelated errors', *International Economic Review*, **17**, 26–45.

Dhrymes P.J. (1970), *Econometrics*, Harper and Row, New York.

Dhrymes P.J. (1971), *Distributed Lags: Problems of Estimation and Formulation*, Holden-Day, San Francisco.

Dhrymes P.J. *et al.* (1972), 'Criteria for evaluation of econometric models', *Annals of Economic and Social Measurement*, **1**, 291–324.

Dhrymes P.J. (1974), 'A note on an efficient two-step estimator', *Journal of Econometrics*, **2**, 301–304.

Dhrymes, P.J. and Erlat H. (1974), 'Asymptotic properties of full information estimators in dynamic autoregressive simultaneous equation models', *Journal of Econometrics*, **2**, 247–260.

Dieudonné J. (1969), *Foundations of Modern Analysis*, Academic Press, New York.

Doob J.L. (1953), *Stochastic Processes*, John Wiley, New York.

Durbin J. (1953), 'A note on regression when there is extraneous information about one of the coefficients', *Journal of the American Statistical Association*, **48**, 799—808.

Durbin J. (1970), 'Testing for serial correlation in least-squares regression when some of the regressors are lagged dependent variables', *Econometrica*, **38**, 410—421.

Durbin J. and Watson G.S. (1950), 'Testing for serial correlation in least squares regression I', *Biometrika*, **37**, 409—428.

Durbin J. and Watson G.S. (1951), 'Testing for serial correlation in least squares regression II', *Biometrika*, **38**, 159—178.

Dwyer P.S. (1967), 'Some applications of matrix derivatives in multivariate analysis', *Journal of the American Statistical Association*, **62**, 607—625.

Eckstein O. and Fromm G. (1968), 'The price equation', *American Economic Review*, **68**, 1159—1183.

Edwards D.A. and Moyal J.E. (1955), 'Stochastic differential equations', *Proceedings of the Cambridge Philosophical Society*, **51**, 663—677.

Fair R.C. (1970), 'The estimation of simultaneous equation models with lagged endogenous variables and first order serially correlated errors', *Econometrica*, **38**, 507—516.

Fair R.C. (1972), 'Efficient estimation of simultaneous equations with autoregressive errors by instrumental variables', *Review of Economics and Statistics*, **54**, 444—449.

Fair R.C. (1974), *A Model of Macroeconomic Activity, Volume 1 : The Theoretical Model*, Ballinger, Cambridge, Mass.

Fair R.C. and Kelejian H.H. (1974), 'Methods of estimation for markets in dis-equilibrium: a further study', *Econometrica*, **42**, 177—190.

Fisher F.M. (1966), *The Identification Problem in Econometrics*, McGraw-Hill, New York.

Fisher F.M. (1970), 'Tests of equality between sets of coefficients in two linear regressions: an expository note', *Econometrica*, **38**, 361—366.

Fishman G.S. (1969), *Spectral Methods in Econometrics*, Harvard University Press, Cambridge, Mass.

Fisk P.R. (1967), *Stochastically Dependent Equations*, Griffin, London.

Friedman M. (1953), 'The methodology of positive economics' in *Essays in Positive Economics*, University of Chicago Press, Chicago.

Gallant A.R. (1975a), 'Seemingly unrelated nonlinear regressions', *Journal of Econometrics*, **3**, 35—50.

Gallant A.R. (1975b), 'Nonlinear regression', *American Statistician*, **29**, 73—81.

Gantmacher F.R. (1959), *Theory of Matrices*, Chelsea, New York.

Godfrey L.G. and Poskitt D.S. (1975), 'Testing the restrictions of the Almon lag technique', *Journal of the American Statistical Association*, **70**, 105—108.

Godfrey L.G. and Wickens M.R. (1977), 'The estimation of incomplete models using subsystem LIML', Essex University Discussion paper, No. 99.

Goldberger A.S. (1964), *Econometric Theory*, John Wiley, New York.

Goldberger A.S. (1972a), 'Structural equation methods in the social sciences', *Econometrica*, **40**, 979—1002.

Goldberger A.S. (1972b), 'Maximum likelihood estimation of regressions containing unobservable independent variables', *International Economic Review*, **13**, 1—15.

Granger C.W.J. and Newbold P. (1973), 'Some comments on the evaluation of economic forecasts', *Applied Economics*, **5**, 35—47.

Granger C.W.J. and Newbold P. (1974), 'Spurious regressions in econometrics', *Journal of Econometrics*, **2**, 111—120.

Green H.A.J. (1971), *Consumer Theory*, Penguin, London.

Grenander U. and Rosenblatt M. (1957), *Statistical Analysis of Stationary Time Series*, John Wiley, New York.

Griliches Z. (1974), 'Errors in variables and other unobservables', *Econometrica*, **42**, 971—998.

Haavelmo T. (1944), 'The probability approach in econometrics, *Econometrica*, Supplement to Volume 12.

Halmos P. (1958), *Finite Dimensional Vector Spaces*, Van Nostrand, Princeton NJ.

Hannan E.J. (1969), 'The identification of vector mixed autoregressive moving average systems', *Biometrika*, **56**, 223—225.

Hannan E.J. (1970), *Multiple Time Series*, John Wiley, New York.

Hannan E.J. (1971), 'Non-linear time series regression', *Journal of Applied Probability*, **8**, 767—780.

Hardy G.H. (1952), *A Course of Pure Mathematics*, Cambridge University Press, London.

Hatanaka M. (1973), 'On the existence and the approximation formulae for the moments of the k-class estimators', *Economic Studies Quarterly*, 24, 1—15.

Hatanaka M. (1974), 'An efficient two-step estimator for the dynamic adjustment model with autoregressive errors', *Journal of Econometrics*, 2, 199—220.

Hatanaka M. (1976), 'Several efficient two-step estimators for the dynamic simultaneous equation model with autoregressive disturbances', *Journal of Econometrics*, 4, 189—204.

Henderson C.R. (1971), 'Comment on "The use of error components models in combining cross section with time series data" ', *Econometrica*, 39, 397—402.

Hendry D.F. (1971), 'Maximum likelihood estimation of systems of simultaneous regression equations with errors generated by a vector autoregressive process', *International Economic Review*, 12, 257—272, plus 'Correction', 15, 260.

Hendry D.F. (1976), 'The structure of simultaneous equations estimators', *Journal of Econometrics*, 4, 51—88.

Hoerl A.E. and Kennard R.W. (1970), 'Ridge regression: biased estimation for non-orthogonal problems', *Technometrics*, 12, 55—82.

Hood W.C. and Koopmans T.C. (eds) (1953), *Studies in Econometric Method*, John Wiley, New York.

Hurwicz L. (1950), 'Least squares bias in time series', in Koopmans T.C. (ed.), *Statistical Inference in Dynamic Economic Models*, John Wiley, New York, Chap. 16, pp 365—383.

Jennrich R.I. (1969), 'Asymptotic properties of non-linear least squares estimators', *Annals of Mathematical Statistics*, 40, 633—643.

Johnston J. (1972), *Econometric Methods*, McGraw-Hill, New York (2nd edn).

Jorgenson D.W., Hunter J. and Nadiri M.I. (1970), 'The predictive performance of econometric models of quarterly investment behaviour', *Econometrica*, 38, 213—254.

Kendall M.G. and Stuart A. (1969), *The Advanced Theory of Statistics*, Volume I, Griffin, London.

Klein L.R. (1962), *An Introduction to Econometrics*, Prentice-Hall, Englewood Cliffs NJ.

Koopmans T.C. (1957), *Three Essays on the State of Economic Science*, McGraw-Hill, New York.

Koopmans T.C. and Hood W.C. (1953), 'The estimation of simultaneous linear economic relationships', in Hood and Koopmans (1953), Chap. 6.

Laidler D.E. (1975), 'Expectations adjustment and the dynamic response of income to policy changes', Chapter 3, 65—81, in Laidler D.E., *Essays on Money and Inflation*, Manchester University Press, Manchester, Chap, 3, pp 65—81.

Lukacs E. and Laha R.G. (1964), *Applications of Characteristic Functions*, Griffin, London.

McGuire T.W., Farley J.W., Lucas R.E. (Jnr) and Ring L. Winston (1968), 'Estimation and inference for linear models in which subsets of the dependent variable are constrained', *Journal of the American Statistical Association*, 63, 1201—1213.

MacDuffee C.C. (1933), *The Theory of Matrices*, Chelsea, New York.

Madansky A. (1976), *Foundations of Econometrics*, North Holland, Amsterdam.
Maddala G.S. (1971a), 'The use of variance components models in pooling cross-section and time-series data', *Econometrica*, 39, 341—358.
Maddala G.S. (1971b), 'Generalised least squares with an estimated covariance matrix', *Econometrica*, 39, 23—34.
Maddala G.S. and Nelson F.D. (1974), 'Maximum likelihood methods of markets in disequilibrium', *Econometrica*, 42, 1031—1044.
Malinvaud E. (1966), *Statistical Methods of Econometrics*, North-Holland, Amsterdam, (1st edn).
Malinvaud E. (1970a), 'The consistency of non-linear regressions', *Annals of Mathematical Statistics*, 41, 956—969.
Malinvaud E. (1970b), *Statistical Methods of Econometrics*, North Holland, Amsterdam, (2nd edn).
Mann H.B. and Wald A. (1943a), 'On the statistical treatment of linear stochastic difference equations', *Econometrica*, 11, 173—220.
Mann H.B. and Wald A. (1943b), 'On stochastic limit and order relationships', *Annals of Mathematical Statistics*, 14, 173—220.
Marcus M. and Mine H. (1964), *A Survey of Matrix Theory and Matrix Inequalities*, Allyn and Bacon, Boston.
Mariano R.S. (1973), 'Approximations to the distribution functions of the ordinary least squares and two-stage least squares estimators in the case of two included endogenous variables', *Econometrica*, 41, 67—77.
Mariano R.S. and Sawa T. (1972), 'The exact finite-sample distribution of the limited information maximum likelihood estimator in the case of two included endogenous variables', *Journal of the American Statistical Association*, 67, 159—163.
de Menil G. (1974), 'Aggregate price dynamics', *The Review of Economics and Statistics*, 56, 129—140.
Mikhail W.M. (1972), 'Simulating the small sample properties of econometric estimators', *Journal of the American Statistical Association*, 67, 620—624.
Moroney J.R. and Mason J.M. (1971), 'The dynamic impacts of autonomous expenditures and the monetary base on aggregate income', *Journal of Money, Credit and Banking*, 3, 793—814.
Nagar A.L. (1959), 'The bias and moment matrix of the general k—class estimators of the parameters in simultaneous equations', *Econometrica*, 27, 575—595.
Nelson C.R. (1972), 'The predictive performance of the FRB—MIT—PENN model of the US economy', *American Economic Review*, 62, 902—917.
Neudecker H. (1968), 'The Kronecker matrix product and some of its applications in econometrics', *Statistica Neerlandica*, 22, 69—82.
Nerlove M. (1971), 'A note on error components models', *Econometrica*, 39, 383—396.
Phillips P.C.B. (1972), 'The structural estimation of a stochastic differential equation system', *Econometrica*, 40, 1021—1041.
Phillips P.C.B. (1976), 'The iterated minimum distance estimator and the quasi-maximum likelihood estimator', *Econometrica*, 44, 449—460.
Phillips P.C.B. (1977), 'Approximations to some finite sample distributions associated with a first-order stochastic difference equation', *Econometrica*, 45, 463—485.
Pigou A.C. (1908), *Economic Science in Relation to Practice*, Macmillan, London.
Popper K.F. (1959), *The Logic of Scientific Discovery*, Hutchinson, London.
Popper K.F. (1963), *Conjectures and Refutations*, Routledge and Kegan Paul, London.
Prais S.J. and Houthakker H.S. (1955), *The Analysis of Family Budgets*, Cambridge University Press, London.
Preston A.J. and Wall K.D. (1973), 'An extended identification problem for state space representations of econometric models', Discussion Paper, Programme of Research into Econometric Methods, Queen Mary College, London.
Rao C.R. (1963), 'Criteria of estimation in large samples', *Sankhya, Series A*, 25, 189—206.

Robinson P.M. (1972), 'Non-linear regression for multiple time series', *Journal of Applied Probability*, 9, 758—768.

Robinson P.M. (1976a), 'The estimation of linear differential equations with constant coefficients', *Econometrica*, 44, 751—764.

Robinson P.M. (1976b), 'Instrumental variables estimation of differential equations', *Econometrica*, 44, 765—776.

Rothenberg T.J. (1971), 'Identification in parametric models', *Econometrica*, 39, 577—591.

Rothenberg T.J. (1973), *Efficient Estimation with a priori Information*, Yale University Press, New Haven.

Rothenberg T.J. and Leenders C.T. (1964), 'Efficient estimation of simultaneous equation systems', *Econometrica*, 32, 57—76.

Rubin H. (1950), 'Consistency of maximum likelihood estimates in the explosive case', in Koopmans T.C. (ed.), *Statistical Inference in Dynamic Economic Models*', John Wiley, New York, Chap. 14, 356—364.

Rudin W. (1964), *Principles of Mathematical Analysis*, McGraw-Hill, New York.

Samuelson P.A. (1954), 'Report of the Evaluate Committee for Econometrica', *Econometrica*, 22, 141—146.

Sargan J.D. (1964a), 'Three-stage least squares and full information maximum likelihood estimates', *Econometrica*, 32, 77—81.

Sargan J.D. (1964b), 'Wages and prices in the United Kingdom: a study in econometric methodology', *Colston Papers*, 16, Butterworths, London.

Sargan J.D. (1972), 'The identification and estimation of sets of simultaneous stochastic equations', mimeographed, London School of Economics (and Discussion Paper No. A1, LSE Econometrics Programme 1975).

Sargan J.D. (1974), 'The validity of Nagar's expansion for the moments of econometric estimators', *Econometrica*, 42, 169—176.

Sargan J.D. (1975), 'Gram Charlier approximations applied to t-ratios of k-class estimators', *Econometrica*, 43, 327—346.

Sargan J.D. (1976), 'Some discrete approximations to continuous time stochastic models', in Bergstrom A.R. (ed.) *Statistical Inference in Continuous Time Economic Models*', North Holland, Amsterdam, Chap. 3, pp 27—79.

Schmetterer L. (1966), 'On the asymptotic efficiency of estimates', in David F.N. (ed.) *Research Papers in Statistics*, (Festschrift for J. Neyman), John Wiley, London, 1966, 301—316.

Schmidt P. (1976), *Econometrics*, Marcel Dekker, New York.

Schönfeld P. (1971), 'A useful central limit theorem for m-dependent variables', *Metrika*, 15, 116—128.

Seber G.A.F. (1964), *The Linear Hypothesis: a General Theory*, Griffin, London.

Shenton L.R. and Johnson W.L. (1965), 'Moments of a serial correlation coefficient', *Journal of the Royal Statistical Society, Series B*, 27, 308—320.

Schiller, R.J. (1973), 'A distributed lag estimator derived from smoothness priors', *Econometrica*, 41, 775—788.

Simon H.A. (1953), 'Causal ordering and identifiability', in Hood and Koopmans (1953), Chap. 3, pp 49—74.

Smyth D.J. and Briscoe G. (1969), 'Investment plans and realisations in United Kingdom manufacturing', *Economica*, 36, 277—293.

Stigum B.P. (1974), 'Asymptotic properties of dynamic stochastic parameter estimates', *Journal of Multivariate Analysis*, 4, 351—381.

Stigum B.P. (1976), 'Least squares and stochastic difference equations', *Journal of Econometrics*, 4, 349—370.

Stone R. (1954), 'Linear expenditure systems and demand analysis: an application to the pattern of British demand', *Economic Journal*, 64, 511—527.

Theil H. (1958), *Economic Forecasts and Policy*, North Holland, Amsterdam.

Theil H. (1971), *Principles of Econometrics*, John Wiley, New York.

Theil H. and Boot J.C.G. (1962), 'The final form of econometric equation systems', *Review of the International Statistical Institute*, 30, 136–152.

Tichmarsh E.C. (1964), *The Theory of Functions*, Oxford University Press, London.

Trivedi P.K. and Pagan A.R. (1976), 'Polynomial distributed lags: a unified treatment', Australian National University, Working Papers in Economics and Econometrics, No. 34.

von Tunzelmann G.N. (1968), 'The new economic history: an econometric appraisal', *Explorations in Entrepreneurial History*, 2nd series, 5.

Wald A. (1943), 'Tests of statistical hypotheses concerning several parameters when the number of observations is large', *Transactions of the American Mathematical Society*, 54, 426–482.

Wallace T.D. and Hussain A. (1969), 'The use of error component models in combining cross-section and time series data', *Econometrica*, 37, 55–72.

Wallis K.F. (1977), 'Multiple time series and the final form of econometric models', *Econometrica*, 45, 1481–1498.

Wegge L. (1965), 'Identifiability criteria for systems of equations as a whole', *Australian Journal of Statistics*, 7, 67–77.

White J.S. (1958), 'The limiting distribution of the serial correlation coefficient in the explosive case', *Annals of Mathematical Statistics*, 29, 1188–1197.

Wickens M.R. (1969), 'The consistency and efficiency of generalised least squares in simultaneous equations systems with autocorrelated errors', *Econometrica*, 37, 651–659.

Wickens M.R. (1972), 'A note on the use of proxy variables', *Econometrica*, 40, 759–762.

Wickens M.R. (1976), 'Rational expectations and the efficient estimation of econometric models', Australian National University, Working Paper in Economics and Econometrics, No. 35.

Wickens M.R. (1977), 'The estimation of incomplete econometric models with autoregressive errors using subsystem estimators', Essex University Discussion Paper, No. 98.

Widder D.V. (1961), *Advanced Calculus*, Prentice Hall, Englewood Cliffs NJ.

Wold H. (1954), 'Causality and econometrics', *Econometrica*, 23, 162–177.

Wolfowitz J. (1965), 'Asymptotic efficiency of the maximum likelihood estimator', *Theory of Probability and its Applications*, 10, 247–254.

Wong E. (1971), *Stochastic Processes in Information and Dynamical Systems*, McGraw-Hill, New York.

Yaglom A.M. (1962), *An Introduction to the Theory of Stationary Random Functions*, Prentice-Hall, Englewood Cliffs NJ.

Zellner A. (1962), 'An efficient method of estimating seemingly unrelated regressions and tests for aggregation bias', *Journal of the American Statistical Association*, 57, 348-368.

Zellner A. (1970), 'Estimation of regression relationships containing unobservable independent variables', *International Economic Review*, 11, 441–454.

Zellner A. and Geisel M.S. (1970), 'Analysis of distributed lag models with applications to consumption function estimation', *Econometrica*, 38, 865–888.

Index